MODERN ALGEBRA
AND TRIGONOMETRY

This book is in the

ADDISON-WESLEY SERIES IN MATHEMATICS

MODERN ALGEBRA
AND TRIGONOMETRY

by

ELBRIDGE P. VANCE

Oberlin College

ADDISON-WESLEY PUBLISHING COMPANY, INC.

READING, MASSACHUSETTS · PALO ALTO · LONDON

Library of Congress Catalog Card No. 62-7115

Second Printing, June 1963

PREFACE

The entire approach to the study of mathematics has been constantly changing in recent years. Although some people have objected to the current trend of unifying or integrating subjects previously taught separately, it is my conviction that such a system seems most efficient. In this way the student acquires a real feeling for the mathematical thought and processes common to all fields of mathematics, in addition to the true integration of the fundamental material itself. It was this conviction which led me to write the book, *Unified Algebra and Trigonometry*.

But many changes in emphasis with regard to both secondary and college mathematics have taken place since that writing. In preparing a revised edition, I found that my efforts have resulted in a significant amount of new material and reflect a completely different point of view. For this reason it now seems wise to consider this an entirely new book, and call it *Modern Algebra and Trigonometry*.

One of the aims of this book is the education of the student in the nature of mathematics as a logical system. He must realize that precise definitions are important, that explicitly stated hypotheses are necessary, and that any system of mathematics consists of these definitions and hypotheses, together with the results which have been derived by logical reasoning. The second aim of this book is more specific. A unified treatment of the basic ideas of algebra and trigonometry is presented, together with a substantial foundation for both. Such material is fundamental to any student's training, whether he wishes to continue in mathematics, the natural sciences, and engineering, or whether his interests lie in the social sciences or economics. With the mastery of the material covered in this book, the student should be well prepared to study mathematical logic, finite mathematics, statistics, and probability, or continue in analytic geometry and calculus.

In writing this book I have been influenced by the Committee on the Undergraduate Mathematical Program of the Mathematical Association of America, the Commission of Mathematics of the College Entrance Board, and the writing of the School Mathematics Study Group. Although much of the material covered will show this influence, the basic outline of the contents is mine.

It has been my aim to write a versatile text, which can be used for any purpose from a one-semester course in the bare essentials, to a full-year course. The moderately well-prepared secondary-school student should have no difficulty with the material, and the number of hours for the course can easily be reduced if the preparation of the student is strong.

The choice of topics, with the integration of algebra and trigonometry where it seems natural, the proportional time spent on each, and the logical treatment throughout are intended to emphasize the modern point of view. The problems which appear at the end of each article are an integral part of the book. They not only help to unify the material, but are frequently used to introduce important concepts and theorems to which later reference is made. Such problems, which are necessary for the continuity of the discussions, are marked with an asterisk, and should always be worked. The answers for the odd-numbered problems are given at the end of the book.

There are several unusual features of the book. The notion of sets is introduced at the beginning and is used throughout the book. The axioms of a Field are explicitly stated, and with these, the Order axioms, and the Completeness property, all the important properties of the real numbers are clearly stated and proved. A rather detailed discussion of complex numbers is also presented. A definite distinction is made between functions and relations, both of which are defined in terms of sets. A brief discussion of the one-dimensional coordinate system leads naturally to the ordinary rectangular coordinate system. The definition of the circular functions in terms of this system is the basic unifying link between trigonometry and analytic geometry, and makes it possible to use many simpler, more direct methods. These functions are first defined for any real number and later applied to the case where the real number is considered as the measure of an angle. The analytic rather than the computational part of trigonometry has been emphasized, although the latter has been included. The emphasis on graphing, the insight into some of the applications of the circular functions in the description of many periodic phenomena, the detailed treatment of determinants, the material on the general inverse function, and the introduction and frequent use of mathematical induction, are other distinguishing features. Every effort has been made to present intuitively each new concept before any detailed rigorous discussion.

Included in the Appendix are tables of powers and roots, four-place tables of the circular functions, logarithms, and the logarithms of the circular functions.

E. P. V.

CONTENTS

CHAPTER 1

SETS AND NUMBERS

The basic quantitative procedures of science involve counting and measurement. Counting characterizes a collection or set of objects by a number. Measurement assigns a number to some property of an object. Counting and measurement are far from simple concepts, as is the notion of a set, and each has been the subject of many studies in the field of scientific methodology. The important thing for us in the present study is the fact that both counting and measurement lead to numbers, and through the use of numbers and sets it is possible to obtain much insight into the workings of nature. We shall begin with a brief discussion of sets, then classify various types of numbers and introduce some basic operations and notions of numbers and sets which are fundamental in all fields of mathematics and science.

1–1 Sets and basic notation. The basic notion of a set, whose importance in mathematics was first considered by Georg Cantor (1845–1918), is so fundamental to the different branches of the subject that it is impossible to give a precise definition in terms of more basic concepts. However, it is so deeply imbedded in our intuition that we shall rely on our experience to consider the notion of set. We may think of a set as a collection (or aggregate) of objects of any sort, restricting ourselves to those objects that are clearly enough described so that there is no question as to whether a certain object does or does not belong to the set. For example, we might consider as sets:

(a) The set of students in the Oberlin College freshman class,
(b) The set of students in this class whose last name begins with the letter V,
(c) The set of positive integers (counting numbers) less than 5,
(d) The set of the authors of this book,
(e) The set of all states in the United States with a population under 10,000,
(f) The set of all straight lines (in a plane) that pass through a given point,
(g) The set of all points that lie on a given line,
(h) The set of all fossils in the world,
(i) The set of letters in the word "Mississippi."

1

If an object belongs to the set, it is called a member or *element* of the set, but, if the object does not belong to the set, it is not an element of the set. To indicate membership in a set we use the symbol ∈. Capital letters are usually used as the names of sets, and small letters as names for the elements. Thus, if a is an object and A is a set, we write $a \in A$ as an abbreviation for "a is an element of A." This also may be read "a is contained in the set A" or "a belongs to the set A." Similarly, if we wish to indicate that a is not an element of A, we write $a \notin A$.

Clearly, as we see from the examples, there are many different sets as well as different sized sets. Each of the examples listed above is different, although some may be of the same size. Examples (a), (b), (c), (d), (e), (h), and (i) are finite, while (f) and (g) are infinite. In general, we say that a set has a finite number of elements if one can enumerate the elements of the set in some order and then count* the elements until a last one is reached. A set is called *finite* if it has a finite number of elements; otherwise it is called *infinite*.

Note that the number of elements in example (i) is four, although there are eleven letters in the word, "Mississippi." Thus, the number of elements in this example and in (c) is the same. As in example (d), a set may have only one element, and in fact, as in example (e), may not have any elements. A set, such as that in (h), may be finite even though very large. The order of enumeration of the elements does not affect the set itself.

The use of sets in elementary mathematics is helpful in the clarification of certain ideas, in the simplification of certain rather complicated concepts, and also in the unification of the studies of different but related concepts. With this in mind, we introduce the two most common methods for describing a set, the *roster* or *tabulation method*, and the *rule* or *defining property method*.

The roster method. We may indicate a set by listing the elements and enclosing them in braces.

The rule method. We may indicate a set by enclosing in braces a descriptive phrase, and agreeing that those objects, and only those, which have the described property are elements of the set.

ILLUSTRATION 1. The set $V = \{a, e, i, o, u\}$ defines the set V of vowels in the English alphabet. This set may also be written†

$$V = \{x, \text{ such that } x \text{ is a vowel in the English alphabet}\}.$$

---

* We assume the intuitive knowledge of the so-called counting numbers, 1, 2, 3, . . . , where the dots signify we do not stop at 3 but keep going indefinitely.

† Note that in these illustrations the "x" is used as a symbol for an arbitrary element of a set, not as a letter of the alphabet.

A shorter and more efficient notation is

$$V = \{x|x \text{ is a vowel in the English alphabet}\},$$

where the vertical bar is read "such that."

ILLUSTRATION 2. If we recall that an even integer is any integer which is divisible by two, the set $E = \{2, 4, 6, 8, 10\}$ may also be written $E = \{x|x \text{ is a positive even integer less than 12}\}$.

ILLUSTRATION 3. It is very difficult to write the set

$$N = \{x|x \text{ is a positive fraction between 1 and 2}\}$$

by the roster method.

ILLUSTRATION 4. It is also difficult to specify the set

$$Z = \{\text{your cat, my Saint Bernard, the earth, Peter, Emily}\}$$

by the rule method.

In any study of sets one of the basic requirements is the ability to compare the sizes of different collections of objects. This is accomplished by one of the great foundational concepts of mathematics, that of "one-to-one correspondence."

DEFINITION 1–1. *A one-to-one correspondence exists between two sets A and B if it is possible to associate the elements of A with the elements of B in such a way that each element of each set is associated with exactly one element of the other.*

For example, the normal human being can associate his fingers with his toes so that each finger is associated with just one toe. In any given group of married couples, there is an obvious correspondence of this type. In the previous illustrations, such a one-to-one correspondence exists between V and E, E and Z, or Z and V. If such is the case, we say the two sets are the same size, although it should be clear that they are not equal.

DEFINITION 1–2. *Two sets A and B are the same size if there exists a one-to-one correspondence between their elements.*

PROBLEMS

Use both the roster method and the rule method to specify the sets in Problems 1 through 5.

1. The members of your immediate family.
2. The counting numbers less than 10.

3. The fractions whose numerator is 1, and whose denominator is a counting number less than 10.

4. The single digits used in our decimal system.

5. The counting numbers which are multiples of 6 and less than 50.

Use the rule method to specify the sets whose elements are tabulated in Problems 6 through 10.

6. $E = \{2, 4, 6, 8\}$

7. $S = \{1, 4, 9, 16, 25\}$

8. $N = \{1, \frac{1}{2}, \frac{1}{3}, \frac{1}{4}\}$

9. $P = \{1, 4, 7, 10, 13\}$

10. $T = \{10, 100, 1000, 10000\}$

Use the rule method to specify the sets described in Problems 11 through 15, and tell why the roster method is difficult or impossible.

11. The counting numbers greater than 100.

12. The students in your school who have been abroad.

13. The United States citizens who have read The Constitution.

14. The books in the Oberlin College library.

15. The set of all triangles whose area is less than 3.

16. Give an example of a set which has just two elements; one element; no elements; an infinite number of elements.

*17. *Two sets A and B* are said to be *equal* if each element of A is an element of B and each element of B is an element of A, and we write $A = B$. Determine whether A and B are the same size and if so, whether $A = B$.

(a) $A = \{1, 3, 5\}$, $B = \{3, 5, 1\}$

(b) $A = \{1, 3, 5\}$, $B = \{a, b, c\}$

Assume x is either -1 or 0 or 1.

(c) $A = \{x|x^2 = 1\}$, $B = \{1, -1\}$

(d) $A = \{1\}$, $B = \{x|x^2 = 1\}$

(e) $A = \{1\}$, $B = \{x|(x - 1)^2 = 0\}$

(f) $A = \{1\}$, $B = \{x|x^2 - x = 0\}$

18. For each of the sets listed below, tell which is finite and which is infinite. For the finite sets, tell which are the same size and which are equal.

(a) The set of the first two odd counting numbers.

(b) The set of all odd counting numbers less than 5.

(c) The set of all odd counting numbers.

(d) The set of letters in the word "Canadian."

(e) The set of points on a given line exactly one unit from a given point on that line.

(f) The set of points in a given plane exactly one unit from a given point in that plane.

(g) The set whose elements are the numbers 1 and 3.

---

* Starred problems are essential to an understanding of later parts of the book, and should be assigned to every student.

1–2 Subsets. Every vowel in the English alphabet is, of course, a letter in this alphabet. If we call A the set of all the letters in the English alphabet, the set V is included in the set A. Similarly, the set E in Illustration 2 of Article 1–1 is included in the set of all even counting numbers. We wish to define this notion in general.

DEFINITION 1–3. *The set A is a* subset *of the set B if every element of A is an element of B. If B has elements that are not elements of A, then A is a* proper subset *of B.*

Since this concept is frequently used, it is convenient to denote this symbolically by $A \subset B$, which is read "A is a subset of B" or "A is included in B." Thus

$$A \subset B \text{ if and only if } x \in A \text{ implies } x \in B.^*$$

It should be noted that every set may be regarded as a subset of itself; that is, for all A, $A \subset A$.

Let us return to the set $A = \{x|x$ is a letter in the English alphabet$\}$. We observed that V was a subset of A. If $C = \{x|x$ is a consonant in the English alphabet$\}$, C is also a subset of A. In this discussion the set A is an over-all set of elements, with which we are concerned throughout our discussion. Such a fixed set in any discussion is called the *universal set*, and is always denoted by U. Of course, different universal sets can be used for different considerations. In one discussion U may be the set of all real numbers, in another, the set of all points in the plane, and so on. In first-grade arithmetic, U was the set of counting numbers.

DEFINITION 1–4. *The* universal set *in any discussion is the totality of members under consideration as elements of any set.*

No element in V was an element of C, and vice versa. Sets related in this way occur frequently, and we say two such sets are *disjoint*. The sets given in Illustrations 2 and 3, Article 1–1, form another example of two disjoint sets.

DEFINITION 1–5. *Two sets, A and B, are* disjoint *if and only if A and B have no elements in common.*

There is one set of special importance. The *empty set*, or *null set*, denoted by $\emptyset$, is the set in any discussion that has no elements. For example, the

---

* The "if and only if" statement in mathematics is an important one. In this case it means: (1) if $x \in A$ implies $x \in B$, then $A \subset B$, and (2) if $A \subset B$, then $x \in A$ implies $x \in B$. In general any such statement consists of two facts. These two can be considered as a theorem and its converse. A definition is always considered an "if and only if" statement.

set consisting of all elements in both V and C is $\emptyset$. Similarly, the set of counting numbers which are perfect squares and end in 7 is $\emptyset$. The statement that the set of elements satisfying a certain condition is empty is equivalent to the statement that no elements satisfying that condition exist. By its very definition, the empty set is a subset of every set.

One further definition should be given.

DEFINITION 1–6.   *Two sets A and B are equal $(A = B)$ if and only if $A \subset B$ and $B \subset A$.*

As a direct consequence of this definition, if one set has an element not in the other, the two are unequal, and we write $A \neq B$.

ILLUSTRATIONS.   The set $X = \{x|x$ is a counting number between 0 and 10$\} = \{1, 2, 3, 4, 5, 6, 7, 8, 9\}$. The set $Y = \{y|y$ is an even counting number less than 7$\} = \{2, 4, 6\}$. The set $Z = \{z|z$ is a counting number and has a perfect square between 3 and 40$\} = \{2, 3, 4, 5, 6\}$. Under these conditions, we may say $Y \subset Z$, $Y \subset X$, and $Z \subset X$. Z is a proper subset of X so that $Z \neq X$. Also, $\{3\} \subset X$, $\{3\} \subset Z$, and $3 \in X$, but we cannot say $3 \subset X$. (Why?).

PROBLEMS

Specify each of the sets in Problems 1 through 4 by the roster method, and in each case give the universal set.

1. The set of subjects you are taking for credit.

2. The ages in years of the members of your family.

3. The counting numbers which are positive integral multiples of 7 and less than 100.

4. The digits in your telephone number.

5. If $A = \{1, 2, 3, 4, 5\}$, $B = \{2, 3, 4\}$, and $C = \{2, 4, 5\}$, which of the following are true?

(a) $A \subset B$?   (b) $A \subset C$?   (c) $B \subset A$?
(d) $B \subset C$?   (e) $C \subset A$?   (f) $C \subset B$?
(g) $C \subset C$?   (h) $\emptyset \subset B$?   (i) $B = C$?

6. For the sets in Problem 5,

(a) What is the set with elements both in B and C?
(b) What is the set with elements in B and $\{1, 5\}$?
(c) What is the set with elements in C and $\{1, 5\}$?

7. If $X = \{1, 2, 3\}$, identify the set Y such that $\{1\} \subset Y$, $Y \subset X$, and $X \neq Y$.

8. (a) List the subsets of the set $\{a, b\}$. Note that there are $2^2 = 2 \times 2$ subsets.

(b) List the subsets of the set $\{a, b, c\}$. Note that there are $2^3 = 2 \times 2 \times 2$ subsets.

9. For the set $\{a, b, c, d\}$, list the possible subsets containing

(a) four elements,   (b) three elements,

(c) two elements,   (d) one element,

(e) no elements.

10. What is the sum of the number of subsets in (a) through (e) in Problem 9? Is this consistent with the results in Problem 8?

11. If $D = \{0, 4, 7\}$, we say that $7 \in D$, or $\{7\} \subset D$, but cannot say $7 \subset D$, since 7 is not a set. Which of the following are true?

(a) $4 \in D$ (b) $4 \subset D$ (c) $0 \in D$

(d) $\emptyset \in D$ (e) $\emptyset \subset D$ (f) $0 \subset D$

(g) $4 = \{4\}$ (h) $4 \in \{4\}$ (i) $0 = \emptyset$

(j) $0 \in \emptyset$

12. If $a \in X$, $b \in Y$, $X \subset Z$, and $Y \subset Z$,

(a) Is $a \in Z$?   (b) Is $b \in Z$?   (c) Is $a \in Y$?

(d) Can there be an element in Z which is an element of both X and Y?

(e) Can there be an element in Z which is an element of X but not Y?

(f) Can there be an element in Z which is neither an element of X nor of Y?

13. Note that Definition 1–5 (the definition that A and B are disjoint) may be written:

If $a \in A$, then $a \notin B$, and if $b \in B$, then $b \notin A$.

Write in a similar notation (Definition 1–6) the definition that $A = B$.

*14. Show by using Definition 1–4 that set equality has the following properties:

(a) Set equality is *reflexive:* For any set A, $A = A$.

(b) Set equality is *symmetric:* For any two sets A and B, if $A = B$, then $B = A$.

(c) Set equality is *transitive:* For any sets A, B, and C, if $A = B$ and $B = C$, then $A = C$.

1–3 Operations on sets. Once more let us return to our example, where the universal set U is the set of all letters in the English alphabet. If $V = \{a, e, i, o, u\}$ again denotes the set whose elements are the vowels, the remaining letters also form a set (in this case the set C, whose elements are all the consonants). In general, such a set is called the complement of the original set, so that C is the complement of V.

DEFINITION 1–7. *The complement of any set A, with respect to any stated or understood universal set, is the set of elements of the universal set that do not belong to A.*

This complement is denoted by A', and is written symbolically

$$A' = \{x | x \in U \text{ and } x \notin A\},$$

or more frequently, since it is understood that $x \in U$,

$$A' = \{x | x \notin A\}.$$

If $B = \{a, b, c, d, e\}$, where this is a subset of the set of all letters in the English alphabet, the set whose elements are either in this set B or in V, or in both, is the set $D = \{a, b, c, d, e, i, o, u\}$. Such a set is called the union of the sets B and V. The set whose elements are in both B and V is the set $E = \{a, e\}$. The set E is called the *intersection* of B and V.

DEFINITION 1–8. *The* union *of two sets A and B is the set of elements that belong to at least one of the sets A and B, that is, to A or B.**

We symbolize this union as $A \cup B$ (read "A union B"), and write

$$A \cup B = \{x | x \in A \text{ or } x \in B\}.$$

DEFINITION 1–9. *The* intersection *of two sets A and B is the set of elements that belong to both A and B.*

We symbolize this intersection as $A \cap B$ (read "A intersection B"), and write

$$A \cap B = \{x | x \in A \text{ and } x \in B\}.$$

Relations among subsets may frequently be clarified by a pictorial representation. With a rectangle representing the universe, any subset A may be indicated by a closed region within the rectangle. Then A', the complement of A, is that closed region within the rectangle but outside A. Such pictures, called Venn diagrams after the English logician John Venn (1834–1883), can, of course, be used for problems with any finite number of sets. Figure 1–1 represents the universe of all letters in the English alphabet, V the set of vowels, and its complement $V' = C$ the set of consonants. Figure 1–2 illustrates the set V and the set B, with the elements a and e in common.

ILLUSTRATION. Let $U = \{1, 2, 3, 4, 5, 6, 7, 8\}$ be the universe, and consider the subsets $X = \{1, 2, 3, 4, 5\}$, $Y = \{1, 2, 3\}$, and $Z = \{4, 6, 8\}$.

* In our everyday language the word "or" in the expression "p or q" sometimes means "p or q or both p and q" and other times "p or q, but not both p and q." In mathematics, it is always taken in the inclusive sense, synonymous with the legal use of "and/or," so that A *or* B means "A or B or both A and B."

FIGURE 1-1   FIGURE 1-2

        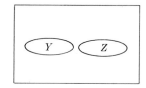

FIGURE 1-3

If we apply the definitions of this section, we have

$$X \cup Y = \{1, 2, 3, 4, 5\},$$
$$Y \cup Z = \{1, 2, 3, 4, 6, 8\},$$
$$Z \cup X = \{1, 2, 3, 4, 5, 6, 8\},$$
$$X \cap Y = \{1, 2, 3\}, \qquad Y \cap Z = \emptyset, \qquad Z \cap X = \{4\}.$$

We can, of course, form complements of these sets, unions and intersections of complements, and so on. For example,

$$X' = \{6, 7, 8\}, \qquad Y' = \{4, 5, 6, 7, 8\}, \qquad Z' = \{1, 2, 3, 5, 7\},$$
$$(X \cup Y)' = \{6, 7, 8\}, \qquad (Y \cap Z)' = \emptyset' = U,$$
$$X' \cup Y' = \{4, 5, 6, 7, 8\}, \qquad X' \cap Y' = \{6, 7, 8\}.$$

In Fig. 1-3, the sets X, Y, Z, taken in pairs, are illustrated by Venn diagrams.

PROBLEMS

1. If $U = \{0, 1, 2, 3, 4, 5, 6, 7, 8, 9\}$, the set of digits in our decimal system, and

$$A = \{0, 1, 2, 3, 4, 5\}, \qquad C = \{4, 5, 6, 7\},$$
$$B = \{2, 3, 4, 5\}, \qquad D = \{6, 7, 8, 9\},$$

find and tabulate

(a) $A \cup B$,   (b) $B \cup C$,   (c) $C \cap D$,
(d) $D \cup A$,   (e) $B \cap D$,   (f) $B \cap C$,
(g) $A \cup \emptyset$,   (h) $B \cap \emptyset$,   (i) $C \cup U$,
(j) $D \cap U$,   (k) B',   (l) C',
(m) $(A \cup B)'$,   (n) $(B \cap D)'$,   (o) $(U \cup \emptyset)'$.

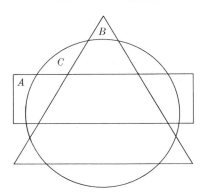

FIGURE 1–4

2. If $U = \{x|x$ is a letter in the English alphabet$\}$,

$A = \{x|x$ is a or one of the next four letters in the English alphabet$\} = \{a, b, c, d, e\}$,

$E = \{x|x$ is e or one of the next four letters in the English alphabet$\}$,

$I = \{x|x$ is i or one of the next four letters in the English alphabet$\}$,

find

(a) $A \cap E$,　　　　　(b) $E \cap I$,　　　　　(c) $I \cap \emptyset$,

(d) $\emptyset \cup A$,　　　　　(e) $A \cup \emptyset$,　　　　　(f) $E \cap U$.

3. Complete the given statements, where X is any subset of the universe U.

(a) $X \cup U$　　　　　(b) $X \cap U$　　　　　(c) $X \cup \emptyset$

(d) $X \cap \emptyset$　　　　　(e) $X \cap X$　　　　　(f) $X \cup X$

(g) $X \cup X'$　　　　　(h) $X \cap X'$　　　　　(i) $\emptyset \cap U$

*4. For any set A, the set of subsets of A is said to be exhaustive if the union of these subsets is A, and is said to be disjoint (recall Definition 1–5) if no two of the subsets have any elements in common. If $A = \{a, b, c\}$, tell whether the following set of subsets is exhaustive; disjoint.

(a) $\{a\}, \{b\}$　　　　　(b) $\{a\}, \{b, c\}$　　　　　(c) $\{a, b\}, \{b, c\}$

(d) $\{a\}, \{a, b\}$　　　　　(e) $\{a\}, \{b\}, \{c\}$

5. If in the diagram in Fig. 1–4, the area of the interior of the rectangle represents set A, the triangle set B, and the circle set C, indicate the area represented by

(a) $A \cup B$,　　　　　(b) $A \cap B$,　　　　　(c) $A \cap C$,

(d) $B \cup C$,　　　　　(e) $(A \cup B) \cap C'$,　　　　　(f) $(A \cup B)' \cap C$.

6. Show by using Venn diagrams that

(a) $A \cup B = B \cup A$,

(b) $A \cup (B \cup C) = (A \cup B) \cup C$,

(c) $A \cap (B \cup C) = (A \cap B) \cup (A \cap C)$,

(d) $(A \cup B)' = A' \cap B'$.

7. Show by using Venn diagrams that

(a) $A \cap B = B \cap A$,

(b) $A \cap (B \cap C) = (A \cap B) \cap C$,

(c) $A \cup (B \cap C) = (A \cup B) \cap (A \cup C)$,

(d) $(A \cap B)' = A' \cup B'$.

8. Show by using Venn diagrams that

(a) $A \cup B = A$ if and only if $B \subset A$,

(b) $A \cap B = B$ if and only if $B \subset A$,

(c) $B \subset A$ if and only if $A' \subset B'$,

(d) $(A')' = A$.

9. Tell under what conditions on the sets A and B we would have each of the following.

(a) $A \cap B = \emptyset$ (b) $A \cap B = U$ (c) $A \cup B = U$

(d) $A \cup B = \emptyset$ (e) $A \cap B = A$ (f) $A \cup B = A$

(g) $A \cap \emptyset = \emptyset$ (h) $A \cap U = A$ (i) $A \cup U = U$

(j) $A \cup U = A$ (k) $A \cup \emptyset = U$ (l) $A \cup \emptyset = \emptyset$

*10. If $n(A)$ represents the number of elements in the set A, we note that $n(A) = 3$ for the set in Problem 4. Give an example of two finite sets A and B, where

(a) $n(A \cup B) = n(A) + n(B)$,   (b) $n(A \cup B) \neq n(A) + n(B)$.

What is the condition on A and B so that (a) will always hold?

*11. Show by using a Venn diagram that for any finite sets A and B,

$$n(A \cup B) = n(A) + n(B) - n(A \cap B).$$

*12. It is sometimes desirable to consider the order of the elements in a set as significant. A pair of elements in which we distinguish one of the elements as the first and the other, not necessarily different, as the second is called an *ordered pair*. We denote such an ordered pair by (x, y), where x is the first and y is the second element. This is quite different from $\{x, y\} = \{y, x\}$, since order is immaterial when we are merely listing the elements of a set. We wish to distinguish between (x, y) and (y, x), and do so by defining the equality of two ordered pairs. *Two ordered pairs, (x_1, y_1) and (x_2, y_2), are equal* if and only if $x_1 = x_2$ and $y_1 = y_2$.

If X and Y are sets, the set of all ordered pairs (x, y) such that $x \in X$ and $y \in Y$ is called the *product set*, or cartesian product,† of X and Y, and is denoted by $X \times Y$. In symbols,

$$X \times Y = \{(x, y) | x \in X \text{ and } y \in Y\}.$$

For example, if $X = \{a, b\}$ and $Y = \{1, 2\}$, then $X \times Y$ is the set of ordered pairs $(a, 1)$, $(a, 2)$, $(b, 1)$, $(b, 2)$. However, $Y \times X$ is the set of ordered pairs $(1, a)$, $(1, b)$, $(2, a)$, $(2, b)$, so that $X \times Y \neq Y \times X$.

---

† The reason for this name will be clear as a result of the discussion in Chapter 4.

Find all the sets of ordered pairs for the product spaces $X \times X$, $X \times Y$, $Y \times X$, and $Y \times Y$ if

    (a) $X = \{a\}$, $Y = \{b\}$,
    (b) $X = \{a, b\}$, $Y = \{c\}$,
    (c) $X = \{a, b, c\}$, $Y = \{1, 2, 3\}$.

1–4 Integers. The first set of numbers encountered by everyone is the set of counting numbers, 1, 2, 3, . . . , to which we frequently referred in our discussion concerning sets. The mathematician calls this set of numbers *the set of positive integers,** or *natural numbers*, and uses it as the foundation for our entire number system. This set of numbers, together with the negative integers −1, −2, −3, . . . and the zero integer constitute the complete *set of integers*, which we shall denote by I.

In a study of any number system, such as the set of integers, in addition to the numbers themselves, we concern ourselves with certain basic operations on these numbers. The two most basic are addition and multiplication.

DEFINITION 1–10. *If A is a set of numbers, A is* closed *under the operation of addition if the sum of any two numbers in A is also in A.*

This is called the closure property of addition. A similar definition can be given for multiplication, or, in fact, any operation. A well-known property of the set of integers is that if any two integers are added or multiplied, the result is an integer. In line with the above definition, we say *I is closed under addition and multiplication.* There are, of course, many sets whose elements are integers which are not closed under either addition or multiplication. The set $\{1, 2, 3\}$ is one such set. Neither the number 5, the sum of 2 and 3, nor number 6, their product, is in the set. The set $\{-1, 0, 1\}$ is not closed under addition, but is closed under multiplication.

PROBLEMS

1. We noticed that the set of integers I was closed under addition and multiplication. Is it closed under: (a) subtraction, (b) division?

2. Is the set of natural numbers closed under: (a) addition, (b) multiplication, (c) subtraction, (d) division?

3. Examine the following sets with regard to closure under addition and multiplication: (a) $\{1\}$, (b) $\{1, 2, 3, 4, 5, 6\}$, (c) $\{1, 0\}$.

---

* Note the distinction between *the* set of positive integers, and *a* set of positive integers. *The* set means the set of all positive integers, while *a* set of positive integers means merely that its elements are integers, but that it does not necessarily contain all the integers.

*4. An *even natural number* is any natural number which may be expressed $2k$, where k is a natural number. Is *the* set of even natural numbers closed under: (a) addition, (b) multiplication?

*5. Define an odd natural number. Is *the* set of odd natural numbers closed under: (a) addition, (b) multiplication?

DEFINITION 1–11. *If a, b, and c are integers such that $a \cdot b = c$, a and b are called* factors *or* divisors *of c, and c is a* multiple *of a or b.*

Thus, 2, 3, and 5 are factors of 30, as are -6 or -15. We recall (Problem 4) that an *even integer* is any integer which has 2 as a factor (or is a multiple of 2). If we define an *odd integer* to be any integer which is not even, it is possible to express any odd integer as $2k + 1$, where k is some integer. The integer -8 is even since $-8 = 2 \cdot -4$, while 9 is odd since $9 = 2 \cdot 4 + 1$.

All positive integers except the number one may be classified as either *composite numbers* or *primes*. A positive integer is called *composite* if it is different from one and can be expressed as the product of two or more positive integers, which are its factors. In certain cases some of these factors may be equal.

For example, 4, 6, 9, and 12 are composite, for $4 = 2 \cdot 2$, $6 = 3 \cdot 2$, $9 = 3 \cdot 3$, and $12 = 3 \cdot 2 \cdot 2$. In fact, every even integer greater than 2 is composite.

A positive integer is called *prime* if it is different from one and is not composite. In other words, it can be expressed as a product of two positive integers only in the trivial way in which one factor is itself and the other the integer one. Examples of prime numbers are 2, 3, 5, and 7.

The *decomposition* of any composite number, that is, the expression of such a number as a product of prime numbers, is most important. Such a decomposition is always possible, since each factor which is composite can be expressed as the product of smaller factors, and ultimately the factors will all be prime. Thus, $60 = 12 \cdot 5 = 4 \cdot 3 \cdot 5 = 2 \cdot 2 \cdot 3 \cdot 5$. Moreover, a decomposition is unique† although the proof of this fact is too advanced for this discussion. Specifically, a composite number can be expressed as a product of prime factors in one and only one way, except for the order of the factors. Thus 60 can also be expressed as $15 \cdot 4 = 5 \cdot 3 \cdot 4 = 5 \cdot 3 \cdot 2 \cdot 2$. Two integers are called *relatively prime* or *prime to each other* if they contain no common prime factors. We shall consider factors again in a more general way in Article 3–5.

---

† For the proof of this statement as well as a general discussion of prime numbers, see R. Courant and H. Robbins, *What Is Mathematics?* New York: Oxford University Press, 1941; and Harriet Griffin, *Elementary Theory of Numbers*. New York: McGraw-Hill Book Company, 1954.

PROBLEMS

1. List all the factors of 12; of 120.

2. List the common divisors of 30 and 50.

3. If E is the set of all even integers and O is the set of all odd integers, notice that $E \subset I$ and $O \subset I$. What can be said about: (a) $E \cup O$, (b) $E \cap O$?

4. If E is the set of all even integers (integral multiples of 2) and T is the set of all integral multiples of 3, what can be said about $E \cap T$?

5. If S is the set of all integral multiples of 6 and T is the set of all integral multiples of 10, what can be said about $S \cap T$? With the result of this and Problem 4, can you state a generalization?

6. List the prime numbers between 1 and 100.

7. In the ninth book of his *Elements*, Euclid (3rd century B.C.) proved that the set $\{p|p$ is a prime number$\}$ is an infinite set. Is this set closed under: (a) addition, (b) multiplication?

8. Many primes occur in pairs separated by one integer. Such pairs are 3 and 5, 5 and 7, 11 and 13, 17 and 19. In fact, it has been conjectured, but never proved, that there is an infinite number of such pairs. List all such pairs less than 100.

9. Many mathematicians have unsuccessfully tried to discover an expression which will always result in a prime number. Consider the expression $p = n^2 - n + 41$.†

(a) What is the value of p for $n = 1, 2, 3, 4, 5$?
(b) What is its value for $n = 9, 10, 11$?
(c) Are the values of p in (a) and (b) prime numbers?
(d) What is the value of p when $n = 41$? Is this a prime number?

10. Recall that any even integer n can be expressed $n = 2k$ for some integer k. Use this definition to show that the set $E = \{x|x$ is an even integer$\}$ is closed under: (a) addition, (b) multiplication.

11. Show that the set $O = \{x|x$ is an odd integer$\}$ is closed under multiplication.

12. Show that the square of an even integer is even and that of an odd integer is odd.

*13. Show that if the square of any integer is even, the integer itself is even. (Recall that any integer is even or odd, and use Problem 12.)

14. Show that if an integer is a multiple of the integer a, its square is also a multiple of a.

1–5 Rational and irrational numbers. The classification of numbers as *rational* involves the formation of the quotient‡ of an integer by an integer. If a is an integer and b is an integer different from zero, then a/b may be defined as the number c which, when multiplied by b, gives a. That is,

---

† n^2 represents n times n.

‡ The word "quotient" is defined in Article 2–4.

c is the quotient and is defined by the equation $cb = a$. Fractions of the form $a/0$ are not defined. We therefore say that $a/0$ does not exist, and division by zero is not permitted.

DEFINITION 1–12. *Any number which can be expressed as the quotient or ratio of two integers (excluding division by zero) is called a* rational number.

The entire set of all such numbers is called *the set of rational numbers*, and is denoted by F. The numbers $\frac{5}{3}$, $-\frac{13}{2}$, and 1.414 are rational numbers. Any integer n, say 3, is a rational number, since $n = (n/1)$. Consequently, $I \subset F$. The number 1.414, which is an approximation for $\sqrt{2}$,* is a rational number, since

$$1.414 = \tfrac{1414}{1000} .$$

Any rational number may be written as a decimal. For example, $\frac{7}{4} = 1.75$, or $\frac{2}{11} = 0.1818 \ldots$. The decimal 1.75 is said to terminate, while the decimal $0.1818 \ldots$ is called a *periodic*† or *repeating decimal* since the two digits 18 repeat themselves. Indeed, a rational number may be identified by the fact that its decimal expansion either terminates or, if unending, is periodic. Numbers which are nonperiodic and unending, when expressed as decimals, are *not rational*. For example, the numbers $\sqrt{2}$, π (the ratio of the circumference of any circle to its diameter), and e (the base for logarithms used in calculus), which cannot be expressed as the quotient of two integers, cannot be written as terminating or unending periodic decimals.

The proofs that π and e are not rational are quite difficult and involve considerably more mathematics than we have at our disposal. However, a comparatively simple proof that $\sqrt{2}$ is not rational is possible. Our method of proof will be to assume that the statement of the theorem we wish to prove is false. On this assumption, we shall work logically with what we know and thus arrive at a contradiction. Because of this contradiction, we realize our assumption was incorrect, and consequently the statement of the theorem must be true. Such an argument is frequently called the method of *indirect proof* or *reductio ad absurdum*.

THEOREM 1–1. *The number $\sqrt{2}$ is not a rational number.*

Proof. Since we wish to prove that no integers p and q exist such that $p/q = \sqrt{2}$, we shall assume two such integers exist. Moreover, if two

---

* A number which, when multiplied by itself, results in 2.

† By "periodic" decimal we mean that a digit or block of digits repeat either from the decimal $(0.161616 \ldots)$ or after a certain stage $(3.2454545 \ldots)$.

such integers exist, we may reduce the fraction p/q to lowest terms by dividing out any common multiple. We therefore have

$$p/q = \sqrt{2}, \qquad (1\text{--}1)$$

where p and q are relatively prime. If we multiply each member of this equation by q, and square, we get

$$p^2 = 2q^2. \qquad (1\text{--}2)$$

Because of the closure property of I, p^2 and q^2 are integers, and in fact, p^2 is an even integer. Because of the result of Problem 13, p is an even integer, and we set it equal to $2r$, where r is an integer. Thus, $p = 2r$. If this value of p is substituted into Eq. (1–2), we have $4r^2 = 2q^2$, or

$$2r^2 = q^2,$$

and therefore q^2 is an even integer. It follows that q is an even integer. We have now arrived at a contradiction, namely, that the two relatively prime integers, p and q, both have 2 as a factor. Our original assumption is thus impossible, and there do *not* exist any integers p and q where $p/q = \sqrt{2}$; that is, $\sqrt{2}$ is not rational.

It is not difficult to prove that F is closed under the operations of addition or multiplication, provided we know the method of adding or multiplying fractions discussed in Articles 3–7 and 3–8. In fact, F is closed under all four of the elementary operations, including subtraction and division (except by zero), so that F is much more useful than I. It is not, however, a system which is completely satisfactory, for it does not permit numbers which, when written as decimals, may continue indefinitely without any period. For example, the number 0.1010010001 . . . is not permitted.

The entire set of numbers expressible as decimals (terminating or not) is called the *set of real numbers*, and those in this set which are not rational form the set of *irrational numbers*. If we let R denote the set of all real numbers, we have $I \subset F \subset R$. Moreover, with R as the universal set, F', the complement of F, can denote the set of all irrational numbers. Unfortunately, F' is not closed under addition since, for example,* the sum of $\sqrt{2}$ and $-\sqrt{2}$ (a number which is easily proved irrational, see Problem 10) is 0, a rational number. Neither is F' closed under multiplication, for $\sqrt{2} \cdot \sqrt{2} = 2$. However, any irrational number can be approximated by a rational number. For example, the rational number which approxi-

---

* If a statement or theorem is proved, it must be proved for all possible cases. If, on the other hand, we are required to disprove a statement, one example for which the statement is false will suffice.

mates $\sqrt{2}$, correct to three decimal places, is 1.414. The rational number $\frac{22}{7}$ is a common approximation for π, while a more accurate one is 3.1416. The set of all real numbers may be classified as follows:

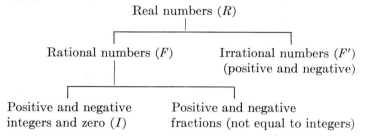

Real numbers (R)

Rational numbers (F)   Irrational numbers (F')
                                          (positive and negative)

Positive and negative   Positive and negative
integers and zero (I)   fractions (not equal to integers)

We shall deal primarily with real numbers in this book, but other types of numbers will arise from generalizations or extensions of real numbers. In Chapter 16, for example, we shall discuss the set of complex numbers, which includes imaginary numbers as well as real numbers. However, unless otherwise stated, all numbers will be regarded as belonging to the set of real numbers, and R will be our universal set.

PROBLEMS

1. Show that the following numbers are rational by Definition 1–12.

(a) 0.6   (b) $4\frac{3}{7}$ (c) −14.73   (d) 0

2. Show that the following are rational numbers.

(a) $-6 + \frac{3}{7}$ (b) $(2/3)/(5/2)$
(c) $(2 + \sqrt{5}) + (7 - \sqrt{5})$

3. Show that the following numbers can be expressed as terminating or periodic decimals and are therefore rational.

(a) $\frac{2}{3}$ (b) $\frac{4}{7}$ (c) $\frac{1}{32}$ (d) $\frac{1}{17}$

4. In expressing $\frac{1}{17}$ as a decimal, (a) what is the periodic repeating block of numbers?

(b) How many digits are there in this block of numbers?
(c) What are the remainders at each stage of the division process used to obtain this block?
(d) Explain why the division of p and q, where the integer p is less than the integer q, will always result in a terminating or periodic decimal. This explanation outlines a proof of what theorem?

5. Show that the following numbers can be expressed as the quotient of two integers.

(a) 3.242424 . . . . [If we let $x = 3.242424$, $100x = 324.242424$ . . . . If we subtract the corresponding members of these two equations, we obtain $99x = 321$, or $x = 107/33$.]

  (b) 6.272727 . . .   (c) 5.818181 . . .

  (d) 0.555 . . .   (e) 0.142857142857 . . .

6. (a) Outline a method which will always result in a solution for Problem 5. (b) Such a method outlines a proof of what theorem?

7. Prove that the set F is closed under: (a) addition [*Hint:* If $a = (p/q)$ and $b = (r/s)$, can $a + b$ be expressed as the quotient of two integers?], (b) multiplication, (c) subtraction, (d) division.

8. Construct a Venn diagram with R for the universe indicating the subsets F, F', and I.

9. If we assume $\sqrt{3}$ is not rational, prove that $5 + \sqrt{3}$ is not rational.

10. Prove that $-\sqrt{2}$ is not rational.

11. Prove that $(a + b\sqrt{2})/c$, where a, b, and c are integers and c is not 0, is not rational.

12. Prove that no rational number exists whose cube is 2.

1–6 Equality. We recall the definition which concerned the equality of two sets. The equality relation in general, we shall assume, is reflexive, symmetric, and transitive (see Problem 14, Article 1–2). Specifically, for all elements a, b, and c of R:

AXIOM E1. *Reflexive* property for equality: $a = a$.

AXIOM E2. *Symmetric* property for equality: If $a = b$, $b = a$.

AXIOM E3. *Transitive* property for equality: If $a = b$ and $b = c$, then $a = c$.

In addition, we shall assume the addition and multiplication properties.

AXIOM E4. *Addition* property for equality: If $a = b$ and $c = d$, then $a + c = b + d$.

AXIOM E5. *Multiplication* property for equality: If $a = b$, and $c = d$, then $a \cdot c = b \cdot d$.

Finally, we shall assume that any quantity may be substituted in any expression for an equal quantity.

We do not intend to belabor what is basic to the idea of equality, but rather wish to point out precisely what assumptions we do make, and we shall ordinarily use them henceforth without specific comment.

There are two main types of equations in mathematics, the *identity* and the *conditional* equation. These two have many of the same properties but differ in meaning. Let us distinguish between them.

DEFINITION 1–13. *An* identity *is a statement of equality which holds true for all permissible values* of the letters involved.*

----

* The *permissible values* are all those values for which both sides of the equation are defined.

Each such identity will be denoted by the symbol $\equiv$, in order to emphasize its nature. The following simple examples will help to clarify the concept.

ILLUSTRATION 1. $x + 2 + 5 - 4 - x \equiv 3$ holds for all values of x.

ILLUSTRATION 2. $x^2 - 4 \equiv (x + 2)(x - 2)$, where x^2 represents x times x, holds for all values of x. This statement may be checked by substituting any value for x in both sides of the identity, and it is proved in Article 3–4.

The conditional equation is more commonly used.

DEFINITION 1–14.   *The conditional equation is a statement of equality which holds true for some, but not all, permissible values of the letters involved.*

One is usually required to solve such an equation, that is, to find all possible values (the solution) for which the equation is true. Later we shall discuss the solving of equations, but now let us consider the following examples.

ILLUSTRATION 3. $x + 2 = 4$ is a conditional equation, since it is true only for $x = 2$.

ILLUSTRATION 4. $x^2 - 7x + 12 = 0$ is a conditional equation, since it is true only for $x = 3$ or 4. Any other value substituted for x in this equation will not satisfy it.

The use of the symbol $\equiv$ for an identity and of $=$ for a conditional equation emphasizes the distinction between the two types of equalities.

CHAPTER 2

THE ALGEBRA OF NUMBERS AS A LOGICAL SYSTEM

We have discussed rather briefly different sets of numbers. In this chapter it is our intention to present the real number system as a *deductive logical system*, and thus give some idea of not only the nature of the numbers themselves, but also the operations on these numbers and the properties they possess. As in any deductive system, we shall state our assumptions and definitions, and outline proofs for the most important theorems, leaving others for the reader to work out. Still others, similar to the theorems we discuss, we shall assume can be established and, as a result, accept without proof. In this way, we hope to convey the idea that any mathematical system involves a certain type of reasoning and that the methods of mathematicians are similar, whether the material be elementary algebra or some much more advanced field of mathematics.

2–1 The deductive system. If we recall the method of proof used in secondary-school geometry or any of the theorems proved in the last chapter, one thing is clear. Each proof involved some hypothesis and conclusion, where the conclusion came as a result of a logical process of reasoning from the hypothesis. But for us to be convinced of the truth of our conclusion, either we must assume the hypothesis true or we must have previously proved it. This hypothesis, in turn, must have been established by the use of facts still earlier established. Such a chain cannot back up indefinitely. There must, at some stage, have been a start. It is at this beginning, then, in a deductive system or argument that we say "We assume that certain facts are true." This beginning must consist of a number of words not defined and a set of statements not proved. Then, as we proceed from statement to statement, precise rules are used. Such basic laws of reasoning, intuitively used by all of us, are rarely stated. One such law states that a proposition is either true or false. Another states that if proposition A follows from proposition B, and B from C, then A follows from C.

A deductive method of reasoning, then, is the process of reasoning which starts with certain *undefined terms*, and certain assumed statements, called *axioms* or *postulates*, uses these to define additional concepts, and applies to these statements and definitions the *rules of deductive logic* to arrive at desired conclusions.

Although from the point of view of mathematical elegance, an irreducible minimum number of axioms is desired for any system, we shall not concern ourselves with a minimum number, but may list some axioms which can be proved from the others in order to present our system more clearly. Certain of these dependent axioms will be mentioned in the problems.

2–2 The real numbers. We are now in a position to present a set of axioms that are by no means unique, but which define or characterize the set of real numbers. It will be clear in considering these axioms that many of them are satisfied individually by other systems as well as the real numbers, and by this type of observation, their true meaning may be all the clearer. We shall separate the axioms into three groups. The first group (Axioms 1 through 6), which we shall consider in this chapter, are called the *axioms of a field*. The other two groups, the *order axioms* and the *completeness property*, will be presented in Chapter 4 and discussed at that time.

We therefore assume that the real-number system is a set of elements R (and form a field). These elements, the undefined terms, are called real numbers. There are also two operations, "+" and "·", called addition and multiplication,* which are defined such that the following axioms hold.

AXIOM 1. *The closure axioms.* For any a and $b \in R$, $a + b$ and $a \cdot b \in R$.

We recall that the sum or product of two integers is an integer, and that the sum or product of two rational numbers is a rational number. Axiom 1 is an equivalent statement for any two real numbers.

AXIOM 2. *The associative axioms.* For any a, b, and $c \in R$,

$$(a + b) + c \equiv a + (b + c),$$
$$(a \cdot b) \cdot c \equiv a \cdot (b \cdot c).$$

The first part of Axiom 2 states that the result is not affected by the way in which we group real numbers for addition. The second part states the same for multiplication. Since addition is associative, we may write $a + b + c$ without parentheses, defining this to mean either $(a + b) + c$ or $a + (b + c)$. In fact, because of closure and the associative property, the sum of any number of real numbers is well defined, and again, a similar statement can be made for the product of any number of real numbers.

_____

* We shall use the usual symbols for grouping two or more numbers as a single quantity, namely parentheses ( ), brackets [ ], or braces { }, when it is clear that they are not used for defining sets. We shall also write ab or $a(b)$, or $(a)b$ or $(a)(b)$, for $a \cdot b$.

Axiom 3. *The commutative axioms.* For any a and $b \in R$,

$$a + b \equiv b + a,$$
$$a \cdot b \equiv b \cdot a.$$

Axiom 3 states that the order in which we either add or multiply real numbers does not affect the result.

Axiom 4. *The distributive axioms.* For any a, b, and $c \in R$,

$$a \cdot (b + c) \equiv (a \cdot b) + (a \cdot c),$$
$$(b + c) \cdot a \equiv (b \cdot a) + (c \cdot a).$$

Axiom 4 states that the result is the same whether we multiply a certain real number by the sum of two real numbers or multiply a number by each of two numbers and then add. The first part of Axiom 4 is called the left-hand distributive law. Neither part of Axiom 4 is independent, but both may be proved by use of the other and the previous axioms. (See Problem 10 below.)

These four axioms may be considered together, for they concern the methods of combining the real numbers by means of the basic operations. They are so simple that you have probably always used them without realizing exactly what properties you were employing. Nevertheless, they are basic. The problems below will provide a better understanding of them and point out where they are used in our ordinary arithmetic and elementary algebra.

PROBLEMS

1. What is meant by the statement that sets are closed under the operation of "$\cup$"? of "$\cap$"?

2. If the operation "$\cup$" for sets $A, B, C, \ldots$ is interpreted as "sum," analogous statements for Axioms 2 and 3, with regard to addition, would be

$$A \cup (B \cup C) \equiv (A \cup B) \cup C \qquad \text{and} \qquad A \cup B \equiv B \cup A.$$

By using Venn diagrams, show that these relations are true.

3. If the operation "$\cap$" for sets $A, B, C, \ldots$ is interpreted as "product," analogous statements for Axioms 2 and 3, with regard to multiplication, would be

$$A \cap (B \cap C) \equiv (A \cap B) \cap C \qquad \text{and} \qquad A \cap B \equiv B \cap A.$$

By using Venn diagrams, show that these relations are true.

4. With the same interpretations as in Problems 2 and 3, Axiom 4 would state that for any three sets A, B, and C,

$$A \cap (B \cup C) \equiv (A \cap B) \cup (A \cap C).$$

Show whether this relation is true by using a Venn diagram.

5. If the $\cap$ and $\cup$ are interchanged in Problem 4, we would have

$$A \cup (B \cap C) \equiv (A \cup B) \cap (A \cup C).$$

Show whether this relation is true by using a Venn diagram. Is the analogous statement true for real numbers?

6. All operations on real numbers are not associative. (a) What can be said about the equality of $2 - (3 - 4)$ and $(2 - 3) - 4$? (b) What can be said about $2 \div (3 \div 4)$ and $(2 \div 3) \div 4$? Give other examples of operations which are not associative.

7. Are the operations "$-$" and "$\div$" commutative for the set R? Give other examples of operations which are not commutative.

8. What real number should appear in the blank spaces below in order that the statements be true? State what axioms are used.

(a) $5 \cdot (4 + \underline{\hspace{1cm}}) = 5 \cdot 4 + 5 \cdot 6$

(b) $3 \cdot (\underline{\hspace{1cm}} + 4) = 3 \cdot 7 + \underline{\hspace{1cm}} \cdot 4$

(c) $4 \cdot 8 + 3 \cdot \underline{\hspace{1cm}} = (\underline{\hspace{1cm}} + \underline{\hspace{1cm}}) \cdot 8$

(d) $\underline{\hspace{1cm}} \cdot (3 + 7) = 8 \cdot \underline{\hspace{1cm}} + 8 \cdot \underline{\hspace{1cm}}$

9. In each of the following, several of the axioms are used to make the assertion of equality. Tell which ones are used and where.

(a) $(x + 2) + a \equiv 2 + (a + x)$

[*Hint*: $(x + 2) + a \equiv (2 + x) + a$ (by Axiom 3)
                  $\equiv 2 + (x + a)$ (by Axiom 2)
                  $\equiv 2 + (a + x)$†   (by Axiom 3)]

(b) $(ab)c \equiv (cb)a$

(c) $a(x + 2) + a(x + 3) \equiv a(2x + 5)$ [We must assume we know $1 + 1 = 2$ and $2 + 3 = 5$.]

(d) $(x + 1)6 + (x + 1)y \equiv (y + 6)(x + 1)$

(e) $(b + c + d)a \equiv ab + ac + ad$

*(f) $(x + y)(a + b) \equiv xa + ay + xb + by$

(g) $(x + 2)(x + 3) \equiv x^2 + 5x + 6$ [We must assume we know $2 + 3 = 5$ and $2 \cdot 3 = 6$.]

*10. Prove the right-hand distributive axiom, $(b + c)a \equiv ba + ca$, by using the left-hand distributive axiom and any others that are needed. State the axioms used.

11. Axioms 1 through 4 have been used so frequently in common practice that we may not always realize when they are used. If we assume addition tables for numbers 1 through 9, and a knowledge of place value of the digits, we can add any two integers, and have the result completely justified. Let us

---

† Note that Axiom E3, the third axiom for equality (Article 1–6), is used several times.

add 37 and 45. Give the reasons for each step. Since $37 = 3 \cdot 10 + 7$, and $45 = 4 \cdot 10 + 5$, we have

$$
\begin{aligned}
37 + 45 &= (3 \cdot 10 + 7) + (4 \cdot 10 + 5) \quad \text{Place value of digits}\\
&= [(3 \cdot 10 + 7) + 4 \cdot 10] + 5\\
&= [3 \cdot 10 + (7 + 4 \cdot 10)] + 5\\
&= [3 \cdot 10 + (4 \cdot 10 + 7)] + 5\\
&= [(3 \cdot 10 + 4 \cdot 10) + 7] + 5\\
&= (3 \cdot 10 + 4 \cdot 10) + (7 + 5)\\
&= (3 + 4) \cdot 10 + (7 + 5)\\
&= 7 \cdot 10 + 12 \quad\quad\quad\quad\quad\quad \text{Addition tables}\\
&= 7 \cdot 10 + (1 \cdot 10 + 2)\\
&= (7 \cdot 10 + 1 \cdot 10) + 2\\
&= (7 + 1) \cdot 10 + 2\\
&= 8 \cdot 10 + 2\\
&= 82.
\end{aligned}
$$

12. Do the same for
(a) $21 + 36$,   (b) $78 + 45$,
(c) 12×16,   (d) 23×36.

(Assume the multiplication tables for integers 1 through 9 and that $10 \cdot 10 = 100$.)

13. Simplify the sum by combining similar terms. Tell what axioms are used. Assume the ordinary addition and multiplication of the integers.

(a) $(x^2 + 2x + 5) + (3x^2 + 5x + 2)$
(b) $3(x^2 + 5x + 6) + 4(2x^2 + 7x + 1)$

14. Express the following products as sums by using Axiom 4, and simplify as in Problem 13. Tell what axioms are used at every step.

(a) $(x + 2y)(x + 3y)$ (b) $(2x + 3y)(x + 5y)$
(c) $(x + 1)(x + 2)(x + 3)$ (d) $(x^2 + 5x + 10)(2x + 3)$

*15. One interpretation of Axiom E4 (Article 1–6) for equality states: If $a \equiv b$ and $c \equiv c$, then $a + c \equiv b + c$. Another might be, if $a \equiv a$ and $c \equiv d$, then $a + c \equiv a + d$. If the first of these properties is always true, we say addition on the right is permitted, while if the second is true, we say addition on the left is permitted. Fortunately, both of these are true for real numbers.

In any system, if addition on the right is permitted, what axiom allows us the further advantage of addition on the left?

16. Show why both multiplication on the right and on the left are permitted for real numbers.

In addition to the four axioms we have just studied, there are more complex axioms involving the properties of the numbers themselves and certain special numbers. Two of these are concerned with identity elements, one for each operation, and, as before, we state them under one number in Axiom 5.

AXIOM 5. *The identity axioms.* For any $a \in R$, there exist two unequal numbers (read "zero" and "one," respectively) such that

$$a + 0 \equiv a,$$
$$a \cdot 1 \equiv a.$$

Since 0 and 1 are elements of R, and, by Axiom 3, these operations in R are commutative, we immediately know that $a + 0 = 0 + a = a$, and $a \cdot 1 = 1 \cdot a = a$. The real number *zero* is called the *identity* or *identity element* for the operation addition, while the number *one* is the *identity element* for multiplication.

There are two other axioms, which again we shall list together, that also imply the existence of certain elements or numbers in our set of real numbers. Since these two axioms are frequently used in proofs that also involve Axiom 5, we shall state them here.

AXIOM 6. *The inverse axioms.* For any $a \in R$, there exists another element of R, denoted by $-a$, (read "minus a" or "the negative of a") such that

$$a + (-a) \equiv 0.$$

Also, for any $a \in R$ ($a \neq 0$), there exists another element of R, denoted by $1/a$ (read "the reciprocal of a") such that

$$a \cdot \frac{1}{a} \equiv 1.$$

In each case, the result of combining (by either operation) any element with its *inverse* is the identity element for that operation. Therefore, by Axiom 6 we are stating that any number has an *inverse* with respect to each of the two operations. Since both addition and multiplication are commutative operations in R, we also have immediately $-a + a \equiv 0$ and $(1/a) \cdot a \equiv 1$. We noted in Article 1–5 that division by zero is undefined. It is for this reason that $a = 0$ is excluded in the second part of Axiom 6.

EXAMPLE 1. Show that $-b + (a + b) \equiv a$.

Solution. By using the commutative and associative axioms, we have

$$-b + (a + b) \equiv -b + (b + a) \equiv (-b + b) + a.$$

Since $-b + b \equiv 0$ and $0 + a \equiv a$, we obtain the required result.

EXAMPLE 2. When there is one and only one element with a given property, we say the element is *unique*. Show that zero, the identity element for addition, is unique.

Solution. If we assume zero is not unique, there is another element $0'$, such that $a + 0' \equiv a$ for all a. Thus, we would have $a + 0' \equiv a$ and $a + 0 \equiv a$ for all a, so that $a + 0' \equiv a + 0$. If we add $-a$ to each member of this equation, by Axiom E4, we have

$$-a + (a + 0') \equiv -a + (a + 0),$$

and by the associative axiom,

$$(-a + a) + 0' \equiv (-a + a) + 0.$$

Since $-a + a \equiv 0$ by Axiom 6, $0 + 0' \equiv 0 + 0$, and therefore, $0' \equiv 0$ (why?). Explain why this completes the proof.

It is also possible to prove that the identity element for multiplication is unique (see Problem 21 below).

PROBLEMS

One or more of the axioms for the set of real numbers R is used to make the statement in each of Problems 1 through 20. Tell precisely which of the six axioms are used and where they are used in each problem.

1. $3 + 0 = 3$
2. $0 + 2 = 2$
3. $-a + 0 = -a$
4. $1 \cdot 6 = 6$
5. $1 \cdot 1 = 1$
6. $0 + 0 = 0$
7. $-1 \cdot 1 = -1$
8. $\pi + (-\pi) = 0$
9. $-\sqrt{2} + \sqrt{2} = 0$
10. $(-5) + [-(-5)] = 0$
11. $3 \cdot \dfrac{1}{3} = 1$
12. $\dfrac{1}{-4} (-4) = 1$
13. $\dfrac{1}{5} \cdot \dfrac{1}{1/5} = 1$
14. $1 \cdot \dfrac{1}{1} = 1$
15. $x + y \equiv x \cdot 1 + y \cdot 1$
16. $0 + 1 \cdot (x + y) \equiv x + y$
17. $-(xy) + xy \equiv 0$
18. $3\sqrt{2x} \cdot \dfrac{1}{3\sqrt{2x}} \equiv 1, \quad (x \neq 0)$
19. $-(a + 0 + b) + (b + a) \equiv 0$
20. $\dfrac{1}{2x + 3y} (2x + 3y) \equiv 1, \quad 2x + 3y \neq 0$

21. Show that the identity element for multiplication, namely one, is unique.

22. Show that for any real number $a \in R$: (a) its inverse for addition is unique, (b) its inverse for multiplication is unique.

23. If we consider the sets A, B, C, ... as elements and consider the set $\emptyset$ as the identity element for the operation "$\cup$" and the set U as the identity element for the operation "$\cap$," to what axioms are the following analogous: $A \cup \emptyset \equiv A$? $A \cap U \equiv A$?

2–3 Certain basic theorems. Let us now prove several theorems that are direct results of the axioms in the last article. Not only are these results important in themselves; the general approach and methods of proof should also be studied and understood, because this material will be useful in the problems and for understanding later work.

In all the theorems and definitions in this article we shall consider the several letters a, b, c, . . . as real numbers, elements of the set R. Moreover, unless there are specifically stated restrictions on these numbers, we shall assume the numbers to be any real numbers that make sense. Many of the theorems involving the operation of addition have a corresponding theorem which involves the operation of multiplication. We shall indicate this by adding an "A" or "M" to the number of the theorem.

Axiom E4, Article 1–6, has been used several times. We are now able to prove the converse of this statement, the so-called *additive cancellation property.*

THEOREM 2–1A. *If $a + c \equiv b + c$, then $a \equiv b$.*

Proof. Since c is a real number, $-c$ is a real number by Axiom 6, and, using Axiom E4, we have $(a + c) + (-c) \equiv (b + c) + (-c)$. Applying the associative axiom, Axiom 2, we get $a + [c + (-c)] \equiv b + [c + (-c)]$, and since $c + (-c) \equiv 0$ (Axiom 6), this becomes $a + 0 \equiv b + 0$. Then, because of Axiom 5, $a \equiv b$, our desired result.

A similar theorem for multiplication is possible.

THEOREM 2–1M. *If $ac \equiv bc$, and $c \not\equiv 0$, then $a \equiv b$.*

Proof. (Give the reasons for each step.) Since $ac \equiv bc$,

$$(ac)\,\frac{1}{c} \equiv (bc)\,\frac{1}{c}.$$

Thus

$$a\left(c \cdot \frac{1}{c}\right) \equiv b\left(c \cdot \frac{1}{c}\right)$$

or, $a \cdot 1 \equiv b \cdot 1$. Thus $a \equiv b$.

A second theorem, similar to that considered in Problem 22(a) of the last article, should be emphasized.

THEOREM 2–2A. *If $a + b \equiv 0$, then $b \equiv -a$.*

Proof. If we add $-a$ on the left (recall Problem 15 in the first set of problems in Article 2–2) to both members of this equation, we have $-a + (a + b) \equiv -a + 0$. If we use the associative axiom, this becomes $(-a + a) + b \equiv -a + 0$; and since $-a + a \equiv 0$ on the left, and $-a + 0 \equiv -a$ on the right, we get, $0 + b \equiv -a$, so that $b \equiv -a$.

Since b represents any number which, when added to a, results in zero, and since we have proved $b \equiv -a$, we have in fact proved that the inverse for addition is unique. Again, there is an analogous theorem for multiplication.

THEOREM 2–2M. *If $ab \equiv 1$ and $a \not\equiv 0$, then $b \equiv (1/a)$.*

There are several theorems, similar in nature (and proof), which show important properties of our number system. We shall prove some of these, and list some other ones as problems. Note that for each such statement which involves addition, there is an analogous statement involving multiplication.

THEOREM 2–3A. *If $a \equiv b$, then $-a \equiv -b$.*

Proof. Since $a \equiv b$, we may add $-a$ to both members of the equation, so that $a + (-a) \equiv b + (-a)$, which gives $0 \equiv b + (-a)$, since $a + (-a) \equiv 0$. If we now look at what we wish to prove and notice the $-b$ on one side of our expected result, our next step is clear. We must add $-b$ to both members of our equation $0 \equiv b + (-a)$. We add $-b$ on the left of each member of the equation (why?) and get $-b + 0 \equiv -b + [b + (-a)]$, which reduces to $-b \equiv -a$ (why?). This may be written $-a \equiv -b$, our desired result.

We now wish to prove one of the fundamental properties of the number zero, which, of course, we have used intuitively since we first began arithmetic. The proof may seem somewhat artificial, but ideas of how to start such proofs and methods for carrying them out come from experience and practice. Therefore the student should not be discouraged when he first encounters them.

THEOREM 2–4. *For all $a \in R$, $a \cdot 0 \equiv 0$.*

Proof. Since $0 + 0 \equiv 0$, we know that $a \cdot (0 + 0) \equiv a \cdot 0$. The left member of this equation may be expanded by the distributive axiom. Since the right member of this equation is the product of two real numbers, and thus a real number, it can be written $a \cdot 0 + 0$, by the identity axiom. Consequently,

$$a \cdot 0 + a \cdot 0 \equiv a \cdot 0 + 0.$$

Application of the left cancellation law for addition (see Problem 1 below), gives us our result.

This theorem might have been stated another way, if we recall that the word "or" in mathematics means "and/or" (see the footnote in Article 1–3).

THEOREM 2–4. *If $a \equiv 0$ or $b \equiv 0$, then $ab \equiv 0$.*

The converse of Theorem 2–4 is one of the most basic theorems in algebra. It is useful in the solutions of quadratic or higher-degree equations when they are solved by the method of factoring. Although we shall refer to it again when we come to that topic, we now state and prove it.

THEOREM 2–5. *If $ab \equiv 0$, then $a \equiv 0$ or $b \equiv 0$.*

Proof. If $a \equiv 0$, the theorem is proved. If not, the number a has an inverse with respect to multiplication, namely $1/a$. If we multiply both members of the equation $ab \equiv 0$ by $1/a$, we get $(1/a) \cdot (ab) \equiv (1/a) \cdot 0$. With the use of the associative law, and the facts that $(1/a) \cdot a \equiv 1$, $1 \cdot b \equiv b$ on the left, and $(1/a) \cdot 0 \equiv 0$ on the right, we have our result.

In addition to studying the theorems we have proved, the student should do all the problems. Then most of the basic ideas in algebra and arithmetic should be clear, and the logical reasons behind the ideas should be apparent.

PROBLEMS

*1. If $c + a \equiv c + b$, show that $a \equiv b$. This is called, the left cancellation property for addition. (Recall Theorem 2–1A.)

*2. If $ca \equiv cb$, and $c \neq 0$, show that $a \equiv b$.

3. Prove Theorem 2–2A, by writing $a + b \equiv 0$ as $a + b \equiv a + (-a)$, using the commutative axiom and Theorem 2–1A.

4. Show that if $a + b \equiv 0$, $a \equiv -b$.

5. Prove Theorem 2–2M.

6. If $a \equiv b$ and neither a nor $b \equiv 0$, show that $(1/a) \equiv (1/b)$.

7. If $a \equiv -b$, show that $-a \equiv b$.

8. If $a \equiv (1/b)$ $(a, b \neq 0)$, show that $b \equiv (1/a)$.

*9. Show that for all a, $-(-a) \equiv a$. [*Hint:* $-(-a) + (-a) \equiv 0.$]

10. State and prove a theorem analogous to that in Problem 9, where the operation is multiplication.

*11. Show that $-0 = 0$. [*Hint:* $0 + 0 = 0$ and $0 + (-0) = 0.$] Give reasons for each of these statements.

12. State and prove a theorem analogous to that in Problem 11, where the operation is multiplication.

13. If $abc \equiv 0$, show that a or b or $c \equiv 0$.

*14. Show that $-(ab) \equiv (-a)b$, giving reasons for each step. We are now able to write $-ab$ for either of these two expressions.

$$[Hint: \quad -(ab) + (ab) \equiv 0 \equiv (-a + a)$$
$$\equiv (-a + a)b$$
$$\equiv (-a)b + ab.]$$

As a result of this problem, we have, for example, $-6 = (-2)(3)$.

*15. Show that $(-1)a \equiv -(1 \cdot a) \equiv -a$. [*Hint:* See Problem 14.]

*16. Show that $(-a)(-b) \equiv ab$. As a result of this problem, we have, for example, $(-2)(-3) = 2 \cdot 3 = 6$.

17. Explain why: (a) $(-1)(-1) = 1$, (b) $(-1)(-1)(-1) = -1$.

2–4 Further theorems. In this chapter we have used the sign "$-$" in only one way, namely, as with a letter such as $-a$, to denote the inverse of a number with respect to addition. We are now able to define subtraction, or the difference of two real numbers, in terms of addition and this inverse element.

DEFINITION 2–1. *The expression $a - b$ is equivalent to $a + (-b)$ and is called "the difference of a and b" or "b subtracted from a."**

As a result of this definition, the sign "$-$" will be used in two different senses, each of which should be clearly understood.

ILLUSTRATION 1. Because of the definition of subtraction (and the associative and commutative axioms), we have

$$a + b - c \equiv a + b + (-c) \equiv a + (-c) + b \equiv a - c + b$$
$$\equiv (-c) + a + b \equiv -c + a + b.$$

As a consequence of this definition and of the results from Article 2–3, we have all the usual properties of subtraction.

THEOREM 2–6. $a(b - c) \equiv ab - ac.$

Proof. Since by definition, $b - c \equiv b + (-c)$, we have $a(b - c) \equiv a[b + (-c)]$, and because of the distributive axiom, this is equal to $ab + a(-c)$. But $a(-c) \equiv -ac$ by Problem 14 of Article 2–3, so that $a(b - c) \equiv ab + (-ac)$, which, as a result of the above definition, may be written $a(b - c) \equiv ab - ac.$

Two additional frequently encountered properties which involve the "$-$" sign appear in Problem 4 below. Special attention should be given to them.

Division of two real numbers is defined in terms of the operation of multiplication.

DEFINITION 2–2. *The expression a/b, where $b \neq 0$, is equivalent to $a \cdot (1/b)$ and is called "the quotient of a by b."*†

ILLUSTRATION 2.   (a) Since $(a/b) \equiv a \cdot (1/b)$ if $b \neq 0$, $b(a/b) \equiv a$;

   (b) Since $(a/1) \equiv a \cdot (1/1) \equiv a \cdot 1$, $(a/1) \equiv a$;

   (c) $(0/a) \equiv 0 \cdot (1/a) \equiv 0$ if $a \neq 0$.

---

* Some mathematicians prefer to use an equivalent, but different, definition. See Problems 5 and 6 below.

† In the discussion of rational numbers in Article 1–5 we said a/b might be defined as that number c such that $a = bc$. This, in fact, may be done, but in the above logical treatment we prefer the definition in terms of a and the inverse of b as stated. (See Problem 14 of this article.)

Many of the properties of division and/or fractions are results of this definition and can be proved directly. Since there is rarely a unique method of proof, the student is encouraged not only to understand any proofs presented, but also to consider other and possibly simpler approaches. We shall give two basic theorems in this article (in addition to those in the problems), and others will appear when the need arises.

THEOREM 2–7. $\dfrac{a}{b} \cdot \dfrac{c}{d} \equiv \dfrac{ac}{bd}$ $(b, d \neq 0)$.

Proof. By definition,

$$\frac{ac}{bd} \equiv ac \cdot \frac{1}{bd}.$$

But

$$ac \cdot \frac{1}{bd} \equiv ac \cdot \frac{1}{bd} \cdot \left(b \cdot \frac{1}{b}\right) \cdot \left(d \cdot \frac{1}{d}\right) \qquad \text{(Why?)}$$

$$\equiv a \cdot c \cdot \left(bd \cdot \frac{1}{bd}\right) \cdot \frac{1}{b} \cdot \frac{1}{d} \qquad \text{(Why?)}$$

$$\equiv \left(a \cdot \frac{1}{b}\right) \cdot \left(c \cdot \frac{1}{d}\right) = \frac{a}{b} \cdot \frac{c}{d}. \qquad \text{(Why?)}$$

The proofs of the next two theorems follow immediately from this theorem. Recall how frequently their results have been assumed in past experience.

THEOREM 2–8. $\dfrac{a}{b} \equiv \dfrac{ax}{bx}$ $(b, x \neq 0)$.

Proof. Since, by Theorem 2–7,

$$\frac{ax}{bx} \equiv \frac{a}{b} \cdot \frac{x}{x},$$

we have

$$\frac{ax}{bx} \equiv \frac{a}{b} \cdot 1 \equiv \frac{a}{b}.$$

THEOREM 2–9. $(a/b) \equiv (c/d)$ if and only if $ad \equiv bc$ $(b, d \neq 0)$.

Proof. We recall that such a statement requires two proofs. (a) We must show that if $(a/b) \equiv (c/d)$, then $ad \equiv bc$. By Axiom E5, and the given condition $(a/b) \equiv (c/d)$, we know

$$\frac{a}{b} \cdot b \cdot d \equiv \frac{c}{d} \cdot b \cdot d,$$

so that

$$a \cdot \left(\frac{1}{b} \cdot b\right) \cdot d \equiv c \cdot \left(\frac{1}{d} \cdot d\right) \cdot b, \qquad \text{or} \qquad ad \equiv bc.$$

(b) Also, we must show that if $ad \equiv bc$, then $(a/b) \equiv (c/d)$. Again, by Axiom E5, and the condition $ad \equiv bc$, we have

$$a \cdot d \cdot \left(\frac{1}{d} \cdot \frac{1}{b} \right) \equiv b \cdot c \cdot \left(\frac{1}{d} \cdot \frac{1}{b} \right),$$

so that

$$a \cdot \frac{1}{b} \cdot \left(d \cdot \frac{1}{d} \right) \equiv c \cdot \frac{1}{d} \cdot \left(b \cdot \frac{1}{b} \right),$$

or

$$\frac{a}{b} \equiv \frac{c}{d}.$$

The reasons for each step should be furnished by the student.

PROBLEMS

1. Explain why $a - a \equiv 0$.

2. Explain why $(a/a) \equiv 1$.

3. Show that $(a - b)c \equiv ac - bc$.

*4. We learned in elementary algebra that the removal of parentheses (or any symbol of grouping) preceded by a minus sign requires a change of each sign within the parentheses. Specifically, (a) $-(a + b) \equiv -a - b$ [Hint: See Problem 15, Article 2–3.]; (b) $-(a - b) \equiv -a + b$. Show that these statements are true.

5. Show that $b + (a - b) \equiv a$.

6. Show that if $a - b \equiv c$, $b + c \equiv a$. Note that this is the property used in elementary school to check subtraction problems.

7. If $x + a = b$, show that $x \equiv b - a$. This is one of the properties frequently used in solving simple equations. Another is stated in Problem 11.

8. If $a \neq 0$, show that $a(b/a) \equiv b$.

9. If $(a/b) \equiv 1$, show that $a \equiv b$.

*10. Show that

$$-\frac{a}{b} \equiv \frac{-a}{b} \equiv \frac{a}{-b}.$$

[Hint: Recall $-(a/b) = -\{a \cdot (1/b)\}$.]

*11. If $ax \equiv b$ $(a \neq 0)$, show that $x \equiv (b/a)$.

12. If $(a/b) \equiv (c/b)(b \neq 0)$, show that $a \equiv c$.

*13. If $c \neq 0$, show that

$$\frac{a + b}{c} \equiv \frac{a}{c} + \frac{b}{c}.$$

*14. Assuming that $b \neq 0$, prove that $(a/b) \equiv c$ if and only if $a \equiv bc$.

*15. Assuming that $b \neq 0$, prove that $(a/b) \equiv c + (d/b)$ if and only if $a \equiv bc + d$.

CHAPTER 3

EXTENSIONS OF THE LOGIC OF ALGEBRA

In this chapter we shall continue our discussion of fundamental notions and processes. Many of the theorems from the last chapter will be used as we construct the algebraic framework for most mathematics. The ideas considered here will appear throughout this book, and they must be thoroughly understood.

3–1 Addition of algebraic expressions. Any combination of symbols and numbers related by the fundamental operations of algebra is called an *algebraic expression*.

ILLUSTRATION 1. $5a + 6b$, $2ax^2$, and $(6x + 5y)2x$ are algebraic expressions.

Any algebraic expression consisting of distinct parts connected by plus or minus signs is called an *algebraic sum*. Each distinct part, together with its sign, is called a *term* of the expression.

ILLUSTRATION 2. In the algebraic sum $2x^2 - 3y^2 - 5$, $2x^2$ is one term, $-3y^2$ another, and -5 is a third term.

In a particular term consisting of two or more factors, any one of the factors or the product of any set of the factors may be called the *coefficient* of the product of the other factors. For example, in the term $2x^2y$, 2 is the coefficient of x^2y, $2x^2$ is the coefficient of y, and $2y$ is the coefficient of x^2. Frequently it is convenient to distinguish between numerical coefficients and letter-symbol coefficients. In determining the sum or difference of two algebraic expressions by combining similar terms, we use coefficients and continue to apply the associative axioms.

ILLUSTRATION 3.   The sum of $2x - 3y + 5$ and $x + 2y - 1$ is

$$(2x - 3y + 5) + (x + 2y - 1) \equiv 2x + x - 3y + 2y + 5 - 1$$
$$\equiv 3x - y + 4.$$

ILLUSTRATION 4.   The difference between $2x - 3y + 5$ and $x + 2y - 1$ is

$$(2x - 3y + 5) - (x + 2y - 1) \equiv 2x - 3y + 5 - x - 2y + 1$$
$$\equiv x - 5y + 6.$$

Both here and in Example 1, below, we use the result established in Problem 4, Article 2–4.

We have stated that algebraic expressions are called algebraic sums when either addition or subtraction is involved. If the expression consists of just one term, it is called a *monomial*. The algebraic sum or difference of two terms is called a *binomial;* and, in general, an algebraic expression consisting of a sum of any number of terms is called a *multinomial*. The expression $2x/3y^2$ is a monomial, while $3x^2 - 2y$ is a binomial.

EXAMPLE 1. Simplify the expression $4x - [2x - 3y - (x + 4y)] + (x - 8)$ by removing parentheses or brackets. Then combine similar terms.

Solution. This is done by repeated application of the result from Problem 4, Article 2–4, and the associative axiom.

$$4x - [2x - 3y - (x+4y)] + (x-8) \equiv 4x - [2x - 3y - x - 4y] + x - 8$$
$$\equiv 4x - 2x + 3y + x + 4y + x - 8$$
$$\equiv 4x + 7y - 8.$$

The removal of parentheses (or any symbol of grouping) preceded by a minus sign requires changing the sign of each term within the parentheses, but parentheses preceded by a plus sign may be removed without changing the expression in the parentheses.

EXAMPLE 2. Find the value of $-2xy + 3x - 4y$ when $x = 3$ and $y = -2$.

Solution. Substitute 3 for x and -2 for y:

$$-2(3)(-2) + 3(3) - 4(-2) = 12 + 9 + 8 = 29.$$

PROBLEMS

In each of the following, (a) find the sum of the expressions, and (b) subtract the second expression from the first.

1. $2a + 3b - 4$ and $a - 2b + 3$ 2. $a - 2b + 3c$ and $2a + 4b - c$
3. $4x + 3y + z$ and $2x + 3y - 2z$ 4. $2x + y + 5$ and $3y - 2z - 4$
5. $2(x - 3y)$ and $-5(2x + y)$ 6. $-(x + 2y - z)$ and $3(x - y + 2z)$

In each of the following, remove all symbols of grouping and combine like terms.

7. $x - (2y + 3x) - 2y$
8. $3x - (2y - 4x) + 6y$
9. $(2x - 3y) - (8x + 6y + 4)$
10. $(2x - 3y) + (y - 4z) - (z - 3x)$
11. $8x + [(3x - 2y) + (6x - 9) - (x + y)]$
12. $3y - [2y + 3x - (2x - 3y)] + 4x$
13. $2x - \{3y - [5x - (7y - 6x)]\}$
14. $9x - (2y - 3x) - \{y - (2y - x)\} - [2y + (4x - 3y)]$

In each of the following expressions, enclose the last three terms in parentheses preceded by a minus sign.

15. $a^2 - b^2 + 2bc - c^2$ 16. $16 - x^2 + 2xy - y^2$
17. $4x^2 - 4y^2 - 4y - 1$ 18. $9x^2 - 9y^2 - 6xy - x^2$

In each of the following expressions, enclose the coefficients of x within parentheses preceded by (a) a plus sign, (b) a minus sign.

19. $cx + dy - ax - by$ 20. $5x - ax + 3 - 4x$
21. $ax - by + bx - ay$ 22. $6x^2 - 8x + 3y - 7y^2 + 6x - 4$

Find the value of each of the following expressions for the given values of the letters.

23. $3x + 4$ when $x = 1$ 24. $x^2 - 7x + 10$ when $x = 2$
25. $3x^2 - 2x + 1$ when $x = -2$ 26. $-3x^2 - 4x + 3$ when $x = -4$
27. $2x + 3y$ when $x = -2, y = 3$ 28. $4x - 3y$ when $x = -1, y = 3$
29. $2x^2 - 3xy + y^2$ when $x = 2, y = -3$
30. $3x^2 + 2xy - 4y^2$ when $x = -3, y = 1$

3–2 Multiplication of algebraic expressions.   When the factors of a product are equal, the product is called a *power* of the repeated factor. We shall introduce a symbol to stand for such a product. The symbol a^2 represents the product $a \cdot a$. Similarly, $a \cdot a \cdot a$ may be represented by a^3, and, in general, we have:

DEFINITION 3–1. *If n is a positive integer, the symbol a^n, the nth power of a, is the product of n factors each equal to a. Thus*

$$a^n \equiv \underbrace{a \cdot a \cdot a \cdots a.}_{n \text{ factors of } a} \tag{3–1}$$

In the symbol a^n, a is called the *base* and n the *exponent* of the power.

ILLUSTRATION 1. $2^5 = 2 \cdot 2 \cdot 2 \cdot 2 \cdot 2 = 32.$

From this definition certain theorems on exponents follow.

THEOREM 3–1. *If n and m are positive integers, and $a \in R$,*

$$\boxed{a^n a^m \equiv a^{n+m}.} \tag{3–2}$$

Proof.

$$a^n \cdot a^m = \underbrace{a \cdot a \cdot a \cdots a}_{n \text{ factors } a} \cdot \underbrace{a \cdot a \cdot a \cdots a}_{m \text{ factors } a} = \underbrace{a \cdot a \cdot a \cdots a}_{n + m \text{ factors } a} = a^{n+m}.$$

The reader should also prove the following two theorems.

THEOREM 3–2. *If n and m are positive integers, and a $\in$ R,*

$$(a^n)^m \equiv a^{nm}. \tag{3-3}$$

THEOREM 3–3. *If n is a positive integer, and a and b $\in$ R,*

$$(ab)^n \equiv a^n b^n. \tag{3-4}$$

ILLUSTRATION 2. $3^2 \cdot 3^4 = 3^6 = 729,$

$a^4 \cdot a^7 = a^{11}.$

ILLUSTRATION 3. $(2^3)^2 = 2^6 = 64,$

$(a^5)^3 = a^{15}.$

ILLUSTRATION 4. $(2 \cdot 3)^3 = 2^3 \cdot 3^3 = 8 \cdot 27 = 216.$

When no exponent is written, the exponent is understood to be 1.

Using these theorems and recalling the distributive axiom, we are now able to perform the multiplication of two algebraic expressions.

EXAMPLE 1. Multiply $2x - 3y$ by $3x + 4y$.

Solution. Each term of the second binomial must be multiplied by the first binomial. [Recall Problem 9(f), Article 2–2.]

$$(2x - 3y)(3x + 4y) \equiv [(2x - 3y) \cdot 3x] + [(2x - 3y) \cdot 4y].$$

Each of these products on the right are expanded again by the right-hand distributive axiom, so that the result is

$$6x^2 - 9xy + 8xy - 12y^2.$$

If we combine similar terms, we have

$$(2x - 3y)(3x + 4y) \equiv 6x^2 - xy - 12y^2.$$

In such problems it is sometimes convenient to arrange both multinomials in ascending (or descending) powers of one letter by the associative axiom, write one below the other, carry out the multiplication, and add the products. Consider the following example.

EXAMPLE 2. Multiply $x^2 - 2y^2 + xy$ by $2x - y$.

Solution.

$$x^2 + xy \quad - 2y^2$$
$$\underline{2x \quad - y}$$
$$2x^3 + 2x^2y - 4xy^2$$
$$\underline{\quad - x^2y - \quad xy^2 + 2y^3}$$
$$2x^3 + \quad x^2y - 5xy^2 + 2y^3$$

PROBLEMS

Perform the indicated operations by using the theorems involving exponents.

1. $a^2 \cdot a^7$ 2. $3x^4 \cdot 2x^3$ 3. $3x^3 \cdot x^4 \cdot x^5$

4. $(-3)^4 \cdot (-3)^5$ 5. $y^{13} \cdot y^{11}$ 6. $(2^3)^4$

7. $(a^5)^4$ 8. $(3b)^5$ 9. $(5c)^3$

10. $(3a)^4$ 11. $(2a^3)^5$ 12. $(x^4)^n$

13. $(a^r \cdot a^s)^t$ 14. $(x^{2m} \cdot x^{3n})^4$ 15. $(2x^n)^n$

Perform the indicated multiplications and collect similar terms. Note that each of Axioms 1 through 4 is used in most of these problems.

16. $(4x - 3)(3x + 6)$ 17. $(x + 3)(2x - 5)$

18. $(5a + 2b)(5a - 2b)$ 19. $(4x + 2y)(4x - 2y)$

20. $(3x - 2)(2x + 5)$ 21. $(r^2 - s^2)(r - s)$

22. $(x - 2y)^2$ 23. $(x^2 - xy + y^2)(x + y)$

24. $(2x + 3x^2 - 1)(3x - 2)$ 25. $(x^2 - 2x - 2)(x + 2x^2 - 4)$

26. $(-xy + 2x^2 - 3y^2)(x^2 - 4y^2 + xy)$

27. $(x - 1)(x + 2)(x - 3)$ 28. $(x - 2)(x + 3)(x + 2)$

29. $(x^4 + 2x^2y^2 + 4y^4)(x^2 - 2y^2)$ 30. $(a^{2n} - 7a^n + 10)(a^n - 1)$

31. $(a^{2n} - 7a^n + 10)(a - 1)$ 32. $(x - 2x^2 + 5 - x^3)(3x - 4 + x^2)$

33. $(x^{2n} + 2x^ny^n + y^{2n})(x^{2n} - 2x^ny^n + y^{2n})$

34. $(x^n - y^n)^3$ 35. $(x - y)^4$

3-3 Division of algebraic expressions. Before we are able to divide one algebraic expression by another, we must establish an additional theorem on exponents.

THEOREM 3-4. *If $a \in R$ ($a \neq 0$) and n and m are positive integers,*

$$\frac{a^n}{a^m} \equiv \begin{cases} a^{n-m} & \text{if } n \text{ is larger than } m, & (3\text{-}5) \\[2mm] \dfrac{1}{a^{m-n}} & \text{if } m \text{ is larger than } n, & (3\text{-}6) \\[2mm] 1 & \text{if } m = n. & (3\text{-}7) \end{cases}$$

Proof. This result is established by writing

$$a^n \over a^m \equiv {\overbrace{a \cdot a \cdot a \cdots a}^{n \text{ factors } a} \over \underbrace{a \cdot a \cdot a \cdots a}_{m \text{ factors } a}},$$

and recalling Theorem 2–7.

ILLUSTRATION 1. $\dfrac{x^8}{x^3} \equiv x^5$; $\dfrac{x^4}{x^{11}} \equiv \dfrac{1}{x^7}$; $\dfrac{x^6}{x^6} \equiv 1.$

We are now prepared to divide any multinomial by a monomial. This is done by dividing each term of the multinomial by the monomial and finding the algebraic sum of the resulting quotients. (Recall Problem 13, Article 2–4.)

EXAMPLE 1.   Divide $12x^3y^4 + 18x^4y^2 - 36xy^3$ by $3x^2y^2$.

Solution. If we use the property stated in Problem 13, Article 2–4, we have

$$\frac{12x^3y^4 + 18x^4y^2 - 36xy^3}{3x^2y^2} \equiv \frac{12x^3y^4}{3x^2y^2} + \frac{18x^4y^2}{3x^2y^2} - \frac{36xy^3}{3x^2y^2}$$

$$\equiv 4xy^2 + 6x^2 - \frac{12y}{x}.$$

We have defined an algebraic expression as the sum of algebraic terms (Article 3–1). Any algebraic term is an *integral rational* term in certain letters representing numbers if it consists of the product of positive integral powers of these numbers and a factor not containing them. For example, ax^2y and $3x^4y^{3/4}$ are integral rational terms in x, and ax^2y and $3x^4y^3$ are integral rational terms in y. The term $by^{1/2}$ is also integral rational in x, since it satisfies the definition. Any multinomial in which each term is integral rational is called an *integral rational expression* or *polynomial*.

ILLUSTRATION 2.   The multinomial $3 - 5x^3 + \frac{2}{5}xy^2$ is a polynomial in x and y. However, $-5/x^3$ is not integral in x, and $5\sqrt{x}$ is neither integral nor rational in x.

The degree of a term which is *integral rational* in some letter is defined to be the *exponent* of that letter. Thus ax^2y and $3x^4y^3$ are terms of the second and fourth degree in x, but first and third degree in y. *The degree of an integral rational term in two or more letters* is defined to be the sum of the exponents of those letters. Thus the degree of ax^2y in x and y is $2 + 1 = 3$, while the degree of $3x^4y^3$ in x and y is 7. *The degree of a polynomial* in certain letters is that of its term (or terms) of highest degree in those letters.

ILLUSTRATION 3.   (a) $2x + 1$, $x^2 - 7x + 10$, and $3x^3 + 5x^2 - 6$ are polynomials of the first, second, and third degree in x, respectively. (b) $3x^2y^5 + 4xy^3 - 7x^3y^2$ is a polynomial of the third degree in x, fifth degree in y, and seventh degree in x and y.

Now let us consider the division of one polynomial by another. Our method will follow that used in arithmetic. The properties we shall use are stated in Problems 14 and 15 of Article 2–4. If we divide 28 by 9, the quotient is 3 and the remainder 1, and we write

$$\tfrac{28}{9} = 3 + \tfrac{1}{9}.$$

To divide one polynomial by another:

1. Arrange each polynomial in descending powers of some common letter.

2. Divide the first term of the dividend (the polynomial to be divided) by the first term of the divisor. This step gives the first term of the quotient.

3. Multiply the divisor by the first term of the quotient, and subtract the product from the dividend.

4. Using the remainder thus obtained as a new dividend, repeat this process, thus finding the second term of the quotient.

5. Continue the process until a remainder is obtained which is either zero or is of lower degree in the common letter than the divisor. If the remainder is zero, the division is exact, and the division is an application of Problem 14, Article 2–4. If the remainder is not zero, the division is not exact, but is an application of Problem 15, Article 2–4.

The work should be arranged as shown in the example.

EXAMPLE 2.   Divide $3x^3 - 4x^2y + 5xy^2 + 6y^3$ by $x^2 - 2xy + 3y^2$.

Solution.

$$
\begin{array}{r}
\text{(Dividend)}\quad 3x^3 - 4x^2y + 5xy^2 + 6y^3 \\
3x^3 - 6x^2y + 9xy^2 \\
\hline
2x^2y - 4xy^2 + 6y^3 \\
2x^2y - 4xy^2 + 6y^3 \\
\hline
0
\end{array}
\left|
\begin{array}{l}
x^2 - 2xy + 3y^2 \quad \text{(Divisor)} \\
\hline
3x + 2y \quad\quad \text{(Quotient)}
\end{array}
\right.
$$

(Remainder)

This result may be expressed in the form

$$\frac{3x^3 - 4x^2y + 5xy^2 + 6y^3}{x^2 - 2xy + 3y^2} \equiv 3x + 2y.$$

EXAMPLE 3. Divide $5x^3 - 14x + 3$ by $x - 2$.

Solution. Since no x^2 term appears in the given dividend, the coefficient of that term is zero, and we have

$$
\begin{array}{r|l}
5x^3 + 0x^2 - 14x + 3 & \underline{x - 2} \\
\underline{5x^3 - 10x^2} & 5x^2 + 10x + 6 \\
10x^2 - 14x + 3 & \\
\underline{10x^2 - 20x} & \\
6x + 3 & \\
\underline{6x - 12} & \\
15 & \\
\end{array}
$$

This results in

$$
\frac{5x^3 - 14x + 3}{x - 2} \equiv 5x^2 + 10x + 6 + \frac{15}{x - 2},
$$

if x is not equal to 2.

A notation frequently used for a polynomial in x is the expression $P(x)$, read "P of x" (this expression does not mean P times x); likewise, a polynomial in x and y might be denoted $Q(x, y)$. In this notation, if $P(x)$ denotes the dividend, $D(x)$ the divisor, $Q(x)$ the quotient, and $R(x)$ the remainder of a division of two polynomials in x, our result could be stated

$$
\frac{P(x)}{D(x)} \equiv Q(x) + \frac{R(x)}{D(x)}, \tag{3-8}
$$

if $D(x)$ is not equal to zero, or

$$
\boxed{P(x) \equiv Q(x) \cdot D(x) + R(x).} \tag{3-9}
$$

(Note the similarity of this equation and the statement in Problem 15, Article 2–4.) Similarly, for division of two polynomials in x and y,

$$
P(x, y) \equiv Q(x, y) \cdot D(x, y) + R(x, y). \tag{3-10}
$$

ILLUSTRATION 4. In Example 2 of this article,

$$P(x, y) = 3x^3 - 4x^2y + 5xy^2 + 6y^3, \qquad D(x, y) = x^2 - 2xy + 3y^2,$$
$$Q(x, y) = 3x + 2y, \qquad R(x, y) = 0.$$

In Example 3,

$$P(x) = 5x^3 - 14x + 3, \qquad D(x) = x - 2,$$
$$Q(x) = 5x^2 + 10x + 6, \qquad R(x) = 15.$$

PROBLEMS

Divide:

1. $9xy^2 - 6x^3$ by $3x$
2. $4x^2y^3 - 24xy^4$ by $2xy^2$
3. $6x^3 - 9x^4y$ by $3xy$
4. $-15x^2y^3 + 20x^3y^2$ by $-5x^2y^2$
5. $3x^2y - 4xy^2 + 6x^3y^3$ by xy
6. $7x^3y^2 - 14x^5y^3 + 28x^8y^5 - 21x^7y^6$ by $7x^3y^2$

Divide, finding the quotient and remainder, and write out the result of each problem in the form of Eq. (3–9) or (3–10).

7. $x^2 - 7x + 10$ by $x - 5$
8. $2y^2 - 5y - 6$ by $2y - 1$
9. $3x^2 - 13x + 4$ by $x - 4$
10. $2x^2 - 5x - 12$ by $2x + 3$
11. $2x^3 - 7x^2 + 11x - 4$ by $2x - 1$
12. $y^3 - 4y^2 - 2 + 5y$ by $y - 1$
13. $x^2y - 6x^3 - 12xy^2 - 6y^3$ by $2x - 3y$
14. $2x^3 - 11x^2y + 13xy^2 - 4y^3$ by $x - 4y$
15. $4x^3 + 5 + 4x^2 - 13x$ by $2x + 5$
16. $4x^3 + 5x - 6$ by $2x - 3$
17. $5x^3 - 2x^2 + 3x - 4$ by $x^2 - 2x + 1$
18. $4x^2 + x - 6x^3 + 3$ by $3x^2 + 5$
19. $x^6 - y^6$ by $x - y$
20. $x^7 - y^7$ by $x - y$

The process of division for polynomials in x (or any one letter) may be greatly simplified when the divisor is in the form $x - a$. This process, known as *synthetic division*, will be illustrated by using the problem of Example 3. Writing only the coefficients, we have

$$
\begin{array}{rr|rrr}
5 + 0 - 14 & 3 & 1 - & 2 & \\
\underline{5 - 10} & & \underline{5} & 10 & 6 \\
10 - 14 & & & & \\
\underline{10 - 20} & & & & \\
6 & 3 & & & \\
\underline{6 - 12} & & & & \\
15 & & & &
\end{array}
$$

We next omit those coefficients that are definite repetitions: the first term in the 2nd, 4th, 6th, ... lines and the second term in the 3rd, 5th, 7th, ... lines. If we compress the remaining terms, write the first coefficient, 5, in the third line, and note that the 1 of the divisor can be omitted, we have

$$
\begin{array}{rrrr|r}
5 & +0 & -14 & 3 & \underline{-2} \\
  & -10 & -20 & -12 & \\
\hline
5 & 10 & 6 & 15 &
\end{array}
$$

The coefficients of the quotient are also omitted, for they appear as the first three coefficients on the third line, while the remainder, 15, appears as the last number.

The final step of simplification is to replace the subtractions by additions, that is, to change the signs in the divisor (-2 to 2) and in the second line. Thus

$$
\begin{array}{rrrr|r}
5 & +0 & -14 & 3 & \underline{2} \\
  & 10 & 20 & 12 & \\
\hline
5 & 10 & 6 & 15 &
\end{array}
$$

This arrangement represents the synthetic division of $5x^3 - 14x + 3$ by $x - 2$. It yields the quotient $5x^2 + 10x + 6$ and the remainder 15.

Let us summarize the process of synthetic division. To divide a polynomial $P(x)$ by a binomial $x - a$, arrange on a line (in order of descending power) the coefficients of $P(x)$, inserting zero for the coefficient of any missing power of x, and write a on the right. Bring down the first coefficient of $P(x)$ to the first position on the third line. Multiply this first coefficient by a, writing the product in the second line under the second coefficient of $P(x)$. The sum of this product and second coefficient is placed in the third line. Multiply this sum by a, add the product to the next coefficient of $P(x)$, again writing the new sum on the third line, and so on, until a product has been added to the final coefficient of $P(x)$.

The last sum in the third line represents the remainder. The preceding numbers represent the coefficients of the powers of x in the quotient, arranged in descending order. The quotient is a polynomial of degree one less than the degree of $P(x)$. The process of synthetic division will be very useful in later work.

EXAMPLE 4. By synthetic division, find the quotient and the remainder of $2x^4 + 3x^3 - 4x^2 + 5x + 6$ divided by $x + 3$.

Solution. In this example $x - a = x - (-3)$, so that $a = -3$.

$$
\begin{array}{rrrrr|r}
2 & +3 & -4 & +5 & +6 & \underline{-3} \\
  & -6 & +9 & -15 & +30 & \\
\hline
2 & -3 & 5 & -10 & 36 &
\end{array}
$$

Thus the quotient is $2x^3 - 3x^2 + 5x - 10$, and the remainder is 36.

PROBLEMS

By synthetic division, find the quotient and the remainder in each of the following divisions.

1. $3x^2 - 2x - 4$ by $x - 3$
2. $2x^3 + 3x^2 - 7$ by $x + 1$
3. $x^3 - 2x^2 + 9$ by $x + 2$
4. $x^3 + 4x - 7$ by $x - 3$
5. $x^4 - 2x^3 - 3x^2 - 4x - 8$ by (a) $x - 2$, (b) $x + 1$
6. $2x^4 - x^3 - 18x^2 - 7$ by (a) $x + 3$, (b) $x - 3$
7. $3x^4 - 7x - 20$ by (a) $x - 2$, (b) $x + 2$
8. $2x^4 - 3x^3 - 20x^2 - 6$ by (a) $x - 4$, (b) $x + 3$

Use synthetic division to find the quotient and remainder in the following divisions and express the answer in the form of Eq. (3–9).

9. $x^3 - 2x^2 + 3x - 4$ by $x - 3$ 10. $2x^3 + x^2 - x + 4$ by $x + 1$
11. $x^4 - 5x^3 + x^2 - 6$ by $x - 1$ 12. $x^3 + 3x^2 - 2x - 5$ by $x + 2$

3–4 Special products. There are certain special products which occur so frequently in algebra that they have been classified. These are given below. *The letters in the formulas may stand for any algebraic expression.* Each is a direct result of the axioms in Chapter 2. The reader should not only verify each by actually carrying out the steps and giving the reasons, but also memorize them, so that he can recognize both the product from the factors and the factors from the product.

$$a(x + y) \equiv ax + ay. \tag{3–11}$$

$$(x + y)(x - y) \equiv x^2 - y^2. \tag{3–12}$$

$$(x \pm y)^2 \equiv x^2 \pm 2xy + y^2. \tag{3–13}*$$

$$(x + a)(x + b) \equiv x^2 + (a + b)x + ab. \tag{3–14}$$

$$(ax + b)(cx + d) \equiv acx^2 + (ad + bc)x + bd. \tag{3–15}$$

$$(x \pm y)^3 \equiv x^3 \pm 3x^2y + 3xy^2 \pm y^3. \tag{3–16}$$

$$(x \pm y)(x^2 \mp xy + y^2) \equiv x^3 \pm y^3. \tag{3–17}$$

The reader should determine which of the above formulas is used in the following illustrations.

ILLUSTRATION 1. $(2x^2 - 3y)(2x^2 + 3y) \equiv (2x^2)^2 - (3y)^2$
$$\equiv 4x^4 - 9y^2.$$

_____

* The sign $\pm$ is read "plus or minus." If the upper (lower) sign is used in the left member, it is also used in the right, so that $(x \pm y)^2 \equiv x^2 \pm 2xy + y^2$ means $(x + y)^2 \equiv x^2 + 2xy + y^2$ and $(x - y)^2 \equiv x^2 - 2xy + y^2$.

ILLUSTRATION 2. $(x + 2)(x + 5) \equiv x^2 + (2 + 5)x + 10$
$$\equiv x^2 + 7x + 10.$$

ILLUSTRATION 3. $(3x + 4y)(2x - 3y) \equiv 6x^2 + (-9 + 8)xy - 12y^2$
$$\equiv 6x^2 - xy - 12y^2.$$

ILLUSTRATION 4.

$(x + y - 1)^3$
$$\equiv [(x + y) - 1]^3$$
$$\equiv (x + y)^3 - 3(x + y)^2 + 3(x + y) - 1$$
$$\equiv x^3 + 3x^2y + 3xy^2 + y^3 - 3x^2 - 6xy - 3y^2 + 3x + 3y - 1.$$

Here $(x + y)$ is considered first as one term.

ILLUSTRATION 5.

$(3x + 2y)(9x^2 - 6xy + 4y^2) \equiv (3x + 2y)[(3x)^2 - (3x)(2y) + (2y)^2]$
$$\equiv (3x)^3 + (2y)^3$$
$$\equiv 27x^3 + 8y^3.$$

PROBLEMS

Find the following products.

1. $2a(3x - 4y)$
2. $-3x(2x + 7y)$
3. $-7xy(3x^2 + 4y)$
4. $4x^2yz(z^2 + xy + yz)$
5. $(2x - 3y)(2x + 3y)$
6. $(7x + 5y^2)(7x - 5y^2)$
7. $(x + 2y)(x - 2y)(x^2 + 4y^2)$
8. $(x - 3)^2$
9. $(2x + 7y)^2$
10. $(3x^2y - 5z^2)^2$
11. $(x - 2)(x - 5)$
12. $(2x + 3)(x - 5)$
13. $(xy^2 - z^2w)^2$
14. $(\frac{1}{2}x + \frac{2}{3}y)^2$
15. $(4x - 3y)(7x + 3y)$
16. $[(x + 1) - z][(x + 1) + z]$
17. $(2x + 3y + 3)(2x + 3y - 3)$
18. $(2x + 3y + 4z)^2$
19. $(x - 2y - z)^2$
20. $(2a + b)^3$
21. $(x + 2)(x^2 - 2x + 4)$
22. $(x - 3)(x^2 + 3x + 9)$
23. $(x + 3y + 2z - 4w)(x + 3y - 2z + 4w)$
24. $(4x - 2y - 3z + 3w)(4x + 2y + 3z + 3w)$
25. $(a - b + c - d)^2$
26. $(2a + 3b - c - 4d)^2$
27. $[2(x + 2y) - 3][2(x + 2y) + 4]$
28. $[2(x - 3y) + 5][3(x - 3y) - 2]$
29. $(2x + 3y)^3$
30. $(5x - 3y)^3$

3–5 Factors and factoring. The process of factoring an algebraic expression is similar to that of finding the factors of a composite number. Recall the discussion of prime and composite integers in Article 1–4. This process, which is usually restricted at this elementary stage to factoring polynomials with rational coefficients and to factors completely free from irrational numbers, is frequently performed by reversing the processes considered in Article 3–4. Such a factorization is considered complete when each algebraic factor is a *prime factor;* that is, an algebraic expression that cannot be factored without violating the above restrictions.

The more common types of factoring are illustrated below. Note the importance and application of the distributive axioms in this discussion.

EXAMPLE 1. Factor $2ax^2 - 4ay^2 + 8a^2x$.

Solution. The polynomial in this problem has $2a$ as a common factor.

$$2ax^2 - 4ay^2 + 8a^2x \equiv 2a(x^2 - 2y^2 + 4ax).$$

EXAMPLE 2. Factor $x(a + 2b) - 3y(a + 2b)$.

Solution. Each of the two expressions has the common term $(a + 2b)$. Therefore,

$$x(a + 2b) - 3y(a + 2b) \equiv (x - 3y)(a + 2b).$$

EXAMPLE 3. Factor $(4x^2/y^2) - (9a - b)^2$.

Solution. This expression is the difference between two perfect squares.

$$\frac{4x^2}{y^2} - (9a - b)^2 \equiv \left(\frac{2x}{y}\right)^2 - (9a - b)^2$$

$$\equiv \left[\frac{2x}{y} + (9a - b)\right]\left[\frac{2x}{y} - (9a - b)\right]$$

$$\equiv \left(\frac{2x}{y} + 9a - b\right)\left(\frac{2x}{y} - 9a + b\right).$$

EXAMPLE 4. Factor $9x^2 - 30xy + 25y^2$.

Solution. This algebraic expression is a perfect square.

$$9x^2 - 30xy + 25y^2 \equiv (3x - 5y)^2.$$

EXAMPLE 5. Factor $27x^3 + (8/y^3)$.

Solution. The algebraic expression is the sum of two cubes. Accordingly,

$$27x^3 + \frac{8}{y^3} \equiv \left(3x + \frac{2}{y}\right)\left(9x^2 - \frac{6x}{y} + \frac{4}{y^2}\right).$$

EXAMPLE 6. Factor $12x^2 + 7xy - 10y^2$.

Solution. This trinomial in the form of Eq. (3–15) is factored by trial and error. The result will be in the form $(ax + by)(cx + dy)$, where

$ac = 12$, $bd = -10$, and $ad + bc = 7$. Here a and c are both plus, and b and d are different in sign. The correct combination, we find, is

$$12x^2 + 7xy - 10y^2 \equiv (4x + 5y)(3x - 2y).$$

EXAMPLE 7. Factor $6x^4 + 7x^2y^2 - 3y^4$.

Solution. This is the same type as Example 6.

$$6x^4 + 7x^2y^2 - 3y^4 \equiv (3x^2 - y^2)(2x^2 + 3y^2).$$

Although the first term on the right is the difference of two squares, it cannot be factored further, for such factorization would introduce irrational quantities.

PROBLEMS

Factor the following completely.

1. $4x - 20$
2. $10x + 15yz$
3. $3y^2 - 9y$
4. $4x^3y^2 + 6x^2y^3$
5. $xy^2z^3 - 3x^2yz^2 + 5xy^3z^2$
6. $a^2b^3c^4 - a^3b^4c^5 + 2a^2b^4c^4$
7. $3y(2x + 5) - 4x(2x + 5)$
8. $3y(4 - y) + 6x^2(4 - y)$
9. $2z^2(x + 3y) - 6xz(x + 3y)$
10. $3x(3 - 2y) - 2xy(3 - 2y)$
11. $9 - a^2$
12. $16x^2 - 9y^2$
13. $225a^8 - 64b^2$
14. $(c^6/d^8) - 121$
15. $x^3y^4 - 25xd^6$
16. $0.01x^4 - 196y^8$
17. $(x + 2y)^2 - z^2$
18. $(3x - 2y)^2 - 25z^2$
19. $(a + b)^2 - (c + d)^2$
20. $9(2x - y)^2 - 4(2a + b)^2$
21. $81(4x - 3y)^2 - 25(3z + w)^2$
22. $x^2 + 6x + 9 - (y^2 + 4y + 4)$
23. $x^2 - 8x + 16$
24. $4a^2 - 12ab + 9b^2$
25. $66xy + 9x^2y^2 + 121$
26. $2x^3 - 28x^2 + 98x$
27. $5z^2 - 30wz + 45w^2$
28. $x^{2n} + 2x^ny^n + y^{2n}$
29. $(3 - x)^2 + 8(3 - x) + 16$
30. $25 - 30(2x - 3y) + 9(2x - 3y)^2$
31. $a^3 - 8$
32. $1 + (8/x^9)$
33. $8x^{6n} + 27y^{3m}$
34. $x^3 - (y^3/64)$
35. $27(x - y)^3 - 8(x + y)^3$
36. $5(a - 2b)^3 - 625(a - 2b)^3$
37. $x^2 - 7x + 12$
38. $y^2 - 2y - 8$
39. $a^2b^2 - ab - 20$
40. $2x^2 + 8x + 6$
41. $35x^2 - 24x + 4$
42. $3y^2 - y - 10$
43. $6a^2 + 7a - 20$
44. $2x^2 - 23xy - 39y^2$
45. $(x + y)^2 - 7(x + y) + 10$
46. $(y + z)^2 + (y + z) - 42$
47. $2(2x + y)^2 - (2x + y) - 10$
48. $6(x + y)^2 + 5(x + y)(y + z) - 6(y + z)^2$
49. $12(a + b)^2 - 14(a + b)(c + d) - 10(c + d)^2$
50. $4(x - 2)^2 + 5(x - 2)(y + 4) - 21(y + 4)^2$

There are many algebraic expressions which, by proper grouping, can be put into one of the forms in the previous examples and then factored.

EXAMPLE 8. Factor $ax - ay - b\overset{\times}{y} + by$.

Solution. If, by the associative axiom, we group the first two terms together, and the last two together, and (use the distributive axiom) factor out the common term, we transform the expression into the form of Example 2.

$$ax - ay - bx + by \equiv a(x - y) - b(x - y)$$
$$\equiv (x - y)(a - b).$$

EXAMPLE 9. Factor $4x^3 - 12x^2 - x + 3$.

Solution. Again we group the first two terms and the last two terms.

$$4x^3 - 12x^2 - x + 3 \equiv 4x^2(x - 3) - (x - 3)$$
$$\equiv (x - 3)(4x^2 - 1)$$
$$\equiv (x - 3)(2x + 1)(2x - 1).$$

In both these examples we could have grouped the first and third, and the second and fourth terms, and obtained the same result.

EXAMPLE 10. Factor $4x^2 - 12xy + 9y^2 + 4x - 6y - 3$.

Solution. If we group the first three terms, the solution becomes clear.

$$4x^2 - 12xy + 9y^2 + 4x - 6y - 3 \equiv (2x - 3y)^2 + 2(2x - 3y) - 3$$
$$\equiv [(2x - 3y) + 3][(2x - 3y) - 1]$$
$$\equiv (2x - 3y + 3)(2x - 3y - 1).$$

EXAMPLE 11. Factor $x^4 + 2x^2y^2 + 9y^4$.

Solution. If the coefficient of the second term were 6, the expression would be a perfect square. Therefore, if we add (and subtract) $4x^2y^2$, our solution becomes evident.

$$x^4 + 2x^2y^2 + 9y^4 \equiv x^4 + 6x^2y^2 + 9y^4 - 4x^2y^2$$
$$\equiv (x^2 + 3y^2)^2 - (2xy)^2$$
$$\equiv (x^2 + 3y^2 + 2xy)(x^2 + 3y^2 - 2xy).$$

PROBLEMS

Factor the following expressions.

1. $ax - ay - by + bx$
2. $ax - 2ay - 6by + 3bx$
3. $x^3 - 2x^2 + 4x - 8$
4. $y^3 - 2y^2 + 5y - 10$
5. $2a - 6 - ab^2 + 3b^2$
6. $x^3 + 3x^2 - 9x - 27$
7. $x^2 - 2x + 1 - y^2$
8. $xy^3 + 2y^2 - xy - 2$

9. $4x^2 - y^2 + 4y - 4$ 10. $x^6 - 7x^3 - 8$

11. $x^2 + 2xy + y^2 - z^2 + 2zw - w^2$

12. $4a^2 - x^2 + b^2 - y^2 - 4ab - 2xy$

13. $x^2 + 4xy + 4y^2 - x - 2y - 6$

14. $x^3 - 5x^2 - x + 5$ 15. $x^4 - 7x^2y^2 + 9y^4$

16. $y^4 + y^2 + 25$ 17. $a^4 + 2a^2b^2 + 9b^4$

18. $x^4 + 4y^4$ 19. $a^8 - b^8$

20. $x^6 + 1$ 21. $x^2 + 2xy - z^2 - 2yz$

22. $(x^2 + 2x - 3)^2 - 4$ 23. $(x - y - 2z)^2 - (2x + y - z)^2$

24. $2(x + 2)^2 (x - 3) + 3(x + 2)(x - 3)^2$

3–6 Simplification of fractions. A basic principle for fractions, algebraic as well as arithmetic, states that the value of a fraction is not changed if its numerator and denominator are both multiplied or both divided by the same quantity (not zero). This principle was stated in Theorem 2–8. Hence, the simplification or reduction of a fraction to lowest terms is always possible. Factor both the numerator and denominator into their prime factors and, by using the basic principle, divide the numerator and denominator by the product of all their common factors.

EXAMPLE 1. Reduce $(8x^4y^7)/(12x^6y^3)$ to lowest terms.

Solution. $$\frac{8x^4y^7}{12x^6y^3} \equiv \frac{2^3x^4y^7}{2^2 \cdot 3x^6y^3} \equiv \frac{2^2x^4y^3 \cdot 2y^4}{2^2x^4y^3 \cdot 3x^2}.$$

By dividing both numerator and denominator by $2^2x^4y^3$, we have

$$\frac{8x^4y^7}{12x^6y^3} \equiv \frac{2y^4}{3x^2}.$$

EXAMPLE 2. Reduce $(x^2 - 7x + 10)/(2x^2 - x - 6)$ to lowest terms.

Solution. If we factor both numerator and denominator, we have

$$\frac{x^2 - 7x + 10}{2x^2 - x - 6} \equiv \frac{(x - 5)(x - 2)}{(2x + 3)(x - 2)},$$

and dividing both numerator and denominator by $x - 2$, that is, applying Theorem 2–8, we get

$$\frac{x^2 - 7x + 10}{2x^2 - x - 6} \equiv \frac{x - 5}{2x + 3}.$$

The elimination of a common factor by dividing the numerator and denominator of a fraction by this factor is called *multiplicative cancellation*. Such a process should be done with care, for Theorem 2–8 is true only when $x \neq 0$. In this case the identity is true for all values of x except $x = 2$ or $x = -\frac{3}{2}$, which are not permissible values.

EXAMPLE 3. Reduce $(12x^2 + 30x - 72)/(52x - 8x^2 - 60)$ to lowest terms.

Solution. $\dfrac{12x^2 + 30x - 72}{52x - 8x^2 - 60} \equiv \dfrac{6(2x - 3)(x + 4)}{4(3 - 2x)(x - 5)} \equiv \dfrac{3(x + 4)}{2(5 - x)}.$

This identity follows from the fact that $2x - 3 = -(3 - 2x)$. (Recall Problem 4, Article 2–4.)

PROBLEMS

Reduce to lowest terms:

1. $\dfrac{28}{63}$

2. $\dfrac{27x^3}{225x^5}$

3. $\dfrac{a^4 x^3 y}{a^2 xy^3}$

4. $\dfrac{a^2 + ab}{3a + 2a^3}$

5. $\dfrac{a^2 x - a^2 y}{ax^2 - ay^2}$

6. $\dfrac{24a^2}{6a^2 - 9a}$

7. $\dfrac{x^2 - 1}{x^2 - x}$

8. $\dfrac{x^2 - 4x + 4}{x^2 - 4}$

9. $\dfrac{x^2 - 16}{x^2 - 8x + 16}$

10. $\dfrac{a^2 - 3a - 4}{a^2 - a - 12}$

11. $\dfrac{y^2 - y - 6}{y^2 + 2y - 15}$

12. $\dfrac{2x^2 + 5x - 12}{4x^2 - 4x - 3}$

13. $\dfrac{6a^2 - 7a - 3}{4a^2 - 8a + 3}$

14. $\dfrac{ax + ay - bx - by}{am - bm - an + bn}$

15. $\dfrac{14x - 24 - 2x^2}{x^2 + x - 20}$

16. $\dfrac{(4x^2 - 9y^2)(18x - 12)}{(2x - 3y)(12x - 8)}$

17. $\dfrac{x^2 - 36}{x^3 - 216}$

18. $\dfrac{2x^2 - 14x + 20}{7x - 2x^2 - 6}$

19. $\dfrac{2(x^2 - y^2)xy + x^4 - y^4}{x^4 - y^4}$

20. $\dfrac{y^6 + 64}{y^4 - 4y^2 + 16}$

3–7 Addition of fractions. The algebraic sum of two or more fractions having the same denominator is a fraction with the common denominator and a numerator which is the algebraic sum of the numerators of the fractions considered. This was proved in Problem 13, Article 2–4.

ILLUSTRATION. $\dfrac{2x^2}{x - 4} - \dfrac{3x}{x - 4} + \dfrac{5}{x - 4} \equiv \dfrac{2x^2 - 3x + 5}{x - 4}.$

To find the algebraic sum of two or more fractions with different denominators, we must replace the fractions with equivalent fractions having the same denominators. It is preferable to use the *least common denominator* (LCD). The LCD of two or more fractions consists of the product of all the unique prime factors in the denominators, each with an exponent equal to the largest exponent with which the factor appears, and is really a result of the following important theorem.

THEOREM 3–5. $\dfrac{a}{b} + \dfrac{c}{d} \equiv \dfrac{ad + bc}{bd}$ $(b, d \neq 0)$.

Proof. We have

$$\frac{a}{b} + \frac{c}{d} \equiv \frac{ad}{bd} + \frac{bc}{bd},$$

by Theorem 2–8. If we now use Problem 13, Article 2–4, we have

$$\frac{ad}{bd} + \frac{bc}{bd} \equiv \frac{ad + bc}{bd},$$

which is our required result.

EXAMPLE 1. Find the LCD of the fractions

$$\frac{3x}{x^2 - 4x + 4}, \qquad \frac{5x^2}{3(x^2 - 4)}, \qquad \frac{2}{2x^2 - x - 6}.$$

Solution. Factoring each denominator, we have

$$x^2 - 4x + 4 \equiv (x - 2)^2,$$
$$3(x^2 - 4) \equiv 3(x + 2)(x - 2),$$
$$2x^2 - x - 6 \equiv (2x + 3)(x - 2).$$

The LCD is $3(x + 2)(x - 2)^2(2x + 3)$.

After the LCD has been determined, equivalent fractions may be formed. Divide the LCD of a given fraction by the denominator of that fraction, and then multiply both numerator and denominator of the given fraction by the result. The equivalent fractions may now be added, as in the illustration above.

EXAMPLE 2. Change the following fractions to equivalent ones, with their LCD as denominator, and find their sum.

$$\frac{4}{x + 2}, \qquad \frac{x + 3}{x^2 - 4}, \qquad \frac{2x + 1}{x - 2}.$$

Solution. The LCD is $(x + 2)(x - 2)$. Therefore,

$$\frac{4}{x + 2} \equiv \frac{4(x - 2)}{(x + 2)(x - 2)}, \qquad \frac{x + 3}{x^2 - 4} \equiv \frac{x + 3}{(x + 2)(x - 2)},$$

$$\frac{2x + 1}{x - 2} \equiv \frac{(2x + 1)(x + 2)}{(x + 2)(x - 2)},$$

and

$$\frac{4}{x + 2} + \frac{x + 3}{x^2 - 4} + \frac{2x + 1}{x - 2}$$

$$\equiv \frac{4(x - 2)}{(x + 2)(x - 2)} + \frac{x + 3}{(x + 2)(x - 2)} + \frac{(2x + 1)(x + 2)}{(x + 2)(x - 2)}$$

$$\equiv \frac{(4x - 8) + (x + 3) + (2x^2 + 5x + 2)}{x^2 - 4}$$

$$\equiv \frac{2x^2 + 10x - 3}{x^2 - 4}.$$

PROBLEMS

Reduce the following to single fractions and simplify.

1. $\frac{2}{3} + \frac{5}{6} - \frac{3}{10}$

2. $5 - \frac{4}{9} - \frac{7}{15}$

3. $\frac{3x}{4y} - \frac{4y}{3x}$

4. $\frac{a^2}{b} - \frac{b^2}{a}$

5. $\frac{2x + 3}{6} - \frac{4x - 7}{9}$

6. $\frac{3x - 1}{5} + \frac{4 - 5x}{6}$

7. $x + y + \frac{x^2}{x - y}$

8. $\frac{x + 1}{x + 2} - \frac{x + 3}{x}$

9. $\frac{3x - 2y}{5x - 3} + \frac{2x - y}{3 - 5x}$

10. $\frac{2}{12x^2 - 3} + \frac{3}{2x - 4x^2}$

11. $\frac{5}{x} - \frac{4}{y} + \frac{3}{z}$

12. $\frac{4}{x^2 - 4x - 5} + \frac{2}{x^2 - 1}$

13. $\frac{2x - 1}{4 - x} + \frac{x + 2}{3x - 12}$

14. $\frac{x + 5}{x^2 + 7x + 10} - \frac{x - 1}{x^2 + 5x + 6}$

15. $\frac{x - 1}{2x^2 - 13x + 15} + \frac{x + 3}{2x^2 - 15x + 18}$

16. $\frac{2x + 3}{3x^2 + x - 2} - \frac{3x - 4}{2x^2 - 3x - 5}$

17. $\frac{3}{a - 3} + \frac{a^2 + 2}{a^3 - 27}$

18. $\dfrac{2xy}{x^3 + y^3} - \dfrac{x}{x^2 - xy + y^2}$

19. $\dfrac{2}{x^2 + 3x + 2} - \dfrac{3}{x^2 + 5x + 6} - \dfrac{4}{x^2 + 4x + 3}$

20. $x + 6 + \dfrac{5x + 1}{12x^2 + 5x - 2} - \dfrac{x}{3x + 2}$

21. $2y - 3 + \dfrac{y - 2}{4y^2 - 12y + 9} + \dfrac{y + 2}{2y^2 - y - 3}$

22. $\dfrac{1}{(x - y)(y - z)} + \dfrac{1}{(y - z)(z - x)} + \dfrac{1}{(z - x)(x - y)}$

23. $\dfrac{x}{(x - y)(y - z)} + \dfrac{y}{(y - z)(z - x)} + \dfrac{z}{(z - x)(x - y)}$

24. $\dfrac{2x - 1}{2x^2 - x - 6} + \dfrac{x + 3}{6x^2 + x - 12} - \dfrac{2x - 3}{3x^2 - 10x + 8}$

3–8 Multiplication and division of fractions. In algebra, as in arithmetic, the product of two or more fractions is a fraction whose numerator is the product of all numerators and whose denominator is the product of all denominators. In obtaining these products, the process of dividing out factors common to the numerator and denominator may be used. Results should be reduced to their simplest form. Note in Illustration 1 that this method is a direct application of Theorem 2–7, followed by an application of Theorem 2–8.

ILLUSTRATION 1. $\dfrac{x - 4}{2x + 8} \cdot \dfrac{4x + 8}{x^2 - 16} \equiv \dfrac{(x - 4) \cdot 2^2 \cdot (x + 2)}{2(x + 4)(x + 4)(x - 4)}$

$$\equiv \frac{2(x + 2)}{(x + 4)^2}.$$

We now have need for a theorem which will establish an expression for the division of two fractions.

THEOREM 3–6. $\dfrac{a}{b} \div \dfrac{c}{d} \equiv \dfrac{a/b}{c/d} \equiv \dfrac{a}{b} \cdot \dfrac{d}{c}$ $(b, c, d \neq 0)$.

Proof. (Give the reasons for each step.)

$$\frac{a/b}{c/d} \equiv \frac{(a/b) \cdot (d/c)}{(c/d) \cdot (d/c)} \equiv \frac{(a/b) \cdot (d/c)}{(cd)/(cd)} \equiv \frac{(a/b) \cdot (d/c)}{1} \equiv \frac{a}{b} \cdot \frac{d}{c}.$$

As a result of this theorem, we are able to state a rule. The quotient of two fractions is the fraction formed by multiplying the dividend by the divisor inverted.

ILLUSTRATION 2. $\dfrac{3x-15}{x+3} \div \dfrac{12x+18}{4x+12} \equiv \dfrac{3x-15}{x+3} \cdot \dfrac{4x+12}{12x+18}$

$$\equiv \frac{3(x-5)}{x+3} \cdot \frac{4(x+3)}{6(2x+3)}$$

$$\equiv \frac{2(x-5)}{2x+3}.$$

PROBLEMS

Perform the indicated operations on the following simple fractions, and reduce the results to simplest form.

1. $\frac{4}{3} \cdot \frac{5}{7}$

2. $\frac{3}{7} \div \frac{13}{11}$

3. $\frac{5}{8} \cdot \frac{4}{15}$

4. $\frac{4}{7} \div \frac{16}{21}$

5. $\frac{7}{22} \cdot \frac{33}{35}$

6. $\frac{6}{7} \div \frac{8}{9}$

7. $\dfrac{3x^3}{4y^2} \cdot \dfrac{5y}{x^2}$

8. $\dfrac{7a}{12b^3} \cdot \dfrac{20b^5}{35a^3}$

9. $\dfrac{40x^3y^2}{24xy^4} \div \dfrac{27xy}{8x^2y^3}$

10. $\dfrac{xy^3}{yz} \div x^2z$

11. $\dfrac{x^2-y^2}{x^3-y^3} \div \dfrac{x+y}{x}$

12. $\dfrac{x^2-2x+y^2}{x^3-y^3} \cdot \dfrac{x^2+xy+y^2}{x-y}$

13. $\dfrac{x^2-6x+9}{x^2-7x+12} \cdot \dfrac{x^3-4x^2+9x-36}{x^4-81}$

14. $\dfrac{y^2-2y-15}{y^2-9} \div \dfrac{12-4y}{y^2-6y+9}$

15. $\dfrac{x^4-y^4}{(x-y)^2} \cdot \dfrac{y^2}{x^2+y^2} \cdot \dfrac{x-y}{xy+y^2}$

16. $(a^2-b^2) \div \left[\dfrac{a^2+ab}{b^2+ab} \div \dfrac{a^2-ab}{b^2-ab} \right]$

17. $\dfrac{9x^2+6x-8}{6x^2+5x-4} \cdot \dfrac{2x^2-7x-4}{2x^2-5x-12} \cdot \dfrac{4x^2+4x-3}{6x^2-x-2}$

18. $\left[\dfrac{y^3+4y^2-5y}{y^2-2y+1} \div \dfrac{y^2+y-2}{y^4+8y} \right] \cdot \dfrac{y-4}{y^2-2y+4}$

19. $\left[\dfrac{2x}{x-1} + \dfrac{x^2}{x^2-1} \right] \div \dfrac{x^3}{1-x}$

20. $\left[\dfrac{3x}{x-3} - \dfrac{3x+2}{x^2-6x+9} \right] \cdot \left[\dfrac{x+2}{x+3} - \dfrac{x}{x^2+6x+9} \right]$

Most of the fractions considered have been simple fractions. Any fraction which contains one or more other fractions in either numerator or denominator, or in both, is called a *complex* fraction. It may be simplified by reducing the numerator and denominator to single fractions and then dividing.

EXAMPLE. Simplify $\dfrac{a - \dfrac{1}{a}}{a - \dfrac{1}{a^2}}$.

Solution. $\dfrac{a - \dfrac{1}{a}}{a - \dfrac{1}{a^2}} \equiv \dfrac{a^2 - 1}{a} \div \dfrac{a^3 - 1}{a^2}$

$$\equiv \frac{(a + 1)(a - 1)}{a} \cdot \frac{a^2}{(a - 1)(a^2 + a + 1)}$$

$$\equiv \frac{a(a + 1)}{a^2 + a + 1} .$$

PROBLEMS

Reduce each of the following to a single fraction in simplest form.

1. $\dfrac{3 + \dfrac{4}{5}}{\dfrac{2}{3} - 1}$

2. $\dfrac{\dfrac{a}{b} + \dfrac{a}{c}}{ab + ac}$

3. $\dfrac{x - \dfrac{x}{y}}{z - \dfrac{z}{y}}$

4. $\dfrac{\dfrac{4x}{5} + \dfrac{2y}{3}}{\dfrac{3x}{5} - \dfrac{3y}{4}}$

5. $\dfrac{\dfrac{2}{x} + \dfrac{5}{y}}{\dfrac{2}{x} - \dfrac{5}{y}}$

6. $\dfrac{\dfrac{1}{x} + \dfrac{1}{y}}{\dfrac{1}{x^2} - \dfrac{1}{y^2}}$

7. $\dfrac{x^2 - \dfrac{1}{x}}{x + 1 + \dfrac{1}{x}}$

8. $\dfrac{\dfrac{1}{2} - \dfrac{4}{x^3}}{\dfrac{1}{x^2} + \dfrac{1}{4} + \dfrac{1}{2x}}$

9. $\dfrac{\dfrac{9x^2 - 4y^2}{x - y}}{\dfrac{}{y - 2x} - 1}$

10. $\dfrac{\dfrac{x}{y} + \dfrac{y^2}{x^2}}{\dfrac{y}{x^2} - \dfrac{1}{x} + \dfrac{1}{y}}$

3–9 Integral and zero exponents. In Article 3–2 we discussed the meaning of a^n ($a \neq 0$) where n was any positive integer. To define a^n where n is any integer, positive, negative, or zero ($n \in I$), we may use the theorems on exponents [Eqs. (3–2) through (3–7)]. We recall from Eq. (3–7) that $a^n/a^n = 1$. If Eq. (3–5) were permissible, we would have $a^{n-n} = a^0 = 1$. This is not permissible because m must not equal n, but we can now use this relationship and Eq. (3–6) to justify the following definitions.

DEFINITION 3–2. *For any $a \in R$ ($a \neq 0$),*

$$a^0 \equiv 1. \qquad (3\text{--}18)$$

DEFINITION 3–3. *For any $a \in R$ ($a \neq 0$) and any positive integer n,*

$$a^{-n} \equiv \frac{1}{a^n} . \qquad (3\text{--}19)$$

We now have the resulting theorems.

THEOREM 3–7. *For any $a \in R$ ($a \neq 0$) and any n and $m \in I$,*

$$a^n a^m \equiv a^{n+m}, \qquad (3\text{--}20)$$

$$(ab)^n \equiv a^n b^n, \qquad (3\text{--}21)$$

$$(a^n)^m \equiv a^{nm}, \qquad (3\text{--}22)$$

and

$$\frac{a^n}{a^m} \equiv a^{n-m}. \qquad (3\text{--}23)$$

Proof. The proofs follow directly from the previous definitions and are left as exercises.

ILLUSTRATIONS.

$$5^0 = 1, \qquad 2x^0 \equiv 2 \cdot 1 \equiv 2, \qquad (2x^2 y)^0 \equiv 1,$$

$$x^{-2} \equiv \frac{1}{x^2}, \qquad (x^3)^4 \equiv x^{12}, \qquad \frac{x^3}{x^5} \equiv x^{-2} \equiv \frac{1}{x^2}.$$

PROBLEMS

Remove the negative and zero exponents and simplify the following expressions.

1. $8x^0$

2. $(8x)^0$

3. $3x^{-2}y^4$

4. $5y^{-2}x^3z^0$

5. $\dfrac{2x^3y^{-2}}{3x^{-2}y^3}$

6. $\dfrac{4x^{-2}y^4}{6x^{-5}y^{-2}}$

7. $\dfrac{a^{-1}+b^{-1}}{(cd)^{-1}}$

8. $\dfrac{x^{-2}+y^{-2}}{x^{-1}+y^{-1}}$

9. $\dfrac{a^{-1}+b^{-1}}{(a+b)^{-1}}$

10. $(a^{-1}+b^{-1})^{-1}$

11. $(x^ny^2)^m$

12. $(-1)^n(-1)^m(-1)^1$

13. Prove Theorem 3–7, (a) Eq. (3–20); (b) Eq. (3–21).

14. Prove Theorem 3–7, (a) Eq. (3–22); (b) Eq. (3–23).

3–10 Rational exponents. In the previous article we extended our definitions involving exponents to zero and negative integers, and now we shall extend the definitions to rational exponents.

DEFINITION 3–4. *Any number a whose nth power (n is any positive integer) is equal to b and which satisfies the equation $a^n = b$, is called an nth root of b.*

We recall, for example, that either 2 or -2 is a square root of 4, since $2^2 = 4$ and $(-2)^2 = 4$. Similarly, since $(-2)^3 = -8$, -2 is a cube root of -8. In general, every number except zero has exactly n distinct nth roots, although most or all of them may be imaginary numbers.* In many cases it is convenient to have a principal nth root defined. The *principal nth root of a positive number* is the positive root. The *principal nth root of a negative number* is the negative root if n is odd. If n is even and the number is negative, no principal nth root is defined, for no real value exists. (Consider, for example, the equation $x^2 = -4$.) The symbol $\sqrt[n]{b}$ means the principal nth root; n is called the index and b the *radicand* of the *radical*.

ILLUSTRATION 1. $\sqrt{9} = 3$, $\sqrt[3]{-8} = -2$, and $\sqrt[4]{81} = 3$ are the principal square root, cube root, and fourth root of 9, -8 and 81, respectively.

We are now able to extend the theorems concerning exponents to the case where $n \in F$. Consider any rational value p/q, where p and q are any two relatively prime positive integers. If $n = 1/q$ where q is any positive integer, and we wish to have our result consistent with Eq. (3–2), that is,

* See Chapter 16.

we wish to have

$$\underbrace{b^{1/q} \cdot b^{1/q} \cdot b^{1/q} \cdots b^{1/q}}_{q \text{ factors } b^{1/q}} \equiv b^{q/q} \equiv b, \qquad (3\text{--}24)$$

we must define $b^{1/q}$ as a qth root of b. In fact, the symbol $b^{1/q}$ is defined as the principal qth root. Likewise, if Eq. (3–3) is to be satisfied, we must define

$$(b^{1/q})^p \equiv b^{p/q}. \qquad (3\text{--}25)$$

This identity states that $b^{1/q}$ is a pth root of $b^{p/q}$ and that $b^{p/q}$ is the pth power of the principal qth root of b. Also, we can now show, by using Eq. (3–25), that

$$\underbrace{b^{p/q} \cdot b^{p/q} \cdot b^{p/q} \cdots b^{p/q}}_{q \text{ factors } b^{p/q}} \equiv b^p, \qquad (3\text{--}26)$$

and thus $b^{p/q}$ is also the principal qth root of b^p. Therefore we have, from Eqs. (3–25) and (3–26) and the previous notation,

$$\boxed{b^{p/q} \equiv (b^p)^{1/q} \equiv \sqrt[q]{b^p},} \qquad (3\text{--}27)^*$$

and also

$$\boxed{b^{p/q} \equiv (b^{1/q})^p \equiv (\sqrt[q]{b})^p.} \qquad (3\text{--}28)$$

It can now be shown that the five theorems on exponents, Eqs. (3–19) through (3–23), hold for all rational exponents (elements of F) as well as for integers (elements of I).

ILLUSTRATION 2. $8^{2/3} = \sqrt[3]{8^2} = \sqrt[3]{64} = 4$, or

$$= (\sqrt[3]{8})^2 = 2^2 = 4.$$

ILLUSTRATION 3. $81^{-3/4} = \dfrac{1}{(\sqrt[4]{81})^3} = \dfrac{1}{3^3} = \dfrac{1}{27}$.

ILLUSTRATION 4. $x^{1/4} \cdot x^{2/3} \equiv x^{1/4+2/3} \equiv x^{11/12} \equiv \sqrt[12]{x^{11}}$.

ILLUSTRATION 5. $x^{1/4} \div x^{2/3} \equiv x^{1/4-2/3} \equiv x^{-5/12} \equiv \dfrac{1}{\sqrt[12]{x^5}}$.

ILLUSTRATION 6. $(x^{-4})^{-3/4} \equiv x^3$.

---

* We must exclude the case where b is negative and q is even, as we did in our definition of principal value.

PROBLEMS

Find the numerical value of the following.

1. $25^{1/2}$ 2. $81^{3/4}$ 3. $(\frac{16}{49})^{1/2}$

4. $(\frac{8}{125})^{-1/3}$ 5. $(\frac{64}{27})^{2/3}$ 6. $32^{-4/5}$

7. $(2^{10})^{-3/5}$ 8. $(2^{-6})^{2/3}$ 9. $3^{7/2} \cdot 3^{1/2}$

Remove the negative exponents, simplify, and express the result in radical form.

10. $x^{1/4} \cdot x^{1/5}$ 11. $x^{1/4} \div x^{1/5}$ 12. $(x^{1/4})^{1/5}$

13. $x^{1/4} \cdot x^{-1/5}$ 14. $(x^{1/4})^{-1/5}$ 15. $(x^{-1/4})^{-1/5}$

Remove the negative and zero exponents and simplify.

16. $(9x^{-4}y^2)^{1/2}$ 17. $(2x^{1/6}y^{5/6})^{-6}$

18. $(2x^{-3}y^4)^3$ 19. $\left(\dfrac{125x^4y^3}{27x^{-2}y^6}\right)^{1/3}$

20. $\left(\dfrac{5^0x^4y^3z}{16x^{-6}yz^5}\right)^{-1/2}$ 21. $(a^{1/2} + b^{1/2})^2$

22. $(a^{1/2} + b^{1/2})(a^{1/2} - b^{1/2})$ 23. $(x^{1/3} + y^{1/3})(x^{2/3} - x^{1/3}y^{1/3} + y^{2/3})$

24. $(x + y)^{-2}(x^{-2} - y^{-2})$ 25. $(x + y^{-1})^2$

3–11 Radicals. In many cases it is more advantageous to express a quantity in terms of radicals than in terms of rational exponents. The laws of radicals follow directly from the previous definitions and theorems on exponents. If m and n are positive integers and a and b are positive where m or n are even,

$$(\sqrt[n]{a})^n \equiv a, \tag{3–29}$$

$$\sqrt[n]{ab} \equiv (ab)^{1/n} \equiv a^{1/n} \cdot b^{1/n} \equiv \sqrt[n]{a} \cdot \sqrt[n]{b}, \tag{3–30}$$

$$\sqrt[n]{\frac{a}{b}} \equiv \left(\frac{a}{b}\right)^{1/n} \equiv \frac{a^{1/n}}{b^{1/n}} \equiv \frac{\sqrt[n]{a}}{\sqrt[n]{b}}, \tag{3–31}$$

$$\sqrt[m]{\sqrt[n]{a}} \equiv (a^{1/n})^{1/m} \equiv a^{1/nm} \equiv \sqrt[mn]{a}. \tag{3–32}$$

ILLUSTRATION 1. $\sqrt{50} = \sqrt{25 \cdot 2} = \sqrt{25} \cdot \sqrt{2} = 5\sqrt{2}.$

ILLUSTRATION 2. $\sqrt[3]{\dfrac{4}{27}} = \dfrac{\sqrt[3]{4}}{\sqrt[3]{27}} = \dfrac{\sqrt[3]{4}}{3}.$

ILLUSTRATION 3. $\sqrt[6]{27} = \sqrt{\sqrt[3]{27}} = \sqrt{3}.$

A complete simplification of radicals by the use of these laws will yield:

(1) no factors which are perfect nth powers under a radical whose index is n, (2) no fractions under the radical sign, (3) the smallest possible index of the radical.

Any radical that satisfies these conditions is said to be in *simplest form*. In addition to the three illustrations above, which are in simplest form, we give the following examples.

EXAMPLE 1. Simplify $\sqrt[3]{81x^5y^7}$.

Solution. In this expression it will be necessary to remove from the radicand all factors that are perfect cubes.

$$\sqrt[3]{81x^5y^7} \equiv \sqrt[3]{27x^3y^6 \cdot 3x^2y} \equiv \sqrt[3]{27x^3y^6} \cdot \sqrt[3]{3x^2y} \equiv 3xy^2\sqrt[3]{3x^2y}.$$

EXAMPLE 2. Simplify $\sqrt{\frac{3}{2}}$.

Solution. For computational reasons, it is important to eliminate any fraction which appears as a radicand. Then the radical may be approximated by only one root extraction and a simple division, rather than by two root extractions and a more complicated division. By introducing a perfect square in the denominator, we may remove it from under the radical.

$$\sqrt{\frac{3}{2}} = \sqrt{\frac{3 \cdot 2}{2 \cdot 2}} = \frac{\sqrt{6}}{2}.$$

EXAMPLE 3. Simplify $\sqrt[4]{64x^2y^4/z^2}$.

Solution. Problems of this type are usually more easily grasped if rational exponents are introduced. We also must eliminate the denominator under the radical.

$$\sqrt[4]{\frac{64x^2y^4}{z^2}} \equiv \left(\frac{2^6x^2y^4}{z^2}\right)^{1/4} \equiv \frac{2^{3/2}x^{1/2}y}{z^{1/2}} \cdot \frac{z^{1/2}}{z^{1/2}} \equiv \frac{2y}{z}\sqrt{2xz}.$$

PROBLEMS

Simplify each of the following.

1. $\sqrt{8}$

2. $\sqrt{98}$

3. $\sqrt{\frac{75}{12}}$

4. $\sqrt[3]{40}$

5. $\sqrt[3]{-625}$

6. $\sqrt[4]{32}$

7. $\sqrt{27x^3y^5}$

8. $\sqrt{192a^3b^7}$

9. $\sqrt[3]{81z^4x^6y^5}$

10. $\sqrt{\frac{3}{5}}$

11. $\sqrt{\frac{125}{63}}$

12. $\sqrt{\frac{1}{9}+\frac{1}{4}}$

13. $\sqrt{a^2b^2+b^2c^2}$

14. $\sqrt{a^{-2}+b^{-2}}$

15. $\sqrt{\frac{3x}{y^3}}$

16. $\sqrt[3]{\dfrac{x^4y}{z^2}}$ 17. $\sqrt[4]{\dfrac{x^7y^6}{243}}$ 18. $\sqrt{x - 2 + \dfrac{1}{x}}$

19. $\sqrt[6]{25}$ 20. $\sqrt[6]{49x^4}$ 21. $\sqrt[3]{\dfrac{5}{3x^2}}$

22. $\sqrt[6]{\dfrac{9}{16}}$ 23. $\sqrt[4]{\dfrac{169x^6z^2}{y^4}}$ 24. $\sqrt[4]{1 - \dfrac{4}{x} + \dfrac{4}{x^2}}$

3–12 Addition and subtraction of radicals. In addition or subtraction of radicals, all similar radicals (that is, those which result in the same index and radicand) are combined into single terms. Consider the example.

EXAMPLE. Simplify by combining similar terms,

$$4\sqrt{12} + 5\sqrt{8} - \sqrt{50} - 7\sqrt{48}.$$

Solution.

$$4\sqrt{12} + 5\sqrt{8} - \sqrt{50} - 7\sqrt{48}$$
$$= 4\sqrt{4\cdot 3} + 5\sqrt{4\cdot 2} - \sqrt{25\cdot 2} - 7\sqrt{16\cdot 3}$$
$$= 8\sqrt{3} - 28\sqrt{3} + 10\sqrt{2} - 5\sqrt{2}$$
$$= 5\sqrt{2} - 20\sqrt{3}.$$

PROBLEMS

Simplify by combining similar terms.

1. $4\sqrt{3} - 5\sqrt{12} + 2\sqrt{75}$ 2. $\sqrt[3]{2} + \sqrt[3]{16} - \sqrt[3]{54}$

3. $5\sqrt{2} - \sqrt[4]{64} + 2\sqrt{32}$ 4. $\sqrt{x^3} + \sqrt{25x^3} + \sqrt{9x}$

5. $\sqrt{4(x + y)} - 2\sqrt{9(x + y)} + 3\sqrt{x + y}$

6. $3\sqrt{18} - 3\sqrt{32} + 3\sqrt{12} - 3\sqrt{3}$ 7. $\sqrt{a^3bc^5} + \sqrt{ab^7c^3} + \sqrt{a^9b^5c}$

8. $\sqrt{\dfrac{a - b}{a + b}} - \sqrt{\dfrac{a + b}{a - b}} + \sqrt{\dfrac{a^2}{a^2 - b^2}}$ 9. $8\sqrt{\dfrac{1}{3}} + \dfrac{3}{2}\sqrt{108} - \sqrt[4]{9}$

10. $\sqrt{\left(\dfrac{x}{y} - \dfrac{y}{x}\right)\dfrac{1}{xy}} - \sqrt{\dfrac{x + y}{x - y}}$ 11. $\dfrac{7 \pm \sqrt{49 - 4\cdot 10}}{2}$

12. $\dfrac{4 \pm \sqrt{16 - 4\cdot 2}}{2}$

3–13 Multiplication and division of radicals. The multiplication of two or more radicals is accomplished by using the rule established in Eq. (3–30). If the radicals have the same index, the result follows immediately. If, however, the radicals are of different indices, they must be converted to radicals with the same index before the multiplication takes place. This is always possible, and may be carried out with the aid of equivalent expressions having rational exponents.

EXAMPLE 1. Find the product of $\sqrt{15ax^3}$ and $\sqrt{45a^2xy^3}$ and simplify.

Solution. Since both radicals have the index 2, we use Eq. (3–30) immediately:

$$\sqrt{15ax^3} \cdot \sqrt{45a^2xy^3} \equiv \sqrt{15^2 \cdot 3a^3x^4y^3}$$
$$\equiv 15ax^2y\sqrt{3ay}.$$

EXAMPLE 2. Multiply $\sqrt{6x^3}$ by $\sqrt[3]{4x^4y^2}$ and simplify.

Solution. By converting the radicals to rational exponents, we have

$$\sqrt{6x^3} \cdot \sqrt[3]{4x^4y^2} \equiv (3 \cdot 2x^3)^{1/2} \cdot (2^2x^4y^2)^{1/3}$$
$$\equiv (3 \cdot 2x^3)^{3/6} \cdot (2^2x^4y^2)^{2/6}$$
$$\equiv (3^3 \cdot 2^3 \cdot x^9 \cdot 2^4x^8y^4)^{1/6}$$
$$\equiv \sqrt[6]{3^3 \cdot 2 \cdot 2^6x^{12} \cdot x^5y^4}$$
$$\equiv 2x^2\sqrt[6]{54x^5y^4}.$$

Division of two radicals is handled in a similar manner, by using Eq. (3–31). Again, if the radicals are of different indices, they must be converted to the same index.

EXAMPLE 3. Divide $6\sqrt[3]{5}$ by $2\sqrt{3}$ and simplify.

Solution. Since $\sqrt[3]{5} = \sqrt[6]{25}$ and $\sqrt{3} = \sqrt[6]{27}$, we have

$$\frac{6\sqrt[3]{5}}{2\sqrt{3}} = 3\sqrt[6]{\frac{25}{27}}.$$

Recalling that a radical in simplest form has a denominator free of radicals, we must multiply the numerator and denominator by $\sqrt[6]{27}$. Thus

$$\frac{6\sqrt[3]{5}}{2\sqrt{3}} \equiv 3\sqrt[6]{\frac{25 \cdot 27}{27 \cdot 27}} \equiv 3\sqrt[6]{\frac{25 \cdot 27}{3^6}} \equiv \frac{3}{3}\sqrt[6]{25 \cdot 27} = \sqrt[6]{675}.$$

The process of eliminating radicals from the denominator, illustrated in Example 3, and Example 2, Article 3–11, is called *rationalizing the denominator.* The problem of eliminating all radicals in a denominator may be more complicated.

EXAMPLE 4. Rationalize the denominator of $(2 + \sqrt{3})/(\sqrt{5} - \sqrt{3})$.

Solution. Since we wish to eliminate both radicals in the denominator, we must find an expression (*rationalizing factor*) which, when multiplied by $\sqrt{5} - \sqrt{3}$, will give a result free of radicals. Since

$$(\sqrt{5} - \sqrt{3})(\sqrt{5} + \sqrt{3}) = 5 - 3,$$

we multiply both numerator and denominator by $\sqrt{5} + \sqrt{3}$.

$$\frac{2 + \sqrt{3}}{\sqrt{5} - \sqrt{3}} \cdot \frac{\sqrt{5} + \sqrt{3}}{\sqrt{5} + \sqrt{3}} = \frac{2\sqrt{5} + \sqrt{15} + 2\sqrt{3} + 3}{5 - 3}$$

$$= \frac{2\sqrt{5} + \sqrt{15} + 2\sqrt{3} + 3}{2}.$$

Problems

Perform the following multiplications, expressing the result in simplest form.

1. $\sqrt{5} \cdot \sqrt{13}$

2. $\sqrt{14} \cdot \sqrt{21}$

3. $\sqrt[3]{4} \cdot \sqrt[3]{26}$

4. $\sqrt[3]{3x^2} \cdot \sqrt{2x}$

5. $\sqrt{x^2 - y^2} \cdot \sqrt{x - y}$

6. $\sqrt{3x^2y^3} \cdot \sqrt{12x^5y}$

7. $\sqrt{x^3 + y^3} \cdot \sqrt{x + y}$

8. $\sqrt[3]{9x} \cdot \sqrt[6]{27x^4}$

9. $\sqrt{2} \cdot \sqrt[3]{3} \cdot \sqrt[4]{4}$

10. $\sqrt{a} \cdot \sqrt[3]{a} \cdot \sqrt[4]{a}$

11. $\sqrt{2}(\sqrt{6} + \sqrt{14})$

12. $(2 + \sqrt{3})(2 - \sqrt{3})$

13. $(\sqrt{3} + \sqrt{5})(\sqrt{3} - \sqrt{5})$

14. $(2\sqrt{3} - 3\sqrt{2})^2$

15. $(\sqrt{5} + 2\sqrt{3})(\sqrt{5} - 3\sqrt{3})$

16. $\sqrt{3 + 2\sqrt{2}} \cdot \sqrt{3 - 2\sqrt{2}}$

17. $\left(\dfrac{\sqrt{5} - 1}{2}\right)^2$

18. $\left(\dfrac{\sqrt{6} - \sqrt{2}}{4}\right)^2$

Perform the following divisions, expressing the result in simplest form.

19. $4\sqrt{28} \div 3\sqrt{7}$

20. $\sqrt[3]{\frac{4}{5}} \div \sqrt[3]{\frac{108}{25}}$

21. $\sqrt[6]{12} \div \sqrt{3}\sqrt{2}$

22. $(2\sqrt{6} + 3\sqrt{14}) \div \sqrt{2}$

23. $\sqrt[4]{24a^3b} \div \sqrt[4]{8ab^3}$

24. $\sqrt{xy^2} \div \sqrt[3]{x^2y}$

Rationalize the denominator of each of the following.

25. $\dfrac{2\sqrt{3}}{4\sqrt{5}}$

26. $\dfrac{2\sqrt[3]{3}}{4\sqrt[3]{5}}$

27. $\dfrac{4}{\sqrt[3]{16}}$

28. $\dfrac{3}{2 + \sqrt{3}}$

29. $\dfrac{5}{\sqrt{7} - \sqrt{3}}$

30. $\dfrac{\sqrt{2} + \sqrt{3}}{\sqrt{2} - \sqrt{3}}$

31. $\dfrac{x}{x + \sqrt{y}}$

32. $\dfrac{y}{\sqrt{x} - \sqrt{y}}$

33. $\dfrac{2\sqrt{7} + \sqrt{3}}{3\sqrt{7} - 5\sqrt{3}}$

34. $\dfrac{1}{\sqrt[3]{a} + \sqrt[3]{b}}$ [*Hint*: $x^3 + y^3 \equiv (x + y)(x^2 - xy + y^2)$.]

35. $\dfrac{2}{2 - \sqrt[3]{3}}$

36. $\dfrac{1}{\sqrt[3]{9} + \sqrt[3]{6} + \sqrt[3]{4}}$

37. $\dfrac{1}{\sqrt{2} + \sqrt{3} + \sqrt{5}}$ [*Hint*: Multiply both numerator and denominator by $(\sqrt{2} + \sqrt{3}) - \sqrt{5}$.]

CHAPTER 4

INEQUALITIES, ABSOLUTE VALUES, AND
COORDINATE SYSTEMS

There are further notions and concepts important in any systematic study of algebra and trigonometry. In Chapter 2 we discussed the field axioms for the real numbers, from which we derived many of the normal properties of the set R. Unfortunately, the ability to compare real numbers does not follow from these field axioms. In addition to them, we must have the four *order axioms*, which we shall give in this chapter, along with the *completeness axiom* (Article 4–3). We shall also consider certain geometric interpretations, together with a brief discussion of other helpful geometric ideas.

4–1 Order axioms for the real numbers. If any field, such as the real numbers, satisfies the following four axioms, the field is said to be *ordered*. The real numbers are considered the undefined elements. The relation "$>$" is defined for these elements by the axioms, and is read "is greater than." Recall that a, b, c ... represent *any* real numbers.

AXIOM O1. *The trichotomy axiom.* If a and $b \in R$, then one and only one of the following statements is true:

$$a > b, \qquad a = b, \qquad b > a.$$

AXIOM O2. *The transitive axiom.* If a, b, and $c \in R$ such that $a > b$ and $b > c$, then $a > c$.

AXIOM O3. *The addition axiom.* If a, b, and $c \in R$ such that $a > b$, then $a + c > b + c$.

AXIOM O4. *The multiplication axiom.* If a, b, and $c \in R$ such that $a > b$ and $c > 0$, then $ac > bc$.

Since both addition and multiplication are commutative operations, the result in Axiom O3 can read $c + a > c + b$, and in Axiom O4, $ca > cb$. The fact that $c > 0$ is a condition in Axiom O4 should be emphasized.

It is often convenient to say one number "is less than" another, rather than always to use the idea of "is greater than." Consequently, we make the following definition of the relation (is less than) on the set R.

DEFINITION 4–1. *If a and $b \in R$, we say $a < b$ (read "a is less than b") if and only if $b > a$.*

As a result of this definition, $a > b$ may be read either "a is greater than b" or "b is less than a." In any of our proofs involving these relations (inequalities) we shall assume that any quantity may be substituted for an equal quantity. For example, if $a > b$ and $b = c$, then $a > c$. Further, we shall define $\geq$ to be $>$ or $=$, and similarly $\leq$ to be $<$ or $=$.

One further definition is in order. You noticed in Chapters 2 and 3 that although we discussed $-a$, $a - b$, and so on, we did not mention in our logical process the idea of positive or negative numbers.* We now define such numbers.

DEFINITION 4–2. *A real number a is* positive *if $a > 0$ and* negative *if $a < 0$.*

It follows immediately from Axiom O1, that zero is neither positive nor negative. Also, because of this definition, Axiom O4 reads, "If $a > b$ and c is positive, then $ac > bc$."

We are now ready to prove several of the more basic theorems.

THEOREM 4–1. *If a and $b \in R$,*
(i) $a > b$ *if and only if* $-a < -b$;
(ii) $a < b$ *if and only if* $-a > -b$.

Proof. We shall prove the statement in (i). The proof of (ii) is similar. If $a > b$, we have by Axiom O3,

$$a + [(-a) + (-b)] > b + [(-a) + (-b)],$$

and by the associative, commutative, and identity axioms, it follows that $0 + (-b) > 0 + (-a)$ or $-a < -b$. Since each of these steps is reversible, the converse follows immediately.

COROLLARY. *If $a > 0$, then $-a < 0$.*

Proof. Recall $0 = -0$ (Problem 11, Article 2–3).

THEOREM 4–2. $1 > 0$.

Proof. By Axiom O1, $1 > 0$, $1 = 0$, or $1 < 0$. By Axiom 5, we know $1 \neq 0$. We shall assume $1 < 0$, arrive at a contradiction, and thus have our result. If we assume $1 < 0$, $-1 > 0$ by Theorem 4–1, and by Axiom O4, $(-1)(-1) > 0(-1)$ or $1 > 0$, which contradicts our assumption. Therefore, $1 > 0$.

COROLLARY. $-1 < 0$.

---

* Note the distinction between "negative number" and "negative of a number" (see Axiom 6, Chapter 2).

As a result of this theorem, we are able to establish order relations between any pair of natural numbers (see Problems 17 through 20), or, in fact, any integers.

It should be emphasized that 1 is a positive number, and, as the discussion has implied, this is by no means trivial.

If in the inequality $5 > 3$, we multiply both numbers by -2, the result is $-10 < -6$, and the relation changes from $>$ to $<$. This is always the case if we multiply by a negative number, and can be stated in general.

THEOREM 4–3. *If $a > b$ and $c < 0$, then $ac < bc$.*

Proof. Since $c < 0$, by Theorem 4–1, $-c > 0$. Now, as a direct result of Axiom O4, $a(-c) > b(-c)$, or $-ac > -bc$, which reduces to $ac < bc$ (Theorem 4–1).

Two further theorems, one involving addition and the other multiplication, should be mentioned.

THEOREM 4–4. *If $a > b$ and $c > d$, then $a + c > b + d$.*

Proof. Since $a > b$, $a + c > b + c$ by Axiom O4. Also, since $c > d$, $b + c > b + d$. If we combine these two statements by Axiom O2, we have

$$a + c > b + d.$$

THEOREM 4–5. *If a, b, c, and d are positive numbers, $a > b$ and $c > d$, then $ac > bd$.*

Proof. (Give the reasons for each step.) Since $a > b$, $ac > bc$. Since $c > d$, $bc > bd$. Therefore, $ac > bd$.

ILLUSTRATIONS. Since $4 > 3$ and $5 > 2$, we may say by Theorem 4–4 that $9 > 5$, and by Theorem 4–5, that $20 > 6$.

Some of these properties of the inequality relations will be used in this chapter. Others, together with those stated in the following set of problems, will be used later, especially in the article in which the solution of inequalities is discussed (Article 7–5).

PROBLEMS

1. Verify each of the order axioms *intuitively* by suitable choices of real numbers. For example, in Axiom O1, if $a = 2$ and $b = -3$, $a > b$, since $2 > -3$.

2. Verify each of the general theorems *intuitively* by suitable choices of real numbers.

3. Prove that $a > b$ if and only if $a - b$ is positive. This property is sometimes taken as the definition of $a > b$.

Prove each of the statements in Problems 4 through 6.

4. If c is positive and $a > b$, then $a + c > b$.

5. If a and b are positive and $a > b$, then $(1/a) < (1/b)$.

6. (a) If a is positive and $a > 1$, then $a^2 > a$.

  (b) If a is positive but $a < 1$, then $a^2 < a$.

  (c) If m and n are positive integers, $m \geq n$ and $a > 1$, then $a^m \geq a^n$.

7. Prove that the relation $a > b$ is true if and only if $a + c > b + c$.

8. Prove that the sum of two positive real numbers is positive.

9. Prove that the sum of two negative real numbers is negative.

*10. Prove that the product ab is positive if and only if a and b are both positive or both negative.

11. Prove that the product ab is negative if and only if a is positive and b is negative or a is negative and b is positive.

*12. Prove that $a^2 \geq 0$. [*Hint:* Use Problem 10.]

13. Prove Theorem 4–2 as a corollary to Problem 12.

14. Prove that if a and b are positive, and $a > l$, then $a^2 > b^2$.

15. Prove that if n is any positive integer, a and b are positive, and $a > b$, then $a^n > b^n$.

16. Prove that if n is any positive integer, a and b are positive, and $a^n > b^n$, then $a > b$. [*Hint:* Assume the statement is not true and use Axiom O1.]

Problems 17 through 20 indicate a method for ordering the integers.

17. Prove that $2 > 1$. Here we must assume that 2 is the symbol indicating $1 + 1$. [*Hint:* $1 > 0$.]

18. Prove that $2 > 0$.

19. If we use the symbol 3 to indicate $2 + 1 = (1 + 1) + 1$, (a) prove that $3 > 2$; (b) prove that $3 > 1$.

20. (a) Prove that $-3 < -2$; (b) prove that $-3 < -1$.

*21. (a) If $a > b$, show that

$$a > \frac{a + b}{2} > b.$$

  (b) Show that $0 < \frac{1}{2} < 1$.

  (c) Show that $\frac{1}{2} < \frac{3}{4} < 1$.

22. If $a > b$, show that $a > \sqrt{ab} > b$. [*Hint:* Use Problem 16.]

23. We recall that $a - c = a + (-c)$. State a property for subtraction, analogous to Axiom O3, and explain why it is true.

24. We recall that if $c \neq 0$,

$$a \cdot \frac{1}{c} = \frac{a}{c}.$$

State a property for division, analogous to Axiom O4, and explain why it is true.

4–2 A one-dimensional coordinate system. The method of associating numbers with points on a line is of considerable help in mathematics and has resulted in great progress in the application of mathematics to science. Any scale which measures quantities, such as a yardstick or thermometer,

$$(-1\tfrac{3}{8}) \qquad (\tfrac{3}{4})$$

$$(-5) \qquad\qquad (-1)\ (0)\ (1) \qquad (\pi)\ (4) \qquad x$$

FIGURE 4–1

makes use of an association of this kind. To each numerical value assumed by the physical quantity there corresponds a position on the scale, and to each position on the scale there corresponds a real number. Such a correspondence establishes a coordinate system. The simplest and most useful coordinate system in one dimension employs a one-to-one correspondence between the set R of real numbers and the set of points on a straight line. Let us consider such a system.

On a fixed straight line of reference of unlimited length, we choose any point O, called the origin, and lay off equal divisions* of arbitrary length in both directions from O. We now associate zero with the origin, the positive integers with the successive points on one side, and the negative integers with the successive points on the other (see Fig. 4–1). The usual convention on such a horizontal line is to consider the integers to the right as positive and those to the left as negative.

The point associated with any rational number can be determined by the simple geometric construction used to divide any line segment into b equal parts. Thus the number $\tfrac{3}{4}$ is represented by a point three-fourths of the way from 0 to the point identified with 1. Also, $-1\tfrac{3}{8}$ is represented by a point at a distance $1\tfrac{3}{8}$ units to the left of 0.

The points associated with some irrational numbers may also be found by geometric construction. For example, the point associated with $\sqrt{2}$ may be located, because $\sqrt{2}$ is the hypotenuse of an isosceles right triangle with each leg one unit in length. Although geometric construction is not possible for all real numbers, *we shall assume that the correspondence can be extended to all real numbers.* This is done by associating every line segment with a real number which represents its length. Thus, with each real number, we have associated one point on the line and, conversely, with each point on the line there is associated one real number.

The *coordinate* of a point is defined to be the number associated with that point. It is written (x) and will be referred to as "the point x."

The coordinate system gives us a graphic interpretation of the relative magnitude of numbers. Thus $5 > 3$ corresponds to the fact that (5) lies to the right of (3), while $-5 < -3$ corresponds to the fact that (-5) is to the left of (-3). The notation $x < y < z$ indicates that y is greater than x but less than z.

---

* There are systems where the subdivisions are not equal. Consider the slide-rule scale.

To express the distance between any two points in this system, we need only subtract the coordinate of the left-hand point from the coordinate of the right-hand point. Thus, if $x_1 < x_2$, where the subscripts 1 and 2 merely denote two distinct values of x, the distance between (x_1) and (x_2) is $x_2 - x_1$, but if $x_2 < x_1$, the distance must be $x_1 - x_2$, since we wish to have the distance always positive. We can avoid the inconvenience of having to distinguish between the two points by employing the notion of absolute value.

The absolute value of x, denoted by $|x|$, indicates its size or magnitude without regard to its sign. For example, $|3| = 3$, and $|-3| = 3$.

DEFINITION 4–3. *The absolute value of a real number x is defined as*

$$|x| \equiv \begin{cases} x & \text{if } x > 0, \\ -x & \text{if } x < 0, \\ 0 & \text{if } x = 0. \end{cases} \tag{4–1}$$

Here we should recall the definition of the square-root sign, $\sqrt{}$. For any positive number a, $\sqrt{a}$ denotes the positive square root of a. Let us emphasize this by the following consistent definition.

DEFINITION 4–4. *For any real number x, x^2 is positive (or zero if $x = 0$) and*

$$\sqrt{x^2} \equiv \begin{cases} x & \text{if } x > 0, \\ -x & \text{if } x < 0, \\ 0 & \text{if } x = 0. \end{cases} \tag{4–2}$$

Thus $\sqrt{7^2} = 7$, and $\sqrt{(-7)^2} = -(-7) = 7$, and in general $|x| = \sqrt{x^2}$. Since Eqs. (4–1) and (4–2) define the same values, either expression can be used to indicate absolute value.

As an immediate consequence of the definition of the absolute value, we have the following theorem.

THEOREM 4–6. *For any $a \in R$,*

$$-|a| \le a \le |a|. \tag{4–3}$$

Proof. Right-hand inequality: If $a \ge 0$, $a = |a|$, but if $a < 0$, (that is, $0 < -a$), $|a| = -a$ so that $0 < |a|$, $a < 0 < |a|$. Thus $a \le |a|$ for all a.

Left-hand inequality: If $a \geq 0$, $-a = -|a| \leq 0 \leq a$. If $a < 0$, $|a| = -a$ or $-|a| = a$, so that for all a, $-|a| \leq a$.

Since two basic properties of absolute value will be used later in work with inequalities, we shall mention them now.

THEOREM 4–7. *If a and b are any two real numbers, the absolute value of their product (or quotient) is equal to the product (or quotient) of their absolute values:*

$$|ab| \equiv |a| \cdot |b|, \tag{4–4}$$

$$\left|\frac{a}{b}\right| \equiv \frac{|a|}{|b|}, \qquad b \neq 0. \tag{4–5}$$

Proof of (4–4). By Definitions 4–3 and 4–4, $|ab| = \sqrt{(ab)^2}$. Thus, $|ab| = \sqrt{(ab)^2} = \sqrt{a^2 b^2} = \sqrt{a^2}\sqrt{b^2} = |a| \cdot |b|$.

THEOREM 4–8. *If a and b are any two real numbers, the absolute value of their sum is less than or equal to the sum of their absolute values:*

$$|a + b| \leq |a| + |b|. \tag{4–6}$$

Proof. See Problem 10 below.

We are now able to give the general expression for the distance between any two points P_1 and P_2.

THEOREM 4–9. *The distance between any two points P_1 and P_2 with coordinates (x_1) and (x_2) may be expressed*

$$d = P_1 P_2 = |x_1 - x_2| \equiv \sqrt{(x_1 - x_2)^2}. \tag{4–7}$$

For example, the distance between the two points (5) and (−3) is given either by the expression $d = \sqrt{[5 - (-3)]^2} = 8$ or by the expression $d = \sqrt{(-3 - 5)^2} = 8$.

PROBLEMS

1. Arrange the following numbers in ascending order of magnitude and plot them on a linear coordinate system such as that of Fig. 4–1: 2.3, 0.333, 2^3, 4, $\frac{1}{3}$, −5, −1, 0, −6.5.

2. State the conditions on a and b in Theorem 4–8, so that the = sign will hold.

3. State in words the geometrical interpretation of the following.

(a) $a < b$

(b) $a < 2$

(c) $a > b$

(d) $a > b > c$

(e) $a - b = 1$

(f) $3.14 < \pi < 3.15$

(g) $1.41 < \sqrt{2} < 1.42$

(h) $|5 - 2| > |1 - 3|$

(i) $|a - b| > 0$

(j) $|x - 2| < 3$

(k) $|x - 1| > 4$

(l) $-1 < x < 1$

4. If the coordinates of two points, P_1 and P_2, on a line are (2) and (8) respectively, show that the coordinate of the midpoint of the segment P_1P_2 is (5).

5. Find the coordinate of the midpoint of the line joining (4) and (-4), (3) and (-5), (-1.7) and (3.7), $(\sqrt{2})$ and $(\sqrt{3})$, (x_1) and (x_2).

6. Solve the following equations for x.

(a) $x = |10|$

(b) $x = |2 - 5|$

(c) $x = \sqrt{3^2}$

(d) $x = \sqrt{(-4)^2}$

(e) $x = |-\frac{3}{2}|$

(f) $x = \sqrt{(-1)^2}$

(g) $x = |\frac{1}{3} - \frac{5}{3}|$

(h) $x = |\frac{1}{3}| + |-\frac{5}{3}|$

7. Solve the following equations for all possible values of x.

(a) $|x| = 2$

(b) $|x| = \sqrt{5}$

(c) $\sqrt{x^2} = 3$

(d) $\sqrt{x^2} = \frac{1}{4}$

(e) $|x - 2| = 5$

(f) $|x - 4| = 0$

(g) $|3 - x| = 6$

(h) $\sqrt{(x - 1)^2} = 5$

(i) $\sqrt{(2 - x)^2} = 4$

(j) $|x - 2| = -3$

(k) $\sqrt{(x - 4)^2} = -1$

(l) $\sqrt{(x - 5)^2} = 3$

8. Prove Eq. (4–5), Theorem 4–7.

*9. If $d \geq 0$, then $|c| \leq d$ if and only if $-d \leq c \leq d$. Give the reasons for each step in the proof of this property, which must consist of two parts:

(a) Proof of the statement that if $|c| \leq d$, then $-d \leq c \leq d$. We know $c \leq |c|$ and $|c| \leq d$, so that $c \leq d$. We know $-d \leq -|c|$ and $-|c| \leq c$, so that $-d \leq c$. Therefore, $-d \leq c \leq d$.

(b) Proof of the statement that if $d \geq 0$ and $-d \leq c \leq d$, then $|c| \leq d$. If $c \geq 0$, $|c| = c$. Since $c \leq d$, we have $|c| \leq d$. If $c < 0$, $|c| = -c$. Since $-d \leq c$ or $-c \leq d$, we again have $|c| \leq d$.

*10. Prove Theorem 4–8. [*Hint:* $-|a| \leq a \leq |a|$ and $-|b| \leq b \leq |b|$. Add these inequalities and use the result in Problem 9.]

*11. Prove $|a - b| \leq |a| + |b|$. [*Hint:* Let b in Theorem 4–8 be equal to $-b$.]

12. Solve the following inequalities for all possible values of x.

(a) $|x - 1| \leq 2$.   By the statement in Problem 9, this is equivalent to $-2 \leq x - 1 \leq 2$.   The left inequality, $-2 \leq x - 1$, gives $x \geq -1$; the right inequality $x - 1 \leq 2$, gives $x \leq 3$. The result may be written $-1 \leq x \leq 3$.

(b) $|3 - x| \leq 5$.

(c) $|2x + 5| < 6$.

(d) $|4 + 3x| < 2$.

*13. Prove that if $d \geq 0$, then $|c| \geq d$ if and only if $c \geq d$ or $c \leq -d$. [*Hint:* See the proof in Problem 9.]

14. Solve the following inequalities for all possible values of x.

(a) $|x - 1| \geq 2$. By the statement in Problem 13, this is equivalent to $x - 1 \geq 2$ or $x - 1 \leq -2$. The first inequality says $x \geq 3$, while the second says $x \leq -1$. Compare these answers with those in Problem 12(a).

(b) $|3 - x| \geq 5$.

(c) $|2x + 6| > 4$.

(d) $|3x + 1| > 8$.

15. Recall from plane geometry that a circle is the locus (totality) of points at a given distance from a given point, where the distance is called the radius and the given point is called the center. In this geometry of one dimension, how many points are at a given distance from a fixed point? Of how many points would a "circle" consist?

16. If (1) is a given point and 2 a given distance, explain how $|x - 1| = 2$ would be the condition that any point (x) must be 2 units distant from (1). This is the condition that the point (x) lies on the "circle" with center (1) and radius 2, and is called the equation of the "circle."

17. In terms of "circles in one dimension," give the geometric significance of each of the equations in Problem 7.

18. Give the equation of a "circle in one dimension" with its center at the point (a) and with radius r.

4–3 The completeness property. Since we wish to characterize the set R completely, it is necessary to give one axiom in addition to the field axioms and order axioms.

Consider the set of rational approximations for $\sqrt{2}$, obtained by the ordinary process of finding a square root. This set $A = \{1, 1.4, 1.41, 1.414, \ldots\}$ is a subset of the set $B = \{x | x \in R \text{ and } x^2 < 2\}$. In neither of these sets is there any element equal to or greater than $\sqrt{2}$, so that $\sqrt{2}$ is called an upper bound of either set. Of course there are many such upper bounds. The numbers $2\frac{1}{2}$, 3, and 4 are also upper bounds, although $\sqrt{2}$ appears to be "the best upper bound," in the sense that it is the smallest of all the upper bounds.

DEFINITION 4–5. *The number v is called an* upper bound *of a set S if $x \leq v$ for all $x \in S$. Similarly, the number u is called a* lower bound *of a set S if $u \leq x$ for all $x \in S$.*

In the examples above, v could be $\sqrt{2}$, 2, $2\frac{1}{2}$, 3, and so on. For the set A, u could be 1, 0, -3, and so on. Are these lower bounds of B? (Why?)

We are not only interested in the bounds of any set, but we also wish to emphasize the smallest of the upper bounds and the largest of the lower bounds, if they exist.

Consider any set of numbers $X = \{x | a < x < b\}$. If $c \in X$, we have, by definition, that $a < c$ and $c < b$. Since, by Problem 21, Article 4–1,

$$a < \frac{a + c}{2} < c,$$

we know that c is not a lower bound of X. Also, since

$$c < \frac{c + b}{2} < b,$$

c is not an upper bound of X. Consequently, b is the smallest upper bound of X, and similarly, a is its largest lower bound.

DEFINITION 4–6. *An upper bound b of a set S is the* least *upper bound if no upper bound is less than b. Similarly, a lower bound a is the* greatest *lower bound if no lower bound is greater than a.*

In the set $X = \{x | a < x < b\}$, b is the least upper bound and a is the greatest lower bound.

The least upper bound and greatest lower bound may or may not be in the set. In the set X they are not in the set, but they are in the set $Y = \{x | a \leq x \leq b\}$. The set of real numbers $\{x | x \geq 0\}$ has a greatest lower bound zero, but no least upper bound. If we recall Theorem 1–1, the set of real numbers $\{x | x \geq 0, x \text{ is rational, and } x^2 \leq 2\}$ has zero for its greatest lower bound, and $\sqrt{2}$ for its least upper bound. Its greatest lower bound, zero, is in the set, but its least upper bound, $\sqrt{2}$, is not. (Why?)

We are now prepared to state the rather intuitive completeness property as our final axiom for the set of real numbers R.

AXIOM C. Every set S where $S \subset R$ and has an upper bound has a least upper bound. Similarly, every such set S that has a lower bound has a greatest lower bound.

EXAMPLE. Show that the set of *positive* integers I_+ has no upper bound.

Solution. We shall show this by assuming the statement is not true and arriving at a contradiction. Let us assume that the set of positive integers I_+ has an upper bound. Since $I_+ \subset R$, it has a *least* upper bound (by Axiom C), which we shall denote by b. Thus, there exists a b such that if $x \in I_+$, $x \leq b$, and b is the least such number. But if $x \in I_+$, $x + 1 \in I_+$, so that $x + 1 \leq b$ for all $x \in I_+$. Therefore, $x \leq b - 1$, which contradicts the fact that b was the least upper bound. This contradiction shows that I_+ has no upper bound.

PROBLEMS

1. Give the least upper bound and the greatest lower bound of each of the following sets (if they exist).

(a) $\{x | x \in R \text{ and } x < -3\}$ (b) $\{x | x \in F, x > 0 \text{ and } x^2 > 2\}$

(c) $\{x | x \in I \text{ and } -3 \le x < 1\}$ (d) $\left\{ \frac{1}{n} \,\middle|\, n \in I \text{ and } n > 0 \right\}$

2. Give an example of a subset of R such that

(a) it has neither an upper nor a lower bound;

(b) it has an upper but no lower bound;

(c) it does not contain its upper or lower bound;

(d) it contains both its upper and lower bound.

3. Show why the set $\{-1, 0, 1\}$ contains its least upper and greatest lower bound. What are they?

4. Show that any finite set $\{a_1, a_2, \ldots, a_n\}$ can be ordered, by recalling Axiom O1. With this knowledge, show that any finite set contains its least upper bound (and greatest lower bound).

5. Let b be the least upper bound of the set S of real numbers. If $x \in S$ and $x < b$, there exists a number $y \in S$ such that $x < y \le b$. If this were not the case, x would be an upper bound of S, contradicting the fact that b is the least upper bound. What is an analogous property for a, the greatest lower bound of the set S of real numbers? Explain.

6. If $r \in R$ and $r > 0$, show that the set $S = \{nr | n \in I_+\}$ has no upper bound. [*Hint:* Assume the statement is not true. Thus there exists some real number t such that $nr \le t$ for all $n \in I_+$. Therefore, $n \le (t/r)$ must hold for all $n \in I_+$. Does this contradict the result of the example?]

7. If $r > 0$, $s > 0$, and r and $s \in R$, there exists a positive integer n such that $nr > s$. Show that this statement is true. [*Hint:* If it were not true, $n \le (s/r)$ for all $n \in I_+$.]

8. If a, b, and c are real numbers such that $a < c < b$, we say c lies between a and b. Show that there is always some rational number between any two unequal rational numbers. [*Hint:* See Problem 21, Article 4–1.]

9. If a and $b \in R$, and $0 < a < b$, show that there is always some *rational* number between a and b. Although the proof of this important result is somewhat involved, each step is comparatively simple. Give the reasons for each step in the proof that follows.

   (i) Since a and 1 are positive, there exists a positive integer n' such that $n'a > 1$.

  (ii) Since $b - a$ and 1 are positive, there exists a positive integer n'' such that $n''(b - a) > 1$.

 (iii) If n is the larger of n' and n'', we have $na > 1$ and $nb > 1 + na$.

 (iv) Since na and 1 are positive, there exists a positive integer m' such that $m' > na$.

  (v) If m is the smallest such m', we have $na + 1 \ge m > na$.

 (vi) Therefore, $nb > m > na$, so that $b > (m/n) > a$.

4–4 A two-dimensional coordinate system. In Article 4–2 we observed a coordinate system that not only enabled us to view the relative magnitudes of numbers in a graphic way, but also allowed us to represent the distance between two points by the magnitude of their differences. But the usefulness of a one-dimensional coordinate system is limited. One of the more important concepts in mathematics is the relation or dependence of two sets of numbers. The corresponding values of two such related sets can be regarded as pairs of numbers; hence a system which produces an association between a point and an ordered pair of numbers would be most advantageous in studying such a relationship. A two-dimensional system provides the association.

We recall the definition of the *cartesian product* of two sets. We are particularly interested here in the case where $X = Y$, and, in fact, where X and Y are both the set of real numbers R. Symbolically this is

$$R \times R = \{(x, y)\,|\,x \in R \text{ and } y \in R\}.$$

Each member of the set is an ordered pair (x, y). We are able to set up an association between this set of all ordered pairs (x, y) of $R \times R$ and the set of all points in the plane. (The student should review the important notion of product set, given in Problem 12, Article 1–3.)

The most frequently used system that sets up an association between each point in a plane and pair of real numbers is the *rectangular cartesian system of coordinates.* In 1637 René Descartes, a French mathematician and philosopher, used this method of associating points with numbers, and by so doing, associated a curve with its equation. Great progress in mathematics and the application of mathematics in science resulted from this unification of algebra and geometry.

Let us construct two perpendicular straight lines and, for convenience, let one of them be horizontal. We shall call these *coordinate axes.* Using the point of intersection as the origin O, set up on each line a one-dimensional system. Ordinarily, the same unit of length is used on both lines, although in some cases it is convenient to do otherwise. We now denote by the expression $(x, 0)$ the point on the horizontal line corresponding to the number x in its one-dimensional system. Similarly, we denote the point on the vertical line corresponding to the number y in its one-dimensional system by the symbol $(0, y)$. The horizontal line is called the *x-axis,* or *axis of abscissas,* while the vertical line is referred to as the *y-axis* or *axis of ordinates.* As is customary, the point on the y-axis $(0, y)$ is above the x-axis when y is positive.

In the reference system of axes shown in Fig. 4–2, consider any specific pair of values of x and y, x_1 and y_1. To find the point corresponding to

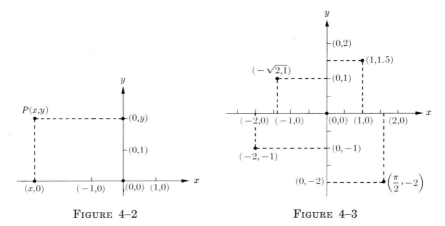

FIGURE 4–2   FIGURE 4–3

this ordered pair of values, we draw lines parallel to the axes through the point $(x_1, 0)$ on the x-axis and the point $(0, y_1)$ on the y-axis. These lines intersect at a point P, a distance x_1 from the y-axis (to the right or left, depending upon whether x_1 is positive or negative) and a distance y_1 from the x-axis (above or below, depending upon whether y_1 is positive or negative). These distances can be called *directed distances*. The point P, determined by the ordered pair of values x_1 and y_1, is denoted by the ordered pair, expressed (x_1, y_1), where x_1 and y_1 are called *coordinates* of P. As might be expected, the x-value is called the *abscissa* of P and the y-value is called its *ordinate*. Clearly, there is only one point determined by any ordered pair of values (x, y). Conversely, for each point there is only one ordered pair of values (x, y), since the point has unique directed distances from the axes. *Thus a one-to-one correspondence is established between all the points in the plane and the set of all ordered number pairs (x, y).* In the discussion which follows it will be convenient to refer to the ordered pair (x, y) as the point (x, y), with coordinates x and y.

The two coordinate axes divide the plane into four parts, called the *first*, *second*, *third*, and *fourth quadrants*. It is helpful to verify that the coordinates of points located in the different quadrants have the signs shown in the table.

Quadrants	Abscissa	Ordinate
I	+	+
II	−	+
III	−	−
IV	+	−

In Fig. 4–3 the plotting of several points is shown.

PROBLEMS

1. Plot the following points:

(a) with abscissa 4 and ordinate 3,

(b) $(4, -3)$

(c) with $x = -4$ and $y = 3$.

2. Plot the points whose coordinates are:

(a) $(2, 6)$, $(-1, 4)$, $(3, -2)$, $(-1, -3)$;

(b) $(4, 0)$, $(-4, 0)$, $(0, 4)$, $(0, -4)$, $(0, 0)$.

3. What are the coordinates of a point (a) three units to the right of the y-axis, and two above the x-axis? (b) four units to the left of the y-axis, and six above the x-axis? (c) five units to the right of the y-axis, on the x-axis?

4. (a) What is the abscissa of any point on the y-axis? (b) What is the ordinate of any point on the x-axis?

5. Without plotting, indicate the quadrant in which each of the following points lies: $(-1, 2)$, $(2, -4)$, $(-3, -7)$, $(4, 6)$, $(-5, 2)$, $(28, -2)$.

6. (a) Give the coordinates of four points which are the vertices of a rectangle. (b) Give the coordinates of three points which are the vertices of a right triangle. (c) Give the coordinates of four points on a circle with its center at $(2, 3)$ and with radius 4.

7. In each of the following, three vertices of a parallelogram are given. Give the three possible sets of coordinates for the fourth vertex.

(a) $(0, 0)$, $(2, 4)$, and $(6, 0)$.

(b) $(-2, 1)$, $(1, 2)$, and $(0, -3)$.

8. Three vertices of a parallelogram are (a, b), $(0, 0)$, and $(c, 0)$. What are the possible coordinates of the fourth vertex?

9. Indicate in a rectangular coordinate system the location of the set of all the points (x, y) whose coordinates satisfy the following conditions.

(a) $x = 2$ (b) $y = -3$ (c) $x > 2$ (d) $y > 4$

(e) $x < -1$ (f) $x = y$ (g) $x > 2$,   (h) $x > y$
$\qquad\qquad\qquad\qquad\qquad\qquad\quad y = 3$

(i) $x < y$ (j) $x > 2$,   (k) $x = 2$,   (l) $x = 2$,
$\qquad\qquad\quad y < 4$ $\qquad\quad y < -1$ $\qquad\quad y = 3$

*10. If, in Fig. 4-4, $P(x, y)$ is the midpoint of the line segment joining $P_1(x_1, y_1)$ and $P_2(x_2, y_2)$, and the line PR is drawn parallel to the y-axis, the

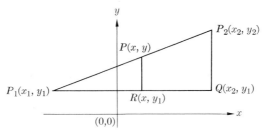

FIGURE 4-4

coordinates of R will be (x, y_1). Since $RP_1 = QR$, $x - x_1 = x_2 - x$. Using this fact, and a similar construction, show that the coordinates of the midpoint of the line joining P_1 and P_2 are

$$x = \frac{x_1 + x_2}{2},$$

(4–8)

$$y = \frac{y_1 + y_2}{2}.$$

11. Find the coordinates of the midpoint of the line joining (a) $(1, 2)$ and $(-3, 5)$; (b) $(6, -2)$ and $(5, -7)$; (c) $(-4, 3)$ and $(2, -3)$.

12. If $A = \{1, 2\}$ and $B = \{-1, 0, 1\}$, plot the set of ordered pairs of $A \times B = \{(x, y) | x \in A \text{ and } y \in B\}$ in a rectangular coordinate system.

13. (a) Describe and plot the points which are members of the set

$$I \times I = \{(x, y) | x \in I \text{ and } y \in I\}.$$

(b) Describe the set of points which are members of the set

$$F \times F = \{(x, y) | x \in F \text{ and } y \in F\}.$$

14. It is sometimes desirable to consider sets of ordered pairs in which the first element is not equal to the second element in any one pair. Such a "deleted cartesian product" has no members of the form (x, x). If $A = \{1, 2, 3\}$, list the members of the deleted cartesian product of A with itself.

*15. The concept of a cartesian product may easily be extended to include any finite number of sets. For example, $R \times R \times R = \{(x, y, z) | x, y, \text{ and } z \in R\}$ has for its members ordered triples. Explain how such a set of triples could be put into one-to-one correspondence with all the points in three-dimensional space. [*Hint:* How did we proceed from a one- to a two-dimensional system?]

4–5 The distance formula. We are now prepared to obtain a formula which has many applications in the mathematics dealt with in this book. To obtain an expression for the distance d between any two points $P_1(x_1, y_1)$ and $P_2(x_2, y_2)$, where the same unit lengths are used on both

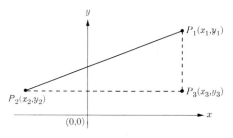

FIGURE 4–5

axes, we make use of the famous theorem of Pythagoras. Considering $P_1(x_1, y_1)$ and $P_2(x_2, y_2)$ any two points in the plane, construct a right triangle, as in Fig. 4–5, with P_1P_2 the hypotenuse, and the two legs parallel to the axes. Call their point of intersection, where the right angle is formed, $P_3(x_3, y_3)$. Since $x_3 = x_1$ and $y_3 = y_2$, the distance between P_2 and P_3 is

$$P_2P_3 = \sqrt{(x_1 - x_2)^2}$$

and the distance between P_1 and P_3 is

$$P_1P_3 = \sqrt{(y_1 - y_2)^2}.$$

Recalling the theorem of Pythagoras, which states that

$$\overline{P_1P_2^2} = \overline{P_2P_3^2} + \overline{P_1P_3^2},$$

we obtain

$$\overline{P_1P_2^2} = (x_1 - x_2)^2 + (y_1 - y_2)^2.$$

This results in the following theorem.

THEOREM 4–10.　*The distance between any two points $P_1(x_1, y_1)$ and $P_2(x_2, y_2)$ is given by*

$$\boxed{d = P_1P_2 = \sqrt{(x_1 - x_2)^2 + (y_1 - y_2)^2}.} \qquad (4\text{–}9)$$

EXAMPLE 1.　The distance between the points $P_1(-4, 2)$ and $P_2(3, -1)$ is

$$P_1P_2 = \sqrt{[3 - (-4)]^2 + (-1 - 2)^2}$$
$$= \sqrt{58}.$$

EXAMPLE 2.　The distance between the origin $(0, 0)$ and any point (x, y) is

$$d = \sqrt{(x - 0)^2 + (y - 0)^2}$$
$$= \sqrt{x^2 + y^2}.$$

EXAMPLE 3.　The triangle with the points $P_1(-5, -1)$, $P_2(2, 3)$, and $P_3(3, -2)$ as vertices is isosceles.

$$P_1P_2 = \sqrt{(-5 - 2)^2 + (-1 - 3)^2}$$
$$= \sqrt{49 + 16} = \sqrt{65},$$

$$P_1P_3 = \sqrt{(-5 - 3)^2 + (-1 + 2)^2}$$
$$= \sqrt{64 + 1} = \sqrt{65}.$$

PROBLEMS

In each of the following exercises, draw the figure on coordinate paper.

1. Find the distance between the given points:
(a) $(3, 2)$ and $(6, 7)$,   (b) $(-4, 3)$ and $(5, -2)$,
(c) $(\frac{5}{2}, -\frac{3}{4})$ and $(\frac{7}{4}, -\frac{3}{2})$,   (d) $(0, 0)$ and $(5, -12)$,
(e) $(-3, 7)$ and $(5, 7)$,   (f) $(-1, 3)$ and (x, y).

2. By proving that two sides of the triangle are equal, show that the triangle whose vertices are $(2, 1)$, $(5, 5)$, and $(-2, 4)$ is an isosceles triangle.

3. Show that the points $(8, 1)$, $(-6, -7)$, and $(2, 7)$ are the vertices of an isosceles triangle.

4. Show that the points $(6, 1)$, $(5, 6)$, $(-4, 3)$, and $(-3, -2)$ are the vertices of a parallelogram.

5. Prove that the points $(2, 3)$, $(-4, -3)$, and $(6, -1)$ are the vertices of a right triangle. Note that we must use the converse of the theorem of Pythagoras to prove this.

6. Show that the points $(12, 9)$, $(20, -6)$, $(5, -14)$, and $(-3, 1)$ are the vertices of a square. What is the length of a diagonal?

7. Test algebraically to see whether or not the following triples of points are collinear (lie on the same line): $(6, 2)$, $(1, 1)$, $(-4, 0)$; $(-6, 5)$, $(3, -10)$, $(-2, -2)$.

8. Find the point on the y-axis which is equidistant from the points $(-4, 4)$ and $(4, 10)$.

9. If two vertices of an equilateral triangle are $(-4, -3)$ and $(4, 1)$, find the remaining vertex.

10. Find those points whose ordinates are -5 and whose distance from the origin is 13.

11. Draw the square whose diagonals lie along the coordinate axes and the length of whose side is a. What are the coordinates of the four vertices?

12. If a circle had its center at the point $(2, 3)$ and passed through $(8, -5)$, what would be its radius? Would it pass through $(-6, 9)$?

13. Consider the circle with its center at the origin and with a radius of 1. Through which of the following points does it pass: $(1, 0)$, $(0, -1)$, $(1, 1)$, $(1/\sqrt{2}, 1/\sqrt{2})$, $(\frac{1}{2}, \frac{1}{2})$, $(-\frac{1}{2}, \sqrt{3}/2)$?

*14. By giving the expression for the distance between the origin and the point (x, y), and equating this distance to 1, we have stated the algebraic condition on x and y which must be satisfied by the coordinates of any point (x, y) lying on the circle whose center is $(0, 0)$ and whose radius is 1. Show that this condition, when simplified, becomes $x^2 + y^2 = 1$. This is called the equation of the unit circle in the plane.

15. If a point lies on a curve, its coordinates must satisfy the equation representing that curve. Check the results of Problem 13 by determining whether the coordinates of the points satisfy the equation of the unit circle obtained in Problem 14, namely, $x^2 + y^2 = 1$.

16. Note that Eq. (4–9) is a generalization of Eq. (4–7). What would be the corresponding generalization in the three-dimensional space described in Problem 15, Article 4–4?

4–6 The circle and its arc length. In any two-dimensional rectangular coordinate system a locus or curve, such as a straight line or circle, may be considered a set of points. The two coordinates of each point in this set satisfy some stated condition* involving these coordinates. Conversely, if the coordinates of any point satisfy this condition, that point must be in this set. For example, let us consider the set of points (ordered pairs) which are members of the set A, where

$$A = \{(x, y) \mid x = y\}.$$

The set A, whose members are the points (x, y) which satisfy the condition $x = y$, is a *locus* or *curve*.† The *equation* of this locus or curve is the condition $x = y$, which the coordinates of the points (and only those points) must satisfy. The *graph* of this locus or curve is the figure we see in Fig. 4–6, namely, the geometric representation of the set of points A in the cartesian coordinate plane.

We have the following three important definitions, and we should distinguish between any two of them.

DEFINITION 4–7. *A locus (or* curve) *is the set of points, and only those points, whose coordinates satisfy certain conditions.*

DEFINITION 4–8. *The* equation *of a locus (or* curve) *is the condition which the coordinates of each of the points of that locus, and only those points, must satisfy.*

DEFINITION 4–9. *The* graph *of a locus (or* curve) *is the geometric representation of the set of points of the locus.*

Several different elementary curves and their equations will be considered in later articles. In this article we are concerned with the circle.

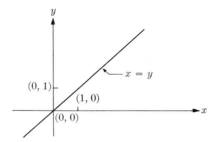

FIGURE 4–6

---

* This condition will be in addition to the fact that $(x, y) \in R$, which we shall always assume unless otherwise stated.

† The word *curve* is used in this restrictive sense in two dimensions.

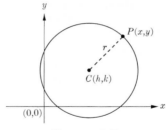

FIGURE 4–7

We recall the definition of a circle as the locus of all points in the plane that are a constant distance from a fixed point. We are, therefore, interested in the set

$C = \{(x, y)|\text{the distance between } (x, y) \text{ and some fixed point is constant}\}.$

If we use the distance formula (Eq. 4–9), it is possible to obtain a general equation of a circle, and be more specific.

With $C(h, k)$ as the center and r as the radius (Fig. 4–7), the condition that any point $P(x, y)$ lying on the circle must satisfy is

$$CP = r,$$

which is the same as having the coordinates of P satisfy the condition

$$\sqrt{(x - h)^2 + (y - k)^2} = r.$$

Conversely, if $CP = r$, then P is on the circle. We therefore have

$$(x - h)^2 + (y - k)^2 = r^2, \qquad (4\text{–}10)$$

which is a general equation of the circle with center (h, k) and with radius r. The circle itself is the set

$$C = \{(x, y)|(x - h)^2 + (y - k)^2 = r^2\}. \qquad (4\text{–}11)$$

EXAMPLE 1. An equation of the circle with its center at $(2, -3)$ and radius 4 is

$$(x - 2)^2 + (y + 3)^2 = 16.$$

The circle itself is the set

$$\{(x, y)|(x - 2)^2 + (y + 3)^2 = 16\}.$$

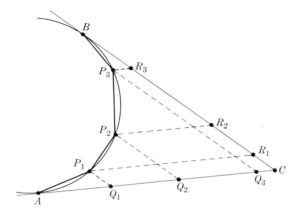

FIGURE 4–8

EXAMPLE 2. An equation of the circle with its center at the origin and a radius of 1 is

$$(x - 0)^2 + (y - 0)^2 = 1,$$

or

$$x^2 + y^2 = 1.$$

This is called an equation of the unit circle, an important special case in our study. Recall Problem 14, Article 4–5. This unit circle is the set $\{(x, y)|x^2 + y^2 = 1\}$.

We are interested not only in the equation of a circle, but also in the notion of length of portions of its circumference. The length of a circular arc is very useful in defining the trigonometric or circular functions as well as in discussing and measuring angles.

By considering a circular arc $\overset{\frown}{AB}$,* as in Fig. 4–8, it is possible to assign to this arc $\overset{\frown}{AB}$ a length s, although it is impossible to measure the length as though it were a straight line. If we denote several points on $\overset{\frown}{AB}$ by $P_1, P_2, P_3, \ldots, P_n$, the length of the polygonal line joining these points is the sum of the lengths of the appropriate chords, obtained by using Eq. (4–9). Let I, called *an inscription* of $\overset{\frown}{AB}$, denote this polygonal line, $AP_1P_2 \ldots P_nB$. Its length can then be expressed

$$|I| = |AP_1| + |P_1P_2| + |P_2P_3| + \cdots |P_nB|.$$

---

* If the arc were larger than half a circle, a slight modification would be possible, and the same result would follow.

We can easily show that the length of any such inscription is less than $|AC| + |CB|$, where AC and CB are tangent lines to the circle at A and B, and C is their point of intersection. From each point P_i draw lines parallel to AC intersecting BC at R_i and parallel to BC intersecting AC at Q_i. Since the length of one side of a triangle is less than the sum of the lengths of the other two sides,

$$|AP_1| < |AQ_1| + |Q_1P_1| = |AQ_1| + |CR_1|.$$

Also, for any P_iP_{i+1},

$$|P_iP_{i+1}| < |Q_iQ_{i+1}| + |R_iR_{i+1}|$$

and

$$|P_nB| < |Q_nC| + |R_nB|.$$

(See Fig. 4–8.) By Theorem 4–4,

$$\begin{aligned}
|I| &= |AP_1| + |P_1P_2| + \cdots |P_iP_{i+1}| + \cdots |P_nB| \\
&< |AQ_1| + |CR_1| + |Q_1Q_2| + |R_1R_2| + \cdots \\
&\quad + |Q_iQ_{i+1}| + |R_iR_{i+1}| + \cdots + |Q_nC| + |R_nB| \\
&= |AQ_1| + |Q_1Q_2| + \cdots + |Q_iQ_{i+1}| + \cdots \\
&\quad + |Q_nC| + |CR_1| + |R_1R_2| + \cdots + |R_iR_{i+1}| + \cdots + |R_nB| \\
&= |AC| + |CB|.
\end{aligned}$$

Thus the length of any inscription of $\overset{\frown}{AB}$ has an upper bound, $|AC| + |CB|$. Since these lengths are real numbers (elements of R), there exists a least upper bound for the set of the lengths of all I's, from which we have the following definition.

DEFINITION 4–10. *The length s of any circular arc $\overset{\frown}{AB}$ is the least upper bound of the set of lengths of all possible inscriptions of the arc.*

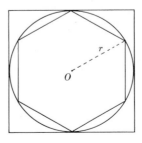

FIGURE 4–9

As an immediate consequence of this definition, we know: (1) for all such inscriptions I, $|I| \leq s$; (2) the arc length $s \leq |AC| + |CB|$.

EXAMPLE. Recall the definition of the real number π, approximately equal to 3.14. The number π is defined as the ratio of the circumference of any circle to its diameter. The circumference or arc length of the entire circle with radius r is, therefore, equal to $2\pi r$, or approximately 6.28 times the radius. Compare this with the two regular geometric figures shown in Fig. 4–9. Since the inscribed hexagon has a perimeter of $6r$ and the circumscribed square has a perimeter of $8r$, the inequality $6r < 2\pi r < 8r$ would be expected.

PROBLEMS

1. Write an equation of the following circles.
(a) center at (3, 1) and radius 5,
(b) center at (4, −2) and radius 3,
(c) center at (−1, 3) tangent to the x-axis,
(d) center at (2, −4) and passing through (5, −8).

2. Write an equation of the circle with its center at the origin and radius r.
3. Describe the following sets.
(a) $A = \{(x, y)|(x - 1)^2 + (y - 1)^2 = 4\}$
(b) $B = \{(x, y)|(x - 2)^2 + (y + 7)^2 \leq 9\}$
(c) $C = \{(x, y)|(x - 2)^2 + (y + 7)^2 \geq 1\}$
(d) $D = \{(x, y)|(x - 3)^2 + (y + 1)^2 = 0\}$
(e) $E = \{(x, y)|(x + 2)^2 + (y - 5)^2 < 0\}$

4. Describe in words the following sets, where reference is made to Problem 3: (a) $B \cup C$, (b) $B \cap C$.

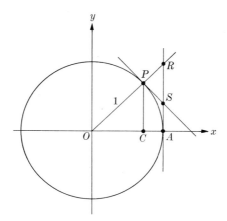

FIGURE 4–10

5. What is the length of the perimeter of the square inscribed in a circle of radius r?

6. Determine the length of the perimeter of the regular hexagon circumscribed about a circle of radius r.

7. Expressing your answer in terms of π, what is the length of the circumference of the unit circle (a circle with a radius of 1)? What is the length of an arc one-fourth the distance around the circle? What is the length of an arc one-sixth the distance around the circle?

8. If P and P' are any two points on a circle such that the chord PP' is not the diameter and D is the point of intersection of the two tangents to this circle at P and P', what can be said about the relative lengths of the chord PP', the arc $\overset{\frown}{PP'}$, and $|P'D| + |PD|$. Why?

*9. In Fig. 4–10 we have a unit circle, center at O, with P the point on the circle and in the first quadrant, and A the point of intersection of the circle and the x-axis. Tangents are drawn to the circle at P and A, and intersect at S. The tangent at A intersects line OP (extended) at R. From P, a perpendicular is drawn to the x-axis, intersecting it at C. Show that $|PC| < |\overset{\frown}{PA}| < |AR|$. [*Hint:* $|PC| < |PA|$, and $|SP| < |SR|$. Why?]

CHAPTER 5

FUNCTIONS AND THEIR GRAPHICAL REPRESENTATION

In mathematics, the concept of a *function* is very important and useful. It appears in almost every branch of the subject. The idea in mathematics, however, has a slightly different meaning than that in ordinary language. We shall use the word *function* to denote a certain specific type of correspondence or association between the elements of two sets. In this book the elements of the two sets will be real numbers, although in the general mathematics context this is not always the case.

5–1 Functions and relations. In considering the unit circle, discussed in Example 2, Article 4–6, we found its equation to be $x^2 + y^2 = 1$. If we subtract x^2 from both members of this equality and take the positive square root, we have

$$y = \sqrt{1 - x^2}, \tag{5-1}$$

the equation of the "top" half of the circle (Fig. 5–1). From the graph of this half-circle, we see that for a particular point to be on the curve, its y-coordinate is determined *uniquely* if its x-coordinate is given. Similarly, from the equation (5–1), there must be a certain value of y which corresponds to any specific value of x. For example, if $x = 0$, y must be 1; if $x = 1$, y must be 0; or if $x = \frac{1}{2}$, y must be $\sqrt{3}/2$. This association or correspondence, which in fact constitutes a specific function, is, of course, more precise than that of any arbitrary product set if no further condition is imposed. Note that the above example satisfies the general definition of a function.

DEFINITION 5–1. *If there is associated with each element of a set X exactly one element of another set Y, then this association constitutes a function from X to Y.*

FIGURE 5–1

This is usually written $f: X \rightarrow Y$, and is read "the function f from X to Y."

In algebra and trigonometry we usually wish to emphasize the elements of the sets as well as the sets themselves. In this case we will write $f: x \rightarrow y$, and read "f takes x into y," where we assume $x \in X$ and $y \in Y$. The set X is called the *domain* of the function f, and the set Y is called its *range*.

The method of association may be accomplished in many ways, although it usually is done by an equation such as $y = \sqrt{1 - x^2}$, by a table of values, or by a graph. The important point is that a function pairs *one and only one* element of Y with each element of X. In the above example, the domain is the set

$$X = \{x \mid x \in R \text{ and } -1 \leq x \leq 1\},$$

and the range is the set

$$Y = \{y \mid y \in R \text{ and } 0 \leq y \leq 1\}.$$

Frequently we may be more specific. If we combine the symbol f for the function with the elements, x, of the domain and regard $f(x)$ as the corresponding element of the range, we may write $f: x \rightarrow f(x)$. The symbol $f(x)$* is, therefore, considered to be the value of f at x, and is read "f of x." In our example, when $x = 0$, $f(0) = 1$; when $x = 1$, $f(1) = 0$, and when $x = \frac{1}{2}$, $f(\frac{1}{2}) = \sqrt{3}/2$. In many cases we may even go further. If the method of defining the association for the function f is an explicit equation for y in terms of x, such as $y = \sqrt{1 - x^2}$, we may write $f: x \rightarrow \sqrt{1 - x^2}$. It should be emphasized that in this discussion x stands for any element in the domain of f, and y [or $f(x)$] stands for the corresponding element in the range. Of course, other letters, such as u, v, or t, may also represent elements of the domain with the corresponding elements $f(u)$, $f(v)$, or $f(t)$ in the range. Any such usage will be clear from the context. There is nothing special about the letter f for denoting a function. Other letters, such as g or h, may also represent the function. In general, a function $f: X \rightarrow Y$, might be indicated as in Fig. 5–2, where two different elements in X may be associated with the same element in Y, but *no two* distinct elements in Y are the correspondent of the same element in X.

Let us summarize the concept of function. There are *three* important parts: the domain X, or set of x-values, the range Y, or set of y-values, and the rule, relationship, or correspondence which associates these two

---

* This symbol, $f(x)$, is not to be confused with f multiplied by x.

FIGURE 5–2

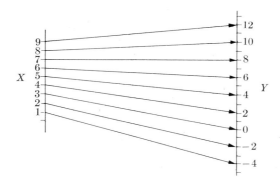

FIGURE 5–3

sets in a certain way. Unless otherwise stated, both the domain and range of any function will be the largest possible set of suitable real numbers.

ILLUSTRATION 1.   Consider the function defined by the equation $y = 2x - 6$ for all positive integers less than 10. Thus, $f: x \rightarrow 2x - 6$, where $X = \{1, 2, \ldots, 9\}$. For this function, $f(1) = -4$, $f(2) = -2$, and so on. The function f is illustrated in Fig. 5–3.

ILLUSTRATION 2.   We recall that the area A of a circle of radius r is given by the expression $A = \pi r^2$. Since π is a quantity which remains fixed in value (called a *constant*), we can consider $A(r) = \pi r^2$ as an equation which defines the function expressing the association between values of the radius and the corresponding area for any circle. This function may be written $A : r \rightarrow \pi r^2$, $(r \geq 0)$. For example, $A(0) = 0$, $A(1) = \pi$, $A(2) = 4\pi$, and so on. The function has for its domain and its range all positive real values, and zero.

ILLUSTRATION 3.   An important, and yet almost trivial, function is the one which associates all real numbers with the same fixed number. Such a function, called a *constant function*, might be written $f: x \rightarrow c$. As a result of this definition, $f(0) = c$, $f(1) = c$, or $f(\pi) = c$ and, in fact, $f(x) = c$ for all $x \in R$, so that the domain of the function is the set R, but its range is the single real number c.

ILLUSTRATION 4. Recall in Article 2–2 that for each real number x, $(x \neq 0)$ there existed a unique inverse with respect to multiplication, $1/x$ (the reciprocal). This association describes the function $r: x \rightarrow 1/x$, whose domain and range are the set R except for zero.

With these illustrations in mind, it should be clear that a function defines a set of ordered pairs, with the added condition that no two pairs have the same first element. For example, in Illustration 4, $(1, 1)$, $(2, \frac{1}{2})$, $(-3, -\frac{1}{3})$, and $(\sqrt{2}, 1/\sqrt{2})$ are specific ordered pairs which belong to this function r. If this point of view is taken, the set X consists of the first members in the ordered pair, and Y the second. We could use the following equivalent definition.

DEFINITION 5–2. *A function from X to Y is a set of ordered pairs (x, y) such that to each $x \in X$, there corresponds a unique $y \in Y$.*

We may, therefore, use the set notation to describe a function:

$$\{(x, y)|y = f(x)\}.$$

If the ordered pair (a, b) belongs to the function, that is, if $f(a) = b$, we say b is the *image* of a under f, so that, in general, the range is the image of its domain.

ILLUSTRATION 5. If $y = a(x)$ is defined so that

$$a(x) = \begin{cases} x & \text{for } x \geq 0, \\ -x & \text{for } x < 0, \end{cases}$$

the function, defined by different expressions over different subsets of the domain, may be written $a: x \rightarrow |x|$. What is the domain and range of this function? The ordered pairs $(3, 3)$ and $(-4, 4)$ belong to this function. Give several other such ordered pairs which also belong to a.

One further illustration will indicate that the method of association need not be an equation.

ILLUSTRATION 6. Let s be the function $s: \theta \rightarrow s(\theta)$, where $\theta \in R$. Let $s(\theta)$ be defined as the ordinate of the point on the unit circle which is reached by starting at $(1, 0)$ and measuring an arc of length $|\theta|$ along the circle (whose equation is $x^2 + y^2 = 1$), in the counterclockwise direction if $\theta > 0$, but in the clockwise direction if $\theta < 0$. This functional value $s(\theta)$ is defined by a rule and is not expressible by an algebraic equation. Verify that $s(0) = 0$, $s(\pi) = 0$, $s(-\pi/2) = -1$, $s(\pi/2) = 1$, $s(3\pi/2) = -1$, $s(4\pi) = 0$. [*Hint:* Recall that the circumference of the unit circle is 2π. The domain of this function is R. What is its range?]

In the definition of a function $f: x \to y$, the value of y is unique, corresponding to any specific value of x. Other possibilities exist, however, so that for a given value of x there may exist two, three, or even an infinite number of corresponding values of y. For example, if we solve the equation of the unit circle, $x^2 + y^2 = 1$, for y, we have

$$y = \pm\sqrt{1 - x^2}.$$

If this is the equation which sets up the association between X and Y, there are two values of y which correspond to any value of x between -1 and 1. Although this might be called a double-valued (and, in general, multiple-valued) function, we prefer to call such a correspondence a *relation*, and not a function of any kind. It could be symbolized by

$$\{(x, y)|x^2 + y^2 = 1\}.$$

It should be clear that any function is a relation, but there exist many relations which are not functions. As in the case of a function, a relation has a domain and range. Although relations will be mentioned in this book, we shall restrict our discussion to functions whenever possible.

PROBLEMS

1. Give the domain and range of the following functions, where x, $y \in R$.

(a) $f: x \to x$ (b) $g: x \to \sqrt{x}$

(c) $p: x \to x^2$ (d) $f: x \to \sqrt{4 - x^2}$

(e) $g: x \to \sqrt{x^2 - 1}$ (f) $h: x \to \dfrac{x}{1 - x}$

(g) $f: x \to \dfrac{1}{x^2 - 1}$ (h) $g: x \to |x| - 2$

2. Which of the following sets describe a function, and which describe only a relation?

(a) $\{(1, 2), (2, 3), (3, 4)\}$ (b) $\{(1, 2), (1, 3), (2, 4)\}$
(c) $\{(x, y)|y = 2x + 4\}$ (d) $\{(x, y)|2x + 3y = 6\}$
(e) $\{(x, y)|x + y^2 = 1\}$ (f) $\{(x, y)|y + x^2 = 1\}$
(g) $\{(x, y)|(x - 2)^2 + (y - 3)^2 = 9\}$

(h) $\{(x, y)|x \le y\}$ (i) $\left\{(x, y)\left|x + \dfrac{1}{y - 3} = 7\right.\right\}$
(j) $\{(x, y)| \ |x| + |y| = 1\}$

3. What is the domain and the range of each of the functions and relations in Problem 2?

4. If $f: x \rightarrow 2x - 5$, find (a) $f(0)$, (b) $f(1)$, (c) $f(3)$, (d) $f(-1)$.

5. If $f: x \rightarrow x^2 - 7x + 10$, find (a) $f(2)$, (b) $f(5)$, (c) $f(3)$, (d) $f(0)$.

6. If $f: x \rightarrow 1/(x - 3)$, find (a) $f(4)$, (b) $f(2)$, (c) $f(-1)$. (d) What can be said about $f(3)$?

7. If $e: x \rightarrow 2^x$, where the domain is the set I, find (a) $e(0)$, (b) $e(1)$, (c) $e(5)$, (d) $e(-5)$.

8. If $g: x \rightarrow x^{1/2}$, find (a) $g(0)$, (b) $g(2)$, (c) $g(4)$, (d) $g(\frac{1}{9})$.

9. Consider the function described by the set $\{(x, y) | 10^y = x\}$. If $y = f(x)$, find (a) $f(1)$, (b) $f(10)$, (c) $f(100)$, (d) $f(\frac{1}{100})$.

10. If $a: x \rightarrow |x - 2|$, find (a) $a(0)$, (b) $a(2)$, (c) $a(4)$, (d) $a(-2)$.

11. If f is a constant function, find $f(2)$ if (a) $f(1) = 6$, (b) $f(6) = -3$, (c) $f(-3) = 4$.

12. If x is the length of one side of a square, express the perimeter P in terms of x.

By using this expression for P we are able to establish a correspondence between the length x and the perimeter of the square. What specific function does this association describe?

13. In Problem 12, express the area A in terms of x. What specific function does this association describe?

14. If x is the length of one side of an equilateral triangle, express the perimeter P in terms of x. Express the area A in terms of x. [*Hint:* In a 30°–60° triangle, the hypotenuse is double the shorter leg. Use the Pythagorean Theorem to find the altitude, and recall that $A = \frac{1}{2}$(base) · (altitude).]

Each of these equations defines a different function. What are these two functions?

15. With s measured in feet and t in seconds, the equation $s = f(t) = -16t^2 + 32t$ expresses the height of a ball above the ground after t seconds if it were thrown upward with a velocity of 32 ft/sec. Find $f(0)$, $f(\frac{1}{2})$, $f(1)$, $f(\frac{3}{2})$, $f(2)$, and explain the result.

16. Verify the values of the function given in Illustration 6.

*17. For the same θ as that described in Illustration 6, define $c(\theta)$ as the abscissa of the point on the unit circle rather than as the ordinate. Find $c(0)$, $c(\pi/2)$, $c(\pi)$, $c(3\pi/2)$, $c(-\pi/2)$, and $c(4\pi)$.

*18. If a function f is defined so that $f(x) = x^2$, show that $f(-x) = f(x)$. Any function satisfying the condition $f(-x) = f(x)$ is called an *even function.* Give another example of such a function.

*19. If a function f is defined so that $f(x) = x^3$, show that $f(-x) = -f(x)$. Any function satisfying this condition is called an *odd function.* Give another example of an odd function.

5–2 Graphical representation of functions and relations. Using the rectangular coordinate system discussed in Article 4–4, we are able to exhibit the association between x and y (or any two variables) in the case of any particular function. Although all the points (x, y) whose coordinates satisfy a given equation $y = f(x)$ cannot be plotted, usually a

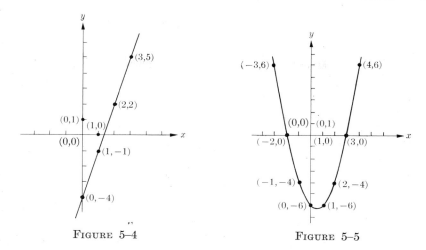

FIGURE 5–4   FIGURE 5–5

sufficient number may be so that a good approximation to a picture of the function may be obtained. The aggregate of all such points forms the graph of the function f, or the curve which represents this function. (Recall Definition 4–9.)

EXAMPLE 1. Draw the graph of the function $f\colon x \to 3x - 4$.

Solution. By assigning arbitrary values for x and computing the corresponding y-values, we can obtain any number of points (x, y) whose coordinates satisfy the equation $y = 3x - 4$. The points, arranged in the table below, are then plotted and joined by a smooth curve. This function is represented by a straight line (Fig. 5–4).

x	0	1	2	3	4
$y = f(x)$	-4	-1	2	5	8

EXAMPLE 2. Draw the graph of the function $q\colon x \to x^2 - x - 6$.

Solution. Again assign values to x, compute the corresponding values of $y = q(x)$, and arrange the results in a table.

x	0	1	2	3	4	-1	-2	-3
$y = q(x)$	-6	-6	-4	0	6	-4	0	6

If we draw a smooth curve through these points (x, y), starting with the point whose abscissa is -3, then -2, -1, and so on, we obtain the result shown in Fig. 5–5. This curve, called a *parabola*, is the required graph. Often, to complete the graph correctly, additional points [e.g., $(\frac{1}{2}, -6\frac{1}{4})$] whose coordinates satisfy the required condition must be found. Although many different curves could be drawn through whatever points are located, the required curve is obtained by sensible "interpolation" between the plotted points.

We have noticed in both Examples 1 and 2 that the graph of the function crosses the x-axis. At any such point, the y-coordinate is zero. The x-value at such points is called a *zero of the function*. In Example 1, the zero of the function is $x = 4/3$; in Example 2, there are two zeros of the function, -2 and 3. In general, a zero of a function is the abscissa of a point where the graph of the function crosses or touches the horizontal axis.

EXAMPLE 3. Draw the graph of the function represented by the set of ordered pairs $\{(x, y)|y = |x - 2|\}$.

Solution. We construct the table,

x	0	1	2	3	4	5	-1
y	2	1	0	1	2	3	3

plot the points, and draw the graph. (See Fig. 5–6.) Note that $x = 2$ is the zero of this function, although the curve does not cross the x-axis.

A relation may be represented graphically by exactly the same method. Such a graph was given in Fig. 4–7 for the relation

$$\{(x, y)|(x - h)^2 + (y - k)^2 = r^2\}.$$

It should be remarked that any vertical line intersects the graph of a function only once at most, although it may intersect a relation's graph any number of times (why?).

EXAMPLE 4. Sketch the graph of the relation $\{(x, y)|y^2 = x\}$.

Solution. If we solve $y^2 = x$ for y, we have $y = \pm\sqrt{x}$, so that the table is relatively easy to construct.

x	0	1	2	4
y	0	± 1	$\pm\sqrt{2}$	± 2

We see, as we would expect, that for each value of x, there are two associated values of y. The graph is shown in Fig. 5–7.

EXAMPLE 5. Draw the graph of the relation $\{(x, y)|y \leq x + 2\}$.

Solution. For the graph of this relation, we first plot the line $y = x + 2$ and then realize that for any particular x the point (x, y) is a member of the required set if its y-coordinate is equal to or less than it would be if the point lay on the line. The required set is thus the line $y = x + 2$, and all points *below* this line. The shaded area indicates the graph (Fig. 5–8) of this relation.

FIGURE 5–6   FIGURE 5–7

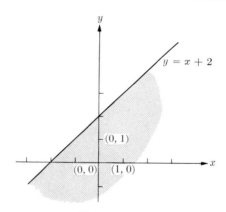

FIGURE 5–8

PROBLEMS

Draw the graph of each of the functions defined by the equations in Problems 1 through 12. Show the scales on both axes and give the zeros of the function in each case.

1. $y = 2x + 5$
2. $y = 6 - 3x$
3. $y = x^2/16$
4. $y = -4x^2$
5. $y = x^2 - 7x + 10$
6. $y = -x^2 - x + 30$
7. $y = |x - 1|$
8. $y = |2x - 3|$

9. $y = \sqrt{x - 1}$. [*Hint:* y is never negative.]
10. $y = x^3$
11. $y = x^3 - x$
12. $y = \sqrt{x(2 - x)}$. What is the domain and the range of this function?
13. Draw the graph of each of the functions given in Problem 1, Article 5–1.
14. In Fig. 5–9, which graphs represent functions and which represent only relations? Why?
15. Draw the graph of each of the sets defined in Problem 2, Article 5–1.
16. Draw the graph of each of the following sets. Which is a function?
(a) $\{(x, y)|yx^2 = 1\}$ (b) $\{(x, y)|y^2x = 1\}$

FIGURE 5–9

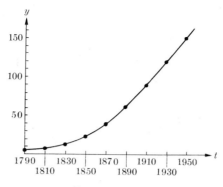

FIGURE 5–10

5–3 Graphical representation of empirical data. Certain functions or relations are expressed most clearly by a table of statistics or scientific data. Often such material cannot be expressed by even a mathematical formula, but an adaptation of the method of graphing may be used. Consider the example showing how our population has grown. The table shows the total population at intervals of twenty years since 1790, when the first census was taken.

Year (t)	1790	1810	1830	1850	1870	1890	1910	1930	1950
Population (y) (in millions)	3.9	7.2	12.9	23.2	39.8	62.9	92.0	122.8	150.7

If the t values are considered the domain and y values the range, we have a finite set of ordered pairs which constitutes a function $p: t \rightarrow y$. This function differs from most of those previously considered, for its domain is a finite set of integers, but we can use an adaptation of our method of graphing to obtain a clear representation of the data. With the t-axis chosen as horizontal, the ordered pairs are plotted as points (t, y) and a smooth curve is drawn through these points *to indicate the general trend.* The graph is shown in Fig. 5–10.

PROBLEMS

Construct a graph representing the data given in each of the following problems. Indicate the scales clearly in each case.

1. This table lists the percentage of the population of the United States which is foreign-born, at ten-year intervals since 1890.

Year (t)	1890	1900	1910	1920	1930	1940	1950
Percentage (y)	14.7	13.6	14.7	13.2	11.6	8.7	6.7

2. This table lists the total horsepower hours of energy (in billions) used from mineral fuel and water power in the United States since 1860.

Year (t)	1860	1880	1900	1920	1940	1950
Energy (y)	25	40	78	190	280	410

3. This table lists the buying power of per capita yearly income for certain years since 1839 in the United States. The figures are adjusted to represent modern purchasing power.

(t)	1839	1859	1879	1899	1919	1929	1933	1941
(y)	198	296	309	482	620	681	495	792

4. This table lists the public school attendance (in millions) of students in the United States, since 1880.

(t)	1880	1890	1900	1910	1920	1930	1940	1950
(y)	6.1	8.2	10.6	12.8	16.2	21.3	22.0	21.7

5. This table lists the number of teachers (in units of 10,000) in the United States, since 1880.

(t)	1880	1890	1900	1910	1920	1930	1940	1950
(n)	28.7	36.4	42.3	52.3	67.9	85.4	87.5	85.9

CHAPTER 6

THE CIRCULAR FUNCTIONS

6–1 Trigonometry. In about 1600 A.D., Bartholomaus Pitiscus, a professor of mathematics at Heidelberg, wrote the first textbook to bear the title *Trigonometry*. He had in mind exactly what the name implies: triangle measurement. Actually, however, trigonometry had its origin in early historical times. It was a part of the attempt to study the celestial sphere in which the sun, moon, and stars were supposed to move, and to calculate the positions of the heavenly bodies by means of angles. The most famous men interested in this development were two Greek astronomers, Hipparchus of Nicaea (2nd century B.C.) and Claudius Ptolemy (2nd century A.D.). As a consequence, one often gains the impression that the principal if not the sole application of trigonometry is the solving of triangles, and thus that the application of trigonometry lies in the fields of astronomy, navigation, and surveying. This may have been true 2000 or even 400 years ago, but it is certainly not the case today.

With the development of trigonometry, the general study of the circular functions has progressed. In fact, we now define trigonometry as that branch of mathematics which is concerned with the properties and applications of the circular or trigonometric functions.

We shall define the circular functions so that both the domain and the range of the functions will be real numbers. As we shall see, this general method of definition has great advantages in many applications of these functions.

6–2 Definitions of the circular functions. Consider the unit circle, with its equation $x^2 + y^2 = 1$, so that its center is the origin of a rectangular coordinate system (Fig. 6–1). If a point P starts at the point $A(1, 0)$ and moves $|\theta|$ units around the circumference of the circle, counterclockwise if $\theta > 0$, clockwise if $\theta < 0$, we can locate the exact position of P for any specific value of θ. If $|\theta| > 2\pi$ (the circumference of the circle), we shall continue around the circle past A until we have traveled the entire distance. Since the arc length of a circle is well defined (Definition 4–10), to every value of θ there is associated a point, called the *terminal point*, whose distance along the arc from $(1, 0)$ is $|\theta|$ units. If we designate this terminal point by $P(\theta)$, we have defined a function

$$\boxed{P : \theta \rightarrow P(\theta),} \tag{6–1}$$

99

whose domain is the set R, and whose range is the set of all points or ordered pairs $\{(x, y)|x^2 + y^2 = 1\}$. Unfortunately, it is somewhat inconvenient to deal with functions which associate real numbers with ordered pairs. We shall simplify the situation by defining two functions, one which takes θ into x, and another which takes θ into y. Specifically,

$$\cos: \theta \to x, \qquad \text{where } x \text{ is the abscissa of } P(\theta),$$

and

$$\sin: \theta \to y, \qquad \text{where } y \text{ is the ordinate of } P(\theta).$$

Since *cos* is the abbreviation for *cosine*, and *sin* is the abbreviation for *sine*, the function values for these two functions are written $x = \cos (\theta)$, or more generally, $x = \cos \theta$, and read "x equals the cosine of θ," and similarly, $y = \sin \theta$, and read "y equals the sine of θ."

Let us repeat these definitions by way of their defining equations.

DEFINITION 6-1. *If the terminal point $P(\theta)$ has the rectangular coordinates x and y,*

$$\cos \theta = x \qquad \text{and} \qquad \sin \theta = y. \tag{6-2}$$

The domain of each function is R. The range of each is the subset of $R = \{r| -1 \leq r \leq 1\}$ (why?). If we recall that the circumference of the unit circle is 2π units in length, the following table should be clear.

θ	$P(\theta)$	$\cos \theta$	$\sin \theta$
0	(1, 0)	1	0
$\pi/2$	(0, 1)	0	1
π	(−1, 0)	−1	0
$3\pi/2$	(0, −1)	0	−1
2π	(1, 0)	1	0

One other circular function of equal importance, that of the *tangent* function, should also be defined.

DEFINITION 6-2. *If the terminal point $P(\theta)$ has the rectangular coordinates x and y,*

$$\tan \theta = \frac{y}{x} \qquad (x \neq 0) \tag{6-3}$$

is the defining equation for the tangent function.

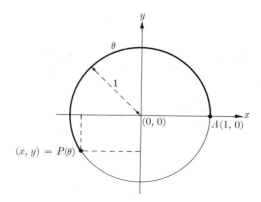

FIGURE 6–1

The domain of this function is the set R excluding the numbers $\pi/2 + n\pi$, where $n \in I$ (why?). Its range is the entire set R. Note the relationship among the three functions which we have defined. Since $\tan \theta = y/x$, we have

$$\tan \theta \equiv \frac{\sin \theta}{\cos \theta},$$ (6–4)

which is defined for all values of θ except where $\cos \theta = 0$. In this case $\tan \theta$ is undefined (why?).

From Article 4–4 we recall the signs of the coordinates of points in the different quadrants. By noting the quadrant in which $P(\theta)$ lies and the signs of x or y, we determine in which quadrants the circular functions are positive or negative. The reader should verify the following table.

Quadrant in which $P(\theta)$ lies	$\sin \theta = y$	$\cos \theta = x$	$\tan \theta = y/x$
I	+	+	+
II	+	−	−
III	−	−	+
IV	−	+	−

The functional values we noticed in the first table were quite special. The fact that the circumference of length 2π is an irrational number and is not an even multiple of any integer indicates that the coordinates of such terminal points as $P(1)$, $P(2)$, and so on are not easily found by elementary processes. This, in fact, is the case, and we shall see later how this is done by using appropriate tables.

There are, however, certain special values of θ whose circular functions we can determine, and we shall do so in Article 6–4. In this article it seems more appropriate to emphasize the relations between the functions.

EXAMPLE 1. For a given θ, let the terminal point $P(\theta)$ lie on the line segment joining the points $(0, 0)$ and $(-3, 4)$, as in Fig. 6–2. Find $\sin \theta$, $\cos \theta$, and $\tan \theta$.

Solution. The distance from $(0, 0)$ to $(-3, 4)$ is $\sqrt{(-3)^2 + 4^2} = 5$. We wish the coordinates of $P(\theta)$, a point on the same straight line but one unit from $(0, 0)$, so that $P(\theta)$'s coordinates are $(-\frac{3}{5}, \frac{4}{5})$. (Show that

FIGURE 6–2

FIGURE 6–3

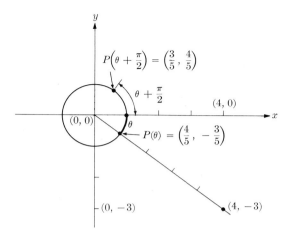

FIGURE 6–4

this is true by similar triangles.)   Thus $\sin \theta = \frac{4}{5}$, $\cos \theta = -\frac{3}{5}$, and $\tan \theta = -\frac{4}{3}$.

EXAMPLE 2.   Find the value of $\cos \theta$ and $\tan \theta$ if $\sin \theta = -\frac{5}{13}$ and $\tan \theta > 0$.

Solution.   Since $\sin \theta = -\frac{5}{13}$ is the y-coordinate of a point on the unit circle, $x^2 + (-\frac{5}{13})^2 = 1$. Thus, $x^2 = 1 - \frac{25}{169} = \frac{144}{169}$, so that $x = \pm\frac{12}{13}$. But since $\sin \theta < 0$ and $\tan \theta > 0$, the terminal point $P(\theta)$ is in the third quadrant. Therefore, $x = \cos \theta = -\frac{12}{13}$ and $\tan \theta = \frac{5}{12}$. (See Fig. 6–3.)

EXAMPLE 3.   Let θ be any real number, and let its associated terminal point $P(\theta)$ lie on the line segment joining the points $(0, 0)$ and $(4, -3)$. (See Figs. 6–4 and 6–5.)   Find the sine, cosine, and tangent of $\theta + \pi/2$ and $\theta + \pi$.

Solution.   As in Example 1, we immediately have $P(\theta) = (\frac{4}{5}, -\frac{3}{5})$. Therefore, by congruent triangles, $P(\theta + \pi/2) = (\frac{3}{5}, \frac{4}{5})$ and $P(\theta + \pi) = (-\frac{4}{5}, \frac{3}{5})$, so that

$$\sin (\theta + \pi/2) = \tfrac{4}{5}, \qquad \sin (\theta + \pi) = \tfrac{3}{5},$$
$$\cos (\theta + \pi/2) = \tfrac{3}{5}, \qquad \cos (\theta + \pi) = -\tfrac{4}{5},$$
$$\tan (\theta + \pi/2) = \tfrac{4}{3}, \qquad \tan (\theta + \pi) = -\tfrac{3}{4}.$$

If θ were increased or decreased by an integral multiple of 2π, $P[\theta + k(2\pi)]$ would coincide with the original $P(\theta)$ so that the two terminal points would have the same coordinates. Therefore we have:

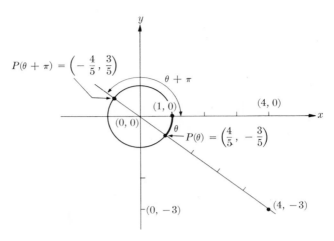

FIGURE 6–5

THEOREM 6–1. *For any* $\theta \in R$ *and any* $k \in I$,

$$\sin\,[\theta + k(2\pi)] \equiv \sin\,\theta, \tag{6–5}$$

and

$$\cos\,[\theta + k(2\pi)] \equiv \cos\,\theta. \tag{6–6}$$

Hence, if we know the values of $\sin\,\theta$ and $\cos\,\theta$ in the range $0 \leq \theta \leq 2\pi$, we know their values of all θ. The sine and cosine functions are called *periodic functions*, with period 2π.*

The tangent function differs from the sine and cosine functions in regard to its period. Since $\tan\,\theta = y/x = -y/-x$, and the point $(-x, -y)$ is also $P(\theta + \pi)$, we have:

THEOREM 6–2. *For any* $\theta \in R$ *and any* $k \in I$,

$$\tan\,(\theta + k\pi) \equiv \tan\,\theta. \tag{6–7}$$

The tangent function is periodic, with period π.

---

* In general, any function f *is said to be periodic*, with period p, provided the function of $\theta + p$ is equal to the function of θ, that is, $f(\theta + p) = f(\theta)$ for all θ. Note that $k = 1$ in Eq. (6–5) gives the smallest value for p, 2π, for which this is true. Usually this smallest value of p is called *the period*.

There are three other circular functions; they are less important than those already defined. The *cosecant, secant,* and *cotangent functions* are defined in terms of the coordinates of $P(\theta) = (x, y)$ as follows:

DEFINITION 6–3.

$$\csc \theta = \frac{1}{y} \quad (y \neq 0), \tag{6–8}$$

$$\sec \theta = \frac{1}{x} \quad (x \neq 0), \tag{6–9}$$

and

$$\cot \theta = \frac{x}{y} \quad (y \neq 0). \tag{6–10}$$

It will be noticed immediately, by using Eqs. (6–2) and (6–3), that

$$\sin \theta \csc \theta \equiv 1, \tag{6–11}$$

$$\cos \theta \sec \theta \equiv 1, \tag{6–12}$$

and

$$\tan \theta \cot \theta \equiv 1. \tag{6–13}$$

Because of Eqs. (6–11) through (6–13), the three functions defined in Definition 6–3 are called the *reciprocal functions.* Recall the definition of the reciprocal of a number, given in Axiom 6, Article 2–2. If $\sin \theta$, $\cos \theta$, and $\tan \theta$ are known, any of the other three function values can be found immediately. For this reason we shall not discuss them further.

PROBLEMS

Which of the following expressions are positive? Which are negative?

1. $\sin 2$
2. $\cos 2$
3. $\tan 4$
4. $\cos 5$
5. $\tan 3.5$
6. $\sin 4.5$
7. $\sin (-1)$
8. $\cot (-2)$
9. $\tan (-2.2)$
10. $\cos 2\pi/3$
11. $\tan 5\pi/4$
12. $\sin (-11\pi/6)$
13. $\cot 9\pi/7$
14. $\sec (-7\pi/8)$
15. $\csc (-\pi/8)$

Assuming that $\theta \in R$, determine the quadrants in which the corresponding $P(\theta)$ may lie under the following conditions.

16. $\sin \theta > 0$
17. $\cos \theta > 0$
18. $\tan \theta > 0$
19. $\sin \theta < 0$

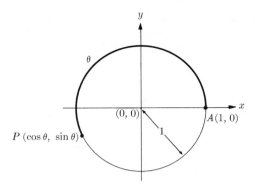

FIGURE 6–6

20. $\cos \theta < 0$

21. $\sec \theta > 0$

22. $\sin \theta > 0$ and $\cos \theta > 0$

23. $\cos \theta > 0$ and $\sin \theta < 0$

24. $\tan \theta > 0$ and $\sin \theta < 0$

25. $\sin \theta > 0$ and $\cos \theta < 0$

26. $\sin \theta < 0$ and $\cos \theta < 0$

In each of the following, the terminal point $P(\theta)$ lies on the line segment joining the origin and the indicated point. Sketch the figure and find the circular function values of each real number θ.

27. $(3, 4)$

28. $(-5, 12)$

29. $(-4, 3)$

30. $(24, -7)$

31. $(-8, -15)$

32. $(10, -8)$

33. $(0, -2)$

34. $(-1, 7)$

35. $(6, 0)$

Find the values of $\sin \theta$, $\cos \theta$, and $\tan \theta$ under the following conditions.

36. $\sin \theta = \frac{5}{13}$, θ in the first quadrant.*

37. $\cos \theta = -\frac{4}{5}$, θ in the third quadrant.

38. $\tan \theta = -\frac{1}{3}$, θ in the second quadrant.

39. $\sin \theta = \frac{2}{3}$, θ not in the first quadrant.

40. $\cot \theta = \frac{4}{3}$, θ not in the first quadrant.

41. $\cos \theta = \frac{5}{6}$, θ not in the first quadrant.

42. $\tan \theta = \frac{1}{2}$, and $\sin \theta$ is positive.

43. $\sin \theta = -\frac{3}{5}$, and $\tan \theta$ is positive.

44. $\cos \theta = -\frac{7}{9}$, and $\tan \theta$ is negative.

45. $\tan \theta = \frac{2}{3}$.

46. $\sec \theta = -\frac{5}{3}$.

47. $\csc \theta = \frac{12}{7}$.

In Problems 48 through 52, the terminal point $P(\theta)$ lies on the line segment joining $(0, 0)$ and $(8, 15)$.

48. Sketch and find the circular functions of $\theta + \pi/2$.

49. Sketch and find the circular functions of $\theta + \pi$.

---

* We shall say θ is in a certain quadrant if $P(\theta)$ lies in that quadrant.

50. Sketch and find the circular functions of $\theta + 3\pi/2$.

51. Sketch and find the circular functions of $\theta - \pi$.

52. Sketch and find the circular functions of $\theta - \pi/2$.

*53. Explain why $P(\theta)$, the terminal point on a unit circle, corresponding to any given real value θ, has coordinates $(\cos\theta, \sin\theta)$. (See Fig. 6–6.) This is a very important concept.

*54. Give the circular function values of $\tan\theta$, $\cot\theta$, $\sec\theta$, and $\csc\theta$ (if they exist) when $\theta = 0$, $\pi/2$, π, $3\pi/2$, 2π. Refer to the table in this article if necessary.

6–3 Behavior of the sine and cosine functions. If we recall the table and Problem 54 in Article 6–2, the functional values of any quadrantal value of θ (any real number which is an integral multiple of $\pi/2$) are also obtained by noting the coordinates of the point $P(\theta)$ on the unit circle.

It is now clear how the values of these functions change as θ increases from 0 to 2π. Verify the following table.

Quadrant in which $P(\theta)$ lies	θ varies from	Value of $\sin\theta$ varies from	Value of $\cos\theta$ varies from
I	0 to $\pi/2$	0 to 1	1 to 0
II	$\pi/2$ to π	1 to 0	0 to -1
III	π to $3\pi/2$	0 to -1	-1 to 0
IV	$3\pi/2$ to 2π	-1 to 0	0 to 1

The fact that the values of the sine and cosine function are never larger than one is apparent from the table. That this must be so is clear, since these values are the coordinates of some point on the unit circle. The tangent, however, can have any positive or negative real number for its value.

We have observed the changes in both $\sin\theta$ and $\cos\theta$ as the point $P(\cos\theta, \sin\theta)$ moves around the unit circle. If we wish to consider the behavior of $\sin\theta$ alone, we can conveniently study the graph of $y = \sin\theta$, with values of θ plotted on the horizontal axis and values of y on the vertical axis. Such a graph may be obtained directly from the unit circle.

Consider a rectangular coordinate system with lengths $\pi/2$ laid off along the θ axis, as in Fig. 6–7. A unit circle is drawn with its center on the θ axis. To obtain the graph of $y = \sin\theta$, the ordinate of $P(\theta)$ is carried over to the point whose abscissa is θ. As many points as may be desired on the graph are obtained by bisecting the arc in each of the four quadrants, then bisecting the resulting arc, and so on. By drawing a smooth

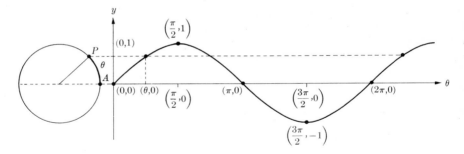

FIGURE 6–7

curve through the points located in this way, we have a graph of $y = \sin \theta$.* The curve continues indefinitely to the right and left, but need only be drawn from 0 to 2π. (Why?) Note how clearly the following properties are shown by the graph of $y = \sin \theta$.

1. This function is periodic with period 2π. (Recall Eq. (6–5).)

2. If θ is in the first quadrant, this function is an increasing function.† (In what other quadrant is this the case?)

3. The values of $\sin \theta$ are positive for θ in the first and second quadrants, and negative in the third and fourth quadrants.

4. The values of $\sin \theta$ lie between -1 and $+1$.

5. The zeros of $\sin \theta$ are at integral multiples of π, $\sin k\pi = 0$ $(k \in I)$.

6. This function has the property that $f(\theta) = -f(-\theta)$, specifically $\sin \theta = -\sin(-\theta)$. [See Eq. (6–27).] Thus the sine function is odd. (Recall Problem 18, Article 5–1).

In Fig. 6–8 the graph of $y = \cos \theta$ is shown. It may be constructed by a procedure similar to the one just described. The use of this graph makes it possible to list properties of the cosine function similar to those given above for the sine function.

We have already noticed certain relations between the various functions, such as Eqs. (6–4), (6–11), (6–12), (6–13). Others can also be derived. Since $\cot \theta \equiv 1/\tan \theta$ (Eq. 6–13) and $\tan \theta \equiv \sin \theta/\cos \theta$ (Eq. 6–4),

$$\cot \theta \equiv \frac{\cos \theta}{\sin \theta}. \qquad (6\text{–}14)$$

---

* Such a graph may also be plotted using points whose coordinates are obtained from Table I in the Appendix. A further discussion of the graphing of circular functions appears in Chapter 14.

† If $\theta_1 > \theta_2$, then $\sin \theta_1 > \sin \theta_2$.

More important, however, are the following results. Since the coordinates of any point on the unit circle are $(\cos \theta, \sin \theta)$, and these coordinates must satisfy the equation of the unit circle, $x^2 + y^2 = 1$, we have

$$\sin^2 \theta + \cos^2 \theta \equiv 1 \qquad (6\text{--}15)$$

for any value of θ, where $\sin^2 \theta$ is the usual notation for $(\sin \theta)^2$, and so on. By dividing each term of Eq. (6–15) by $\cos^2 \theta$, we get

$$\frac{\sin^2 \theta}{\cos^2 \theta} + 1 \equiv \frac{1}{\cos^2 \theta},$$

or

$$\tan^2 \theta + 1 \equiv \sec^2 \theta. \qquad (6\text{--}16)$$

By dividing each term of Eq. (6–15) by $\sin^2 \theta$, we obtain

$$1 + \frac{\cos^2 \theta}{\sin^2 \theta} \equiv \frac{1}{\sin^2 \theta},$$

or

$$1 + \cot^2 \theta \equiv \csc^2 \theta. \qquad (6\text{--}17)$$

EXAMPLE. Find all six functions of θ if $\cos \theta = \frac{3}{5}$.

Solution. This example is similar to Example 2, Article 6–2. We can now solve it by a second method. Using Eq. (6–12), we have $\sec \theta = \frac{5}{3}$. From Eq. (6–15),

$$\sin \theta \equiv \pm\sqrt{1 - \cos^2 \theta} = \pm\sqrt{1 - \tfrac{9}{25}} = \pm\sqrt{\tfrac{16}{25}} = \pm\tfrac{4}{5}.$$

The sign depends on the quadrant in which $P(\theta)$ lies. Since $\cos \theta > 0$, we know $P(\theta)$ is in the first or fourth quadrant. If it were in the first, the plus sign would appear before the $\frac{4}{5}$; if it were in the fourth, the minus sign would be chosen. From Eq. (6–4), $\tan \theta = \sin \theta / \cos \theta = \pm\tfrac{4}{5}/\tfrac{3}{5} = \pm\tfrac{4}{3}$. Using Eq. (6–11), we have $\cot \theta = \pm\tfrac{3}{4}$, and Eq. (6–8) gives us $\csc \theta = \pm\tfrac{5}{4}$.

PROBLEMS

1. How do the values of the six circular functions of 2π compare with those for $\theta = 0$?

2. What are the values of the six circular functions of $-\pi/2$?

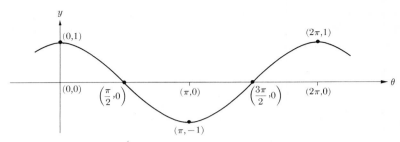

FIGURE 6–8

3. What are the values of the six circular functions of the following values of θ?

(a) 3π (b) $7\pi/2$ (c) $9\pi/2$
(d) 16π (e) 15π (f) 100π
(g) $5\pi/2$ (h) 4π (i) 5π

4. What are the values of the six circular functions of the following values of θ?

(a) -5π (b) $-\pi/2$ (c) $-3\pi/2$
(d) -6π (e) $-11\pi/2$ (f) -40π
(g) $-\pi$ (h) $-7\pi/2$ (i) $-5\pi/2$

5. Verify the table in this article for the variation of $\sin \theta$ and $\cos \theta$.

6. Make a similar table for the variation of $\tan \theta$ and $\cot \theta$.

7. Make a similar table for the variation of $\sec \theta$ and $\csc \theta$.

8. Do Problems 36 through 47 of Article 6–2 by the method outlined in the example of this article.

9. Show that $\sin (k\pi) = 0$ and $\cos (k\pi) = (-1)^k$ for any $k \in I$.

*10. Construct a graph of $y = \cos \theta$, as in Fig. 6–8, indicating the procedure used. From the graph list properties for $\cos \theta$, similar to those listed for $\sin \theta$.

11. In the same rectangular coordinate system, sketch both the curve $y = \sin \theta$ and $y = \cos \theta$, one curve superimposed on the other. Although the following facts will be proved later in this chapter, could they be deduced from the figure?

(a) $\sin (\pi/2 + \theta) \equiv \sin (\pi/2 - \theta)$ (b) $\sin (-\theta) \equiv -\sin \theta$
(c) $\cos (\pi/2 - \theta) \equiv -\cos (\pi/2 + \theta)$ (d) $\cos (-\theta) \equiv \cos \theta$
(e) $\cos \theta \equiv \sin (\pi/2 - \theta)$ (f) $\sin \theta \equiv \cos (\pi/2 - \theta)$

*12. Obtain an expression in terms of θ for the length of any chord (in a unit circle) whose corresponding arc is of length $|\theta|$. [*Hint:* In Fig. 6–6 the coordinates of A are $(1, 0)$ and those of $P(\theta)$ are $(\cos \theta, \sin \theta)$. If we use the distance formula (Eq. 4–9), we have

$$AP = \sqrt{(1 - \cos \theta)^2 + \sin^2 \theta}$$

$$= \sqrt{1 - 2 \cos \theta + \cos^2 \theta + \sin^2 \theta},$$

or

$$\text{Length of chord} = \sqrt{2 - 2 \cos \theta}.]$$ (6–18)

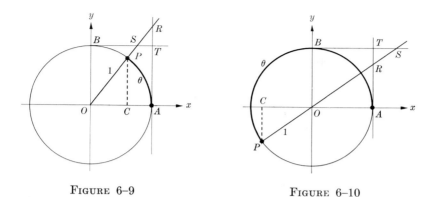

FIGURE 6–9   FIGURE 6–10

13. Find the length of the chord in a unit circle if the length of the corresponding arc is (a) $\pi/2$, (b) π.

14. In Fig. 6–9 we have a terminal point $P(\theta)$ on the unit circle, corresponding to any real number θ. Draw the tangent to the circle at $A(1, 0)$ and a line from the origin O through $P(\theta)$. The point at which these lines intersect can be called R. Draw the tangent to the circle through $B(0, 1)$. This tangent line will intersect the line from O through $P(\theta)$ and the tangent line to the circle at A. Call these points of intersection S and T respectively. (a) Verify for this figure that $\tan \theta$ is equal in magnitude to the length of the line segment AR. Draw a line from $P(\theta)$ perpendicular to the x-axis. Call the foot of this perpendicular C. Then triangle OPC is similar to ORA. Use the ratio of similar sides of these triangles to obtain the result. (b) Verify that $\cot \theta$ is equal in magnitude to the length of the line segment BS.

15. Figure 6–10 has been drawn in the same manner as Fig. 6–9, except that $P(\theta)$ is in the third quadrant. In a similar manner, construct two other figures,

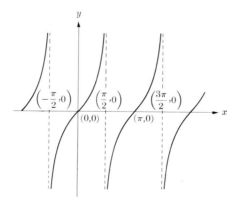

FIGURE 6–11

one where $P(\theta)$ is in the second quadrant and one where $P(\theta)$ is in the fourth quadrant.

16. Using the figures from Problem 15, Fig. 6–9 and Fig. 6–10, and the results of Problem 14, verify that the following definitions are equivalent to the original definitions: (a) $\tan \theta$ is the y-coordinate of the point R, (b) $\cot \theta$ is the x-coordinate of the point S.

*17. By using the unit circle and the definition for $\tan \theta$ given in Problem 16, construct a graph of $y = \tan \theta$. (See Fig. 6–11.)

18. From the graph of $y = \tan \theta$ given in Fig. 6–11, list properties for this function similar to those listed for the sine function.

*19. For values of θ such that $0 < \theta < \pi/2$, show that $\sin \theta < \theta < \tan \theta$. [*Hint:* See Problem 9, Article 4–6.]

6–4 Values of the circular functions of special real numbers. In Article 6–2 we mentioned that the exact value of circular functions for certain numbers (other than the quadrantal values) can be found. Two of these values are $\pi/6$ and $\pi/3$. If P_1 and P_2 in Fig. 6–12 are the tri-section points of the unit circle arc of length $\pi/2$ from $(1, 0)$ to $(0, 1)$, $P_1 = P(\pi/6)$ and $P_2 = P(\pi/3)$. If we recall from plane geometry that in a 30°–60° right triangle the length of the hypotenuse is twice that of the shorter leg, it should be clear that $P(\pi/6) = (\sqrt{3}/2, \frac{1}{2})$ while $P(\pi/3) = (\frac{1}{2}, \sqrt{3}/2)$. (Since, in either right triangle shown in the figure, the length of the hypotenuse is one, and the length of the shorter leg is $\frac{1}{2}$, the length of the third side is $\sqrt{3}/2$ by the Pythagorean Theorem.)

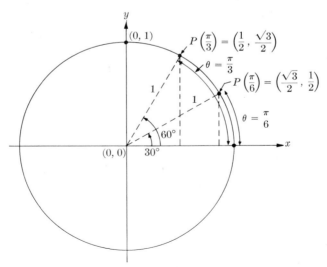

FIGURE 6–12

Therefore,

$$\sin\frac{\pi}{6} = \frac{1}{2}, \qquad \cot\frac{\pi}{6} = \sqrt{3},$$

$$\cos\frac{\pi}{6} = \frac{\sqrt{3}}{2}, \qquad \sec\frac{\pi}{6} = \frac{2}{\sqrt{3}},$$

$$\tan\frac{\pi}{6} = \frac{1}{\sqrt{3}}, \qquad \csc\frac{\pi}{6} = 2.$$

Similarly, by using $P(\pi/3)$, we have

$$\sin\frac{\pi}{3} = \frac{\sqrt{3}}{2}, \qquad \cot\frac{\pi}{3} = \frac{1}{\sqrt{3}},$$

$$\cos\frac{\pi}{3} = \frac{1}{2}, \qquad \sec\frac{\pi}{3} = 2,$$

$$\tan\frac{\pi}{3} = \sqrt{3}, \qquad \csc\frac{\pi}{3} = \frac{2}{\sqrt{3}}.$$

By properly placing a 30°–60° triangle in the unit circle, with one end of its hypotenuse at the center, the coordinates of the terminal point of any nonquadrantal value for θ of size $k(\pi/6)$, with $k \in I$, can be found. From these coordinates, the values of the circular functions of any such real number result.

Another special value is any odd multiple of $\pi/4$. For example, if $\theta = 3\pi/4$, $P(3\pi/4)$ is the midpoint of the arc from $(0, 1)$ to $(-1, 0)$. (See Fig. 6–13.) This point lies on the unit circle and has x- and y-coordinates equal in size, with $y = -x$ so that by substituting, we have $x^2 + x^2 = 2x^2 = 1$, or $x = \pm 1/\sqrt{2}$. Since $P(3\pi/4)$ lies in the second quadrant, we choose the minus sign, so that $x = -1/\sqrt{2}$. Hence,

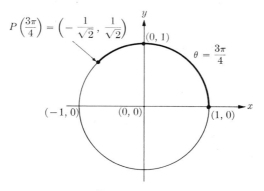

FIGURE 6–13

$$\sin \frac{3\pi}{4} = \frac{1}{\sqrt{2}}, \qquad \cot \frac{3\pi}{4} = -1,$$

$$\cos \frac{3\pi}{4} = \frac{-1}{\sqrt{2}}, \qquad \sec \frac{3\pi}{4} = -\sqrt{2},$$

$$\tan \frac{3\pi}{4} = -1, \qquad \csc \frac{3\pi}{4} = \sqrt{2}.$$

The values of the circular functions of any other odd multiple of $\pi/4$ can be obtained by similar methods.

PROBLEMS

Draw a figure showing each real number θ in the unit circle and verify the following by finding the exact values.

1. (a) $\sin \pi/3 = \cos \pi/6$
   (b) $\sin \pi/6 = \cos \pi/3$

2. (a) $\sin \pi/6 = \sin 5\pi/6$
   (b) $\cos 5\pi/6 = -\cos \pi/6$

3. (a) $\tan \pi/4 = \tan 5\pi/4$
   (b) $\cot 3\pi/4 = \cot 7\pi/4$

4. (a) $\sec 11\pi/6 = \sec \pi/6$
   (b) $\csc 2\pi/3 = -\csc 4\pi/3$

5. (a) $\sin 2\pi/3 = \sin (4\pi/3)$
   (b) $\cos 7\pi/6 = \cos (-5\pi/6)$

6. (a) $\sin \pi/3 = 2 \sin \pi/6 \cos \pi/6$
   (b) $\sin \pi/2 = 2 \sin \pi/4 \cos \pi/4$

7. (a) $\sin \dfrac{\pi}{6} = \sqrt{\dfrac{1 - \cos \pi/3}{2}}$

   (b) $\cos \dfrac{\pi}{6} = \sqrt{\dfrac{1 + \cos \pi/3}{2}}$

8. $\tan \dfrac{\pi}{6} = \dfrac{1 - \cos \pi/3}{\sin \pi/3} = \dfrac{\sin \pi/3}{1 + \cos \pi/3}$

9. $\cos \dfrac{\pi}{3} = \cos^2 \dfrac{\pi}{6} - \sin^2 \dfrac{\pi}{6} = 2 \cos^2 \dfrac{\pi}{6} - 1$

Find the exact numerical values of the following.

10. (a) $\sin^2 \dfrac{\pi}{6} + \cos^2 \dfrac{\pi}{6}$ (b) $\sin^2 0 + \cos^2 0$

11. (a) $\sec^2 \dfrac{\pi}{3} - \tan^2 \dfrac{\pi}{3}$ (b) $\sec^2 \dfrac{5\pi}{4} - \tan^2 \dfrac{5\pi}{4}$

12. (a) $\csc^2 \dfrac{7\pi}{4} - \cot^2 \dfrac{7\pi}{4}$ (b) $\csc^2 \dfrac{3\pi}{4} - \cot^2 \dfrac{3\pi}{4}$

13. $\sin \dfrac{2\pi}{3} + \cos \dfrac{7\pi}{6} + \tan \dfrac{5\pi}{3}$

14. $\tan \dfrac{5\pi}{4} + \cot \dfrac{7\pi}{4} - \sec \dfrac{5\pi}{6}$

15. $\csc \dfrac{5\pi}{6} - \cos \dfrac{4\pi}{3} + \tan \dfrac{2\pi}{3}$

16. $\sin \dfrac{2\pi}{3} \cos \dfrac{5\pi}{6} + \cos \dfrac{2\pi}{3} \sin \dfrac{5\pi}{6}$

17. $\cos \dfrac{3\pi}{4} \cos \dfrac{\pi}{4} - \sin \dfrac{3\pi}{4} \sin \dfrac{\pi}{4}$

18. $\sin \dfrac{11\pi}{6} \cos \dfrac{\pi}{3} \tan \dfrac{3\pi}{4}$

19. $\left(\cos \dfrac{11\pi}{6} + \sin \dfrac{\pi}{3} \right) \left(\tan \dfrac{\pi}{6} + \cot \dfrac{4\pi}{3} \right)$

20. $\left(\tan \dfrac{5\pi}{4} + \sin \dfrac{3\pi}{2} \right) \cos \dfrac{5\pi}{6}$

Find all the values for θ between 0 and 2π that satisfy each of the following equations.

21. $\sin \theta = \frac{1}{2}$ 22. $\cos \theta = -\frac{1}{2}$
23. $\tan \theta = 1/\sqrt{3}$ 24. $\sin \theta = -\sqrt{3}/2$
25. $\tan \theta = -1$ 26. $\cos \theta = -\sqrt{2}/2$
27. $\sin \theta = \sqrt{2}/2$ 28. $\sec \theta = 2$
29. $\cot \theta = -\sqrt{3}$ 30. $\csc \theta = 2/\sqrt{3}$

31. By drawing a figure for each of the following values of θ in the unit circle, make a table giving the six circular functions of each: 0, $\pi/6$, $\pi/4$, $\pi/3$, $\pi/2$, $2\pi/3$, $3\pi/4$, $5\pi/6$, π, $7\pi/6$, $5\pi/4$, $4\pi/3$, $3\pi/2$, $5\pi/3$, $7\pi/4$, $11\pi/6$, 2π.

32. Using Eq. (6–18), find the length of the chord in a unit circle if the corresponding θ is (a) $\pi/6$, (b) $\pi/3$, (c) $2\pi/3$.

6–5 Exact values of the circular functions for $\theta = \pi/5$. There is one other special value which is of interest. Although a slightly more complicated construction is required for $\pi/5$, we are able to find exact values for the circular functions of this number, and thus in all have exact values for the functions of π, $\pi/2$, $\pi/3$, $\pi/4$, $\pi/5$, and $\pi/6$.

Consider the unit circle with center O and radius OA. (See Fig. 6–14.) Locate the point E on the radius OA so that

$$\frac{\text{Length } OA}{\text{Length } OE} = \frac{\text{Length } OE^*}{\text{Length } EA}.$$

---

* This location is possible with the use of ruler and compass, and is essentially the same as that used for constructing a regular pentagon.

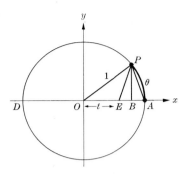

FIGURE 6–14

By letting t denote the length of OE, we have the relationship

$$\frac{1}{t} = \frac{t}{1-t}. \tag{6-19}*$$

Solving this quadratic equation† for the positive value of t, we find $t = (\sqrt{5} - 1)/2$.

Locate P so that the length of the chord AP is equal to t. Then the triangles OPA and AEP are similar, and thus triangle AEP is isosceles, so that the length of PE is equal to t, and triangle OEP is also isosceles. From this it follows directly that $\angle OAP$ is twice $\angle POA$. (See Problems 3, 4, and 5.) Since $\angle OAP$ is measured by $\frac{1}{2}\widehat{PD}$,‡ $\angle POA$ is measured by $\frac{1}{4}\widehat{PD}$. Also $\angle POA$ is measured by $\widehat{PA}$. Thus, the length of $\widehat{PD}$, $|\widehat{PD}| = 4|\widehat{AP}|$. But $|\widehat{PD}| + |\widehat{AP}| = \pi$. As a direct result, $|\widehat{AP}| = \pi/5$.

---

* The ratio defined by Eq. (6–19) has been considered since the time of the Greek mathematicians, and is called the *golden section*. Much has been written on this subject that would be of interest to the student. For example:

1. H. V. Barravalle, "The Geometry of the Pentagon and the Golden Section," *Mathematics Teacher*, Jan. 1948.

2. W. W. Rouse Ball, *Mathematical Recreations and Essays*, rev. by H. S. M. Coxeter, 11th Ed. London: Macmillan and Company, Ltd., 1940.

3. R. Courant and H. Robbins, *What Is Mathematics?*. New York: Oxford University Press, 1941.

4. Jay Hambridge, *The Elements of Dynamic Symmetry*. New York: Brentano's, 1926.

5. Tobias Dantzig, *Bequest of the Greeks*, 1955.

† The solution of quadratic equations is discussed in Article 7–4. (See Problem 3, second list.)

‡ Use is made of the theorem in plane geometry which states that an angle inscribed in a circle is measured by one-half the intercepted arc.

By considering PB perpendicular to OA at B, we easily find the exact lengths of OB and PB, that is, the x- and y-coordinates of $P = P(\pi/5)$, or the cosine and sine of $\pi/5$. The length of EA is

$$1 - t = 1 - \frac{\sqrt{5} - 1}{2} = \frac{3 - \sqrt{5}}{2};$$

thus the length of EB is $(3 - \sqrt{5})/4$. Therefore the length of OB is

$$OB = \frac{\sqrt{5} - 1}{2} + \frac{3 - \sqrt{5}}{4} = \frac{\sqrt{5} + 1}{4}.$$

Also, in the right triangle OPB,

$$(\text{length of } PB)^2 = 1 - \left(\frac{\sqrt{5} + 1}{4}\right)^2 = \frac{5 - \sqrt{5}}{8}.$$

Thus

$$\sin \frac{\pi}{5} = \sqrt{\frac{5 - \sqrt{5}}{8}}, \qquad \cos \frac{\pi}{5} = \frac{\sqrt{5} + 1}{4}. \tag{6–20}$$

Should the numerical values of the other functions be desired, they can now be found.

PROBLEMS

Referring to Fig. 6–14, prove the following in detail.
1. Triangle AEP is isosceles.
2. Triangle OEP is isosceles.
3. Angles AOP, OPE, and EPA are equal.
4. $\angle OPA = \angle OAP$.
5. $\angle PAO = $ twice $\angle POA$.
6. Using Eq. (6–18), find the length of the chord in a unit circle if the corresponding θ is $\pi/5$. How does this value compare with the value of t?

6–6 The fundamental circular function identities. In the last few articles we have considered some of the useful relations between the different circular functions. There are eight of these, known as *the fundamental circular function identities*, and from these, other simple identities may be proved. They consist of the three reciprocal relations, Eqs. (6–11), (6–12), (6–13), the tangent and cotangent relations, Eqs. (6–4) and (6–14), and the Pythagorean relations, Eqs. (6–15), (6–16), (6–17).

With the use of these relations, all the circular functions may be expressed in terms of any one circular function. Consider the following example.

EXAMPLE 1. Express the six circular functions of θ in terms of sin θ.

Solution. Of course sin θ = sin θ. By Eq. (6–15),

$$\cos^2 \theta \equiv 1 - \sin^2 \theta,$$

and therefore

$$\cos \theta \equiv \pm\sqrt{1 - \sin^2 \theta},$$

where the choice of the sign will depend on the quadrant of θ. From this and Eq. (6–4),

$$\tan \theta \equiv \pm \frac{\sin \theta}{\sqrt{1 - \sin^2 \theta}}.$$

The reciprocal relations, Eqs. (6–11) through (6–13), are used for the other three functions:

$$\csc \theta \equiv \frac{1}{\sin \theta},$$

$$\sec \theta \equiv \pm \frac{1}{\sqrt{1 - \sin^2 \theta}},$$

$$\cot \theta \equiv \pm \frac{\sqrt{1 - \sin^2 \theta}}{\sin \theta}.$$

Another example will illustrate the method of proving any circular function identity with the aid of the fundamental identities. Supply the reason for each step.

EXAMPLE 2. By transforming the left member to the form of the right, prove that

$$\frac{1}{\sin \theta} - \sin \theta \equiv \cot \theta \cos \theta.$$

Solution.

$$\frac{1}{\sin \theta} - \sin \theta \equiv \frac{1 - \sin^2 \theta}{\sin \theta} \equiv \frac{\cos^2 \theta}{\sin \theta} \equiv \frac{\cos \theta}{\sin \theta} \cos \theta \equiv \cot \theta \cos \theta.$$

Unfortunately, there is no uniform procedure to be followed in proving identities. Factoring and the addition of fractions or other algebraic simplifications are often advantageous, but the introduction of radicals should be avoided whenever possible. If in doubt, it may be helpful to express all the functions in terms of sines and cosines and simplify. The establishing of an identity is accomplished by transforming (1) the left member into the exact form of the right, (2) the right into the exact form of the left, or (3) each side separately into the same form. In the following examples, give the reason for each step.

EXAMPLE 3. By transforming each side separately to the same form, prove that $\tan \theta \sin \theta \equiv \sec \theta - \cos \theta$.

Solution.

$$\tan \theta \sin \theta \qquad \sec \theta - \cos \theta$$

$$\frac{\sin \theta}{\cos \theta} \sin \theta \qquad \frac{1}{\cos \theta} - \cos \theta$$

$$\frac{\sin^2 \theta}{\cos \theta} \qquad \frac{1 - \cos^2 \theta}{\cos \theta}$$

$$\frac{\sin^2 \theta}{\cos \theta} \equiv \frac{\sin^2 \theta}{\cos \theta}.$$

EXAMPLE 4. Prove the identity

$$\frac{1 - \sin \theta}{\cos \theta} \equiv \frac{\cos \theta}{1 + \sin \theta}.$$

Solution.

$$\frac{1 - \sin \theta}{\cos \theta} \equiv \frac{(1 - \sin \theta)(1 + \sin \theta)}{\cos \theta (1 + \sin \theta)}$$

$$\equiv \frac{1 - \sin^2 \theta}{\cos \theta (1 + \sin \theta)}$$

$$\equiv \frac{\cos^2 \theta}{\cos \theta (1 + \sin \theta)}$$

$$\equiv \frac{\cos \theta}{1 + \sin \theta}.$$

There are three different reasons for learning to prove identities such as those in the following set of problems. By working with and proving such relationships, one more easily masters the formulas and definitions of the circular functions. One also matures mathematically through the acquisition or review of certain algebraic manipulations. Most important, however, many such identities are often used in more advanced mathematics and in practical applications.

PROBLEMS

By means of the fundamental identities, express each of the following in terms of $\sin \theta$ only.

1. $\csc \theta$ 2. $\cos^2 \theta$ 3. $\cos \theta$
4. $\sec \theta$ 5. $\tan \theta$ 6. $\cot \theta$

By means of the fundamental identities, express each of the following in terms of $\cos \theta$ only.

7. $\sec \theta$ 8. $\sin^2 \theta$ 9. $\sin \theta$

10. $\csc \theta$ 11. $\tan \theta$ 12. $\cot \theta$

13. Express all six functions of θ in terms of $\tan \theta$. [*Hint:* Use the identity $\sec^2 \theta \equiv 1 + \tan^2 \theta$.]

14. Express $(\sin \theta + \tan \theta)/(\sec \theta + 1)$ in terms of $\sin \theta$ only.

15. Express $(\tan \theta + \cot \theta)/(\sec \theta \sin \theta)$ in terms of $\cos \theta$ only.

Prove the following identities.

16. $\tan \theta + \cot \theta \equiv \sec \theta \csc \theta$

17. $1 - 2 \sin^2 \theta \equiv 2 \cos^2 \theta - 1$

18. $\sin \theta \cos \theta \sec \theta \csc \theta \equiv 1$

19. $\dfrac{1}{1 + \sin \theta} + \dfrac{1}{1 - \sin \theta} \equiv 2 \sec^2 \theta$

20. $\cos \theta + \tan \theta \sin \theta \equiv \sec \theta$

21. $\cos^4 \theta - \sin^4 \theta \equiv \cos^2 \theta - \sin^2 \theta$

22. $\dfrac{\tan \theta - \cot \theta}{\tan \theta + \cot \theta} \equiv 2 \sin^2 \theta - 1$

23. $\dfrac{\sin \theta}{1 + \cos \theta} + \dfrac{1 + \cos \theta}{\sin \theta} \equiv 2 \csc \theta$

24. $\dfrac{1 - \cos \theta}{\sin \theta} \equiv \dfrac{\sin \theta}{1 + \cos \theta}$

25. $\cos^2 \theta - \sin^2 \theta \equiv \dfrac{1 - \tan^2 \theta}{1 + \tan^2 \theta}$

26. $\cot \theta + \tan \theta \equiv \cot \theta \sec^2 \theta$

27. $\dfrac{1 + \tan^2 \theta}{\tan^2 \theta} \equiv \csc^2 \theta$

28. $(\csc \theta - \cot \theta)^2 \equiv \dfrac{1 - \cos \theta}{1 + \cos \theta}$

29. $(\sec \theta - \tan \theta)^2 \equiv \dfrac{1 - \sin \theta}{1 + \sin \theta}$

30. $(\cos \theta - \sin \theta)^2 + 2 \sin \theta \cos \theta \equiv 1$

31. $\dfrac{\cot^2 \theta - 1}{1 + \cot^2 \theta} \equiv 2 \cos^2 \theta - 1$

32. $\dfrac{1 + \csc \theta}{\csc \theta - 1} \equiv \dfrac{1 + \sin \theta}{1 - \sin \theta}$

33. $\dfrac{\tan \theta}{1 - \cot \theta} + \dfrac{\cot \theta}{1 - \tan \theta} \equiv 1 + \tan \theta + \cot \theta$

34. $\dfrac{1 - \tan^2 \theta}{1 + \tan^2 \theta} \equiv 1 - 2 \sin^2 \theta$

35. $\dfrac{2 \sin^2 \theta - 1}{\sin \theta \cos \theta} \equiv \tan \theta - \cot \theta$

36. $\sec \theta \csc \theta - 2 \cos \theta \csc \theta \equiv \tan \theta - \cot \theta$

37. $\dfrac{\cos \theta - \sin \theta}{\cos \theta + \sin \theta} \equiv \dfrac{\cot \theta - 1}{\cot \theta + 1}$

38. $\dfrac{\sin \theta}{\csc \theta - \cot \theta} \equiv 1 + \cos \theta$

39. $\dfrac{(\cos^2 \theta - \sin^2 \theta)^2}{\cos^4 \theta - \sin^4 \theta} \equiv 1 - 2 \sin^2 \theta$

40. $\dfrac{\sec^2 \theta}{1 + \sin \theta} \equiv \dfrac{\sec^2 \theta - \sec \theta \tan \theta}{\cos^2 \theta}$

41. $1 + \cot \theta \equiv \dfrac{(1 - \cot^2 \theta) \sin \theta}{\sin \theta - \cos \theta}$

42. $\dfrac{\sec \theta + \tan \theta}{\cos \theta - \tan \theta - \sec \theta} \equiv -\csc \theta$

43. $\sin \theta + \cos \theta + \dfrac{\sin \theta}{\cot \theta} \equiv \sec \theta + \csc \theta - \dfrac{\cos \theta}{\tan \theta}$

44. $\dfrac{\sin \theta \cos \theta + \cos \theta \sin \theta}{\cos \theta \cos \theta - \sin \theta \sin \theta} \equiv \dfrac{\tan \theta + \tan \theta}{1 - \tan \theta \tan \theta}$

6–7 Proof of the formula for $\cos (\alpha - \beta)$. We are now in a position to deal with two additional general types of circular function relations. They differ from those studied thus far in that they contain functions of more than one number. The problem of expressing a circular function of θ plus some multiple of $\pi/2$ as a function of only θ (as in Example 3, Article 6–2) is by no means the only situation frequently encountered; often we wish to consider circular functions of two numbers in general. Such functions, we shall see, can be expressed in terms of functions of each number separately. More specifically, we know that $\sin (\pi/4 + \pi/3)$ is not equal to $\sin \pi/4 + \sin \pi/3$, since the latter is equal to $1/\sqrt{2} + \sqrt{3}/2$ (a value greater than one), an impossible value for the sine function. However, $\sin (\pi/4 + \pi/3)$ can be expressed in terms of functions of $\pi/4$ and $\pi/3$ and its value readily obtained. We find it convenient to develop first a formula for $\cos (\alpha - \beta)$, one of the truly basic formulas of trigonometry.

THEOREM 6–3. *For any α and $\beta \in R$,*

$$\cos (\alpha - \beta) \equiv \cos \alpha \cos \beta + \sin \alpha \sin \beta. \qquad (6\text{–}21)$$

Proof. As in Fig. 6–15, let α and β be any two real numbers and $P(\alpha)$ and $P(\beta)$ their corresponding terminal points on the unit circle. Since the coordinates of $P(\alpha)$ are $(\cos \alpha, \sin \alpha)$ and of $P(\beta)$ are $(\cos \beta, \sin \beta)$, the distance d between these two points, Eq. (4–9), is given by

$$d = \sqrt{(\cos \alpha - \cos \beta)^2 + (\sin \alpha - \sin \beta)^2}$$

$$= \sqrt{\cos^2 \alpha - 2 \cos \alpha \cos \beta + \cos^2 \beta + \sin^2 \alpha - 2 \sin \alpha \sin \beta + \sin^2 \beta}$$

$$= \sqrt{2 - 2 (\cos \alpha \cos \beta + \sin \alpha \sin \beta)}.$$

By recalling Eq. (6–18), the expression for the length of any chord whose corresponding arc has length $|\theta|$ in the unit circle, we have another expression for d. Since d represents the length of the chord whose associated number is γ, where $\gamma = (\alpha - \beta) \pm$ (some integral multiple of 2π),

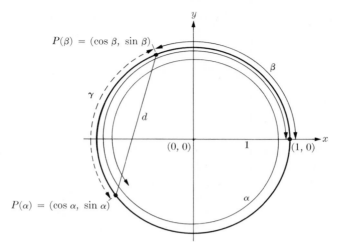

FIGURE 6–15

$$d = \sqrt{2 - 2 \cos \gamma}$$
$$= \sqrt{2 - 2 \cos (\alpha - \beta)}.$$

Upon equating these two expressions for d and simplifying, we see that

$$\cos (\alpha - \beta) \equiv \cos \alpha \cos \beta + \sin \alpha \sin \beta,$$

which was to be proved. It should be emphasized that this formula expresses the cosine of $\alpha - \beta$ in terms of the functional values of α and β themselves, and *holds for any value of α or β*. It is in this respect that the formula becomes important, as will be evident in the remaining articles in this chapter.

6–8 Special reduction formulas. As is probably somewhat evident by this time, any circular function of any real number can be expressed as a function of a real number between zero and $\pi/4$. This is shown by using certain reduction formulas derived from Eq. (6–21) with special values for α or β.

If we replace α by $\pi/2$ in Eq. (6–21), we obtain

$$\cos (\pi/2 - \beta) \equiv \cos \pi/2 \cos \beta + \sin \pi/2 \sin \beta.$$

Since $\cos \pi/2 = 0$ and $\sin \pi/2 = 1$, we have

$$\cos (\pi/2 - \beta) \equiv \sin \beta. \qquad (6\text{–}22)$$

It should again be emphasized that relations such as Eq. (6–22) hold for all real numbers α or β, and the reader should observe this as the formulas are derived. If in Eq. (6–22) we replace β by $\pi/2 - \beta$, the relation

$$\cos [\pi/2 - (\pi/2 - \beta)] \equiv \sin (\pi/2 - \beta)$$

holds for all β. Simplifying, we find

$$\sin (\pi/2 - \beta) \equiv \cos \beta. \qquad (6\text{–}23)$$

From Eqs. (6–22) and (6–23), we immediately see that

$$\tan (\pi/2 - \beta) \equiv \cot \beta, \qquad (6\text{–}24)$$

and

$$\cot (\pi/2 - \beta) \equiv \tan \beta. \qquad (6\text{–}25)$$

Although true for all values, these four results are especially useful in the computation of functional values for numbers less than $\pi/2$.

ILLUSTRATION 1.

(a) $\sin 1 = \cos (\pi/2 - 1) =$ approximately $\cos (1.5708 - 1) = \cos 0.5708$.

(b) $\tan \pi/3 = \cot \pi/6$.

We have noted that circular functions have names which can be paired. In each pair, one function is the cofunction of the other. The sine is the cofunction of the cosine, and the cosine is the cofunction of the sine, and so on. The four relations above can be stated: *The cofunction of any number equals the function of $\pi/2$ minus the number.*

The relationship between the function of any number and its negative is very useful, and also follows from Eq. (6–21). Letting $\alpha = 0$,

$$\cos (0 - \beta) \equiv \cos 0 \cos \beta + \sin 0 \sin \beta.$$

Since $\cos 0 = 1$ and $\sin 0 = 0$,

$$\cos (-\beta) \equiv \cos \beta. \qquad (6\text{–}26)$$

Also, if we replace β by $-\beta$ in Eq. (6–22),

$$\cos (\pi/2 + \beta) \equiv \sin (-\beta).$$

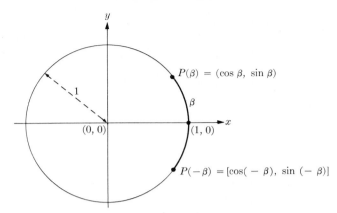

FIGURE 6–16

Since $\pi/2 + \beta = \beta - (-\pi/2)$,

$$\sin (-\beta) \equiv \cos [\beta - (-\pi/2)]$$
$$\equiv \cos \beta \cos (-\pi/2) + \sin \beta \sin (-\pi/2)$$
$$\equiv (\cos \beta)(0) + (\sin \beta)(-1),$$

or

$$\boxed{\sin (-\beta) \equiv -\sin \beta.} \qquad (6\text{--}27)$$

It follows directly from Eqs. (6–26) and (6–27) that

$$\tan (-\beta) \equiv -\tan \beta. \qquad (6\text{--}28)$$

ILLUSTRATION 2.
(a) $\sin (-\pi/4) = -\sin \pi/4$.
(b) $\tan (-\pi/3) = -\tan \pi/3$.
(c) $\cos (-\pi/6) = \cos \pi/6$.

Note the significance of Eqs. (6–26) and (6–27) in Fig. 6–16.

6–9 General addition formulas.   We shall now derive the general formulas for the sine, cosine, and tangent of the sum or difference of two numbers. Since

$$\cos (\alpha + \beta) \equiv \cos [\alpha - (-\beta)]$$
$$\equiv \cos \alpha \cos (-\beta) + \sin \alpha \sin (-\beta).$$

we have

$$\boxed{\cos (\alpha + \beta) \equiv \cos \alpha \cos \beta - \sin \alpha \sin \beta.} \qquad (6\text{--}29)$$

Also,

$$\sin (\alpha + \beta) \equiv \cos [\pi/2 - (\alpha + \beta)]$$
$$\equiv \cos [(\pi/2 - \alpha) - \beta]$$
$$\equiv \cos (\pi/2 - \alpha)\cos \beta + \sin (\pi/2 - \alpha) \sin \beta,$$

and we have

$$\sin (\alpha + \beta) \equiv \sin \alpha \cos \beta + \cos \alpha \sin \beta. \tag{6–30}$$

Replacing β by $-\beta$ in Eq. (6–30), we immediately find

$$\sin (\alpha - \beta) \equiv \sin \alpha \cos \beta - \cos \alpha \sin \beta. \tag{6–31}$$

The tangent formulas,

$$\tan (\alpha + \beta) \equiv \frac{\tan \alpha + \tan \beta}{1 - \tan \alpha \tan \beta} \tag{6–32}$$

and

$$\tan (\alpha - \beta) \equiv \frac{\tan \alpha - \tan \beta}{1 + \tan \alpha \tan \beta}, \tag{6–33}$$

result from the fact that $\tan \theta \equiv \sin \theta/\cos \theta$.

By using Eqs. (6–29) and (6–30), we have

$$\tan (\alpha + \beta) \equiv \frac{\sin (\alpha + \beta)}{\cos (\alpha + \beta)}$$

$$\equiv \frac{\sin \alpha \cos \beta + \cos \alpha \sin \beta}{\cos \alpha \cos \beta - \sin \alpha \sin \beta}$$

$$\equiv \frac{\dfrac{\sin \alpha \cos \beta}{\cos \alpha \cos \beta} + \dfrac{\cos \alpha \sin \beta}{\cos \alpha \cos \beta}}{\dfrac{\cos \alpha \cos \beta}{\cos \alpha \cos \beta} - \dfrac{\sin \alpha \sin \beta}{\cos \alpha \cos \beta}}$$

$$\equiv \frac{\tan \alpha + \tan \beta}{1 - \tan \alpha \tan \beta}.$$

Equation (6–33) may be derived in a similar way, or by using Eq. (6–28).

EXAMPLE 1. Compute $\sin 7\pi/12$ from the functions of $\pi/3$ and $\pi/4$.

Solution. $\sin 7\pi/12 = \sin (\pi/3 + \pi/4)$
$$= \sin \pi/3 \cos \pi/4 + \cos \pi/3 \sin \pi/4$$
$$= \sqrt{3}/2 \cdot \sqrt{2}/2 + \tfrac{1}{2} \cdot \sqrt{2}/2$$
$$= \sqrt{6}/4 + \sqrt{2}/4 = (\sqrt{6} + \sqrt{2})/4.$$

EXAMPLE 2. Compute $\cos \pi/12$.

Solution. $\cos \pi/12 = \cos (\pi/3 - \pi/4)$
$$= \cos \pi/3 \cos \pi/4 + \sin \pi/3 \sin \pi/4$$
$$= \tfrac{1}{2} \cdot \sqrt{2}/2 + \sqrt{3}/2 \cdot \sqrt{2}/2$$
$$= \sqrt{2}/4 + \sqrt{6}/4 = (\sqrt{2} + \sqrt{6})/4.$$

EXAMPLE 3. Consider $\sin \alpha = \tfrac{12}{13}$, with $P(\alpha)$ in the first quadrant, and $\cos \beta = \tfrac{3}{5}$, with $P(\beta)$ in the first quadrant.   In what quadrant does $P(\alpha + \beta)$ lie?

Solution. Since $P(\alpha)$ and $P(\beta)$ are both in the first quadrant, $P(\alpha + \beta)$ is either in the first or second quadrant. Since the cosine is positive in the first and negative in the second, it will suffice to find $\cos (\alpha + \beta)$. We are able to find $\cos \alpha$ and $\sin \beta$ as in Article 6–2: $\cos \alpha = \tfrac{5}{13}$ and $\sin \beta = \tfrac{4}{5}$. Thus,

$$\cos (\alpha + \beta) = \cos \alpha \cos \beta - \sin \alpha \sin \beta$$
$$= \tfrac{5}{13} \cdot \tfrac{3}{5} - \tfrac{12}{13} \cdot \tfrac{4}{5}$$
$$= \tfrac{15}{65} - \tfrac{48}{65} = -\tfrac{33}{65}.$$

Since $\cos (\alpha + \beta)$ is negative, it follows that $P(\alpha + \beta)$ is in the second quadrant.

EXAMPLE 4. Show that $\sin (3\pi/2 - \theta) \equiv -\cos \theta$.

Solution. In Eq. (6–31) let $\alpha = 3\pi/2$ and $\beta = \theta$. Therefore,

$$\sin (3\pi/2 - \theta) \equiv \sin 3\pi/2 \cos \theta - \cos 3\pi/2 \sin \theta$$
$$\equiv (-1) \cos \theta - (0) \sin \theta$$
$$\equiv -\cos \theta.$$

EXAMPLE 5. Express $3 \sin \theta + 4 \cos \theta$ in the form $k \sin (\theta + \theta_1)$, where $P(\theta_1)$ is in the first quadrant.

Solution. By multiplying and dividing the expression by $\sqrt{3^2 + 4^2} = 5$, we have

$$5(\tfrac{3}{5} \sin \theta + \tfrac{4}{5} \cos \theta) \equiv 5 (\sin \theta \cdot \tfrac{3}{5} + \cos \theta \cdot \tfrac{4}{5}).$$

Letting $\cos \theta_1 = \tfrac{3}{5}$, we find that $\sin \theta_1 = \tfrac{4}{5}$; thus the above expression becomes

$$5(\tfrac{3}{5} \sin \theta + \tfrac{4}{5} \cos \theta) \equiv 5 \sin (\theta + \theta_1),$$

where θ_1 has its sine equal to $\tfrac{4}{5}$ and its cosine equal to $\tfrac{3}{5}$.

PROBLEMS

1. Find the exact value of the sine, cosine, and tangent of $5\pi/12$ by setting $\alpha = \pi/4$ and $\beta = \pi/6$ in one of the formulas previously derived.

2. Find the exact value of $\sin \pi/12$ and $\tan \pi/12$ by taking $\pi/12 = \pi/3 - \pi/4$.

3. Find the exact value of $\cos 7\pi/12$ and $\tan 7\pi/12$, as done in Example 1.

4. Find the exact values of the sine, cosine, and tangent of $11\pi/12$ by setting $\alpha = 3\pi/4$ and $\beta = \pi/6$.

It is interesting to note that with the results of Problems 1–4 and previously known results, the exact values of the circular functions of any integral multiple of $\pi/12$ have been or can be readily found.

5. If $\sin \alpha = \tfrac{4}{5}$, $\sin \beta = \tfrac{12}{13}$, $0 \le \alpha \le \pi/2$, and $0 \le \beta \le \pi/2$, find

(a) $\sin (\alpha + \beta)$,   (b) $\cos (\alpha + \beta)$,   (c) $\tan (\alpha + \beta)$,
(d) $\sin (\alpha - \beta)$,   (e) $\cos (\alpha - \beta)$,   (f) $\tan (\alpha - \beta)$.

6. If $\cos \alpha = -\tfrac{24}{25}$, $\tan \beta = \tfrac{9}{40}$, $\pi/2 \le \alpha \le \pi$, and $\pi \le \beta \le 3\pi/2$, find

(a) $\sin (\alpha + \beta)$,   (b) $\cos (\alpha + \beta)$,   (c) $\tan (\alpha + \beta)$,
(d) $\sin (\alpha - \beta)$,   (e) $\cos (\alpha - \beta)$,   (f) $\tan (\alpha - \beta)$.

7. (a) In what quadrant is $P(\alpha + \beta)$ in Problem 5? (b) In what quadrant is $P(\alpha - \beta)$ in Problem 6?

Find $\sin (\alpha + \beta)$ and $\cos (\alpha + \beta)$, given that:

8. $\tan \alpha = \tfrac{3}{4}$, $\sec \beta = \tfrac{13}{5}$, and neither $P(\alpha)$ nor $P(\beta)$ is in the first quadrant.

9. $\tan \alpha = -\tfrac{15}{8}$, $\sin \beta = -\tfrac{7}{25}$, and neither $P(\alpha)$ nor $P(\beta)$ is in the fourth quadrant.

Express each of the following in terms of functions of θ only.

10. $\cos (\pi/4 + \theta)$ 11. $\tan (\theta + \pi/6)$ 12. $\sec (\theta - \pi/4)$
13. $\cot (\pi/4 + \theta)$ 14. $\sin (\theta + \pi/3)$ 15. $\csc (\theta - \pi/6)$
16. $\cos (\pi/6 - \theta)$ 17. $\sin (\theta - \pi/4)$

Show that the following statements are true.

18. $\tan (\theta + \pi/4) - \tan (\theta - 3\pi/4) \equiv 0$

19. $\sin (\theta - \pi/6) + \cos (\theta - \pi/3) \equiv \sqrt{3} \sin \theta$

20. $\cot (\alpha + \beta) \equiv \dfrac{\cot \alpha \cot \beta - 1}{\cot \alpha + \cot \beta}$

21. $\tan (\theta + \pi/4) \equiv (1 + \tan \theta)/(1 - \tan \theta)$

22. $\sin (\alpha + \beta)/\cos \alpha \cos \beta \equiv \tan \alpha + \tan \beta$

*23. (a) $\sin (\alpha + \beta) + \sin (\alpha - \beta) \equiv 2 \sin \alpha \cos \beta$
    (b) $\sin (\alpha + \beta) - \sin (\alpha - \beta) \equiv 2 \cos \alpha \sin \beta$

24. (a) $\cos (\alpha + \beta) + \cos (\alpha - \beta) \equiv 2 \cos \alpha \cos \beta$
    (b) $\cos (\alpha + \beta) - \cos (\alpha - \beta) \equiv -2 \sin \alpha \sin \beta$

*25. By letting $\alpha + \beta = x$, $\alpha - \beta = y$, and dividing the respective members of Problems 23(a) and (b), prove

$$\frac{\sin x - \sin y}{\sin x + \sin y} \equiv \frac{\tan \frac{1}{2}(x - y)}{\tan \frac{1}{2}(x + y)}.$$

Show that the following relations are true.

26. (a) $\sin (\alpha + \beta) \sin (\alpha - \beta) \equiv \sin^2 \alpha - \sin^2 \beta$
    (b) $\cos (\alpha + \beta) \cos (\alpha - \beta) \equiv \cos^2 \alpha - \sin^2 \beta$

27. $\cos (\alpha + \beta) \cos \beta + \sin (\alpha + \beta) \sin \beta \equiv \cos \alpha$

28. $\sin (\alpha - \beta) \cos \beta + \cos (\alpha - \beta) \sin \beta \equiv \sin \alpha$

Express the following in the form $k \sin (\theta + \theta_1)$, where θ_1 is between $-\pi/2$ and $\pi/2$.

29. $5 \sin \theta + 12 \cos \theta$ 30. $15 \sin \theta + 8 \cos \theta$

31. $4 \sin \theta - 3 \cos \theta$ 32. $24 \sin \theta + 7 \cos \theta$

33. $\sin \theta + \cos \theta$ 34. $2 \sin \theta - 5 \cos \theta$

6–10 General reduction formulas. It is often necessary to express the circular functions of a given number in terms of functions of a number between 0 and $\pi/2$. We are able to do this by using reduction formulas obtained from Eq. (6–21). If we wish to reduce a number by multiples of $\pi/2$, in order to work with the smaller number, we can recall (Problem 9, Article 6–3) that

$$\sin (2k \cdot \pi/2) = 0 \quad \text{and} \quad \cos (2k \cdot \pi/2) = (-1)^k$$

for any integer $k \in I$. Since

$$\sin (2k \cdot \pi/2 + \beta) \equiv \sin (2k \cdot \pi/2) \cos \beta + \cos (2k \cdot \pi/2) \sin \beta,$$

we have

$$\sin (2k \cdot \pi/2 + \beta) \equiv (-1)^k \sin \beta. \tag{6–34}$$

and similarly,

$$\cos (2k \cdot \pi/2 + \beta) \equiv (-1)^k \cos \beta. \tag{6–35}$$

These two relationships are for β increased or decreased by even multiples of $\pi/2$. The function is not changed, although the sign may be. For odd multiples of $\pi/2$, the function is changed to its cofunction, and again the sign may also change, for

$$\sin [(2k + 1)\pi/2 + \beta]$$
$$\equiv \sin [\pi/2 + (2k \cdot \pi/2 + \beta)]$$
$$\equiv \sin \pi/2 \cos (2k \cdot \pi/2 + \beta) + \cos \pi/2 \sin (2k \cdot \pi/2 + \beta)$$
$$\equiv \cos (2k \cdot \pi/2 + \beta),$$

and therefore, by Eq. (6–35),

$$\sin [(2k + 1)\pi/2 + \beta] \equiv (-1)^k \cos \beta. \qquad (6\text{--}36)$$

Moreover,

$$\begin{aligned}
\cos &[(2k + 1)\pi/2 + \beta] \\
&\equiv \cos [\pi/2 + (2k \cdot \pi/2 + \beta)] \\
&\equiv \cos \pi/2 \cos (2k \cdot \pi/2 + \beta) - \sin \pi/2 \sin (2k \cdot \pi/2 + \beta) \\
&\equiv -(-1)^k \sin \beta,
\end{aligned}$$

and thus,

$$\cos [(2k + 1)\pi/2 + \beta] \equiv (-1)^{k+1} \sin \beta. \qquad (6\text{--}37)$$

The special case of Eqs. (6–34) and (6–35), where k has the value 2, is important, since

$$\sin (\beta + 2\pi) \equiv \sin \beta \qquad (6\text{--}38)$$

and

$$\cos (\beta + 2\pi) \equiv \cos \beta. \qquad (6\text{--}39)$$

It was for this reason that these functions were called *periodic functions*, with periods of 2π. [Recall Eqs. (6–5) and (6–6).]

These formulas are of special importance and most useful when applied to angular measurement. This will be illustrated in Chapter 15.

EXAMPLE 1. Express sin 10.8909 as a function of a number where $0 < \theta < \pi/4$ (=0.7854).

Solution. Since

$$10.8909 = 6(1.5708) + 1.4661,$$

by using Eq. (6–34), we have sin 10.8909 = −sin 1.4661. From Eq. (6–22),

$$-\sin 1.4661 = -\cos (1.5708 - 1.4661) = -\cos 0.1047,$$

and we have sin 10.8909 = −cos 0.1047.

EXAMPLE 2. Express cos 21.6945 as a function of a number θ, when $0 < \theta < \pi/4$.

Solution. Again, 21.6945 = 13(1.5708) + 1.2741. Thus, using Eq. (6–37), cos 21.6945 = −sin 1.2741, and by Eq. (6–22), we have

$$\cos 21.6945 = -\cos 0.2967.$$

EXAMPLE 3. Do the same for cos (−8.6743).

Solution. Since

$$-8.6743 = -5(1.5708) - 0.8203,$$

we have

$$\cos(-8.6743) = -\sin 0.8203 = -\cos 0.7505.$$

Now that the procedure is familiar to us, we should be able to write the answer without the use of Eqs. (6–24) through (6–37). Draw a figure, choose the sign of the functional value to be simplified, depending upon the quadrant, and with this sign, write the corresponding number between 0 and $\pi/2$. In considering Example 1, since 10.8909 is such that $P(10.8909)$ is in the third quadrant, sin 10.8909 is negative, and the corresponding θ is 1.4661, so that sin 10.8909 = $-\sin 1.4661$.

PROBLEMS

Express each of the following as a function of a real number θ, where $0 < \theta < \pi/4 = 0.7854$.

1. sin 3.4209	2. cos 2.5656	3. sin 5.5676
4. cos 4.4331	5. tan 5.1313	6. cos 12.7060
7. sin (−10.9083)	8. cos (−7.5922)	9. tan 17.5231
10. sin 8	11. cos 2	12. tan 3
13. cos 4	14. tan 5	15. sin 6

By using Eq. (6–21), or Eqs. (6–29) through (6–33), show that each of the following statements is true. Check those involving sines or cosines by Eqs. (6–34) through (6–37).

16. $\sin(\pi + \theta) \equiv -\sin\theta$	17. $\cos(\pi + \theta) \equiv -\cos\theta$
18. $\sin(\pi - \theta) \equiv \sin\theta$	19. $\cos(\pi - \theta) \equiv -\cos\theta$
20. $\tan(3\pi/2 - \theta) \equiv \cot\theta$	21. $\cos(\theta - \pi) \equiv -\cos\theta$
22. $\cos(3\pi/2 + \theta) \equiv \sin\theta$	23. $\sin(\theta + 3\pi/2) \equiv -\cos\theta$
24. $\tan(\pi + \theta) \equiv \tan\theta$	25. $\cos(2\pi - \theta) \equiv \cos\theta$
26. $\sin(2\pi - \theta) \equiv -\sin\theta$	

27. In Problem 24 we showed that $\tan(\theta + \pi) \equiv \tan\theta$. This was proved as a special case of Eq. (6–7), with $k = 1$. What is the period of $\tan\theta$?

28. What are the periods of the cotangent, secant, and cosecant functions?

6–11 General identities. We have emphasized throughout that the general identities

$$\sin(\alpha \pm \beta) \equiv \sin\alpha\cos\beta \pm \cos\alpha\sin\beta, \qquad (6\text{–}40)$$

$$\cos(\alpha \pm \beta) \equiv \cos\alpha\cos\beta \mp \sin\alpha\sin\beta, \qquad (6\text{–}41)$$

$$\tan(\alpha \pm \beta) \equiv \frac{\tan\alpha \pm \tan\beta}{1 \mp \tan\alpha\tan\beta} \qquad (6\text{–}42)$$

were proved for all real numbers. As the fundamental identities were used to prove the simple identities (Article 6–6), so these can be used to prove other identities, several of which appear in the next list of problems. Also, they are used to obtain the important multiple value identities. Since Eqs. (6–40) through (6–42) are true for any α and β, letting $\alpha = \beta$, we immediately have

$$\sin 2\alpha \equiv \sin (\alpha + \alpha)$$
$$\equiv \sin \alpha \cos \alpha + \cos \alpha \sin \alpha,$$

or

$$\boxed{\sin 2\alpha \equiv 2 \sin \alpha \cos \alpha.} \qquad (6\text{–}43)$$

Also,

$$\cos (\alpha + \alpha) \equiv \cos \alpha \cos \alpha - \sin \alpha \sin \alpha,$$

or

$$\boxed{\begin{aligned} \cos 2\alpha &\equiv \cos^2 \alpha - \sin^2 \alpha \\ &\equiv 1 - 2 \sin^2 \alpha \qquad \text{(Why?)} \\ &\equiv 2 \cos^2 \alpha - 1. \qquad \text{(Why?)} \end{aligned}}$$

$$(6\text{–}44)$$
$$(6\text{–}45)$$
$$(6\text{–}46)$$

Moreover,

$$\tan (\alpha + \alpha) \equiv \frac{\tan \alpha + \tan \alpha}{1 - \tan \alpha \tan \alpha},$$

or

$$\boxed{\tan 2\alpha \equiv \frac{2 \tan \alpha}{1 - \tan^2 \alpha}.} \qquad (6\text{–}47)$$

Other identities in terms of $\theta/2$ are also readily established. If we use Eq. (6–45) with $2\alpha = \theta$, or $\alpha = \theta/2$,

$$\cos \theta \equiv 1 - 2 \sin^2 \frac{\theta}{2}.$$

Solving for $\sin \theta/2$, we have

$$2 \sin^2 \frac{\theta}{2} \equiv 1 - \cos \theta, \qquad (6\text{–}48)$$

so that

$$\boxed{\sin \frac{\theta}{2} \equiv \pm \sqrt{\frac{1 - \cos \theta}{2}},} \qquad (6\text{–}49)$$

where the choice of the sign before the radical is determined by the size of $\theta/2$. Similarly, if we use Eq. (6–46) with the same substitution $\alpha = \theta/2$,

$$\cos \theta \equiv 2 \cos^2 \frac{\theta}{2} - 1,$$

and solving for $\cos \theta/2$, we get

$$2 \cos^2 \frac{\theta}{2} \equiv 1 + \cos \theta, \tag{6–50}$$

or

$$\boxed{\cos \frac{\theta}{2} \equiv \pm \sqrt{\frac{1 + \cos \theta}{2}},} \tag{6–51}$$

with the choice of the sign again depending on the size of $\theta/2$.

There are two identities for $\tan \theta/2$, and these can be obtained by using Eqs. (6–48) and (6–50). In the identity

$$\tan \frac{\theta}{2} \equiv \frac{\sin \theta/2}{\cos \theta/2},$$

by multiplying the numerator and denominator of the right member by $2 \sin \theta/2$, we have

$$\tan \frac{\theta}{2} \equiv \frac{2 \sin^2 \theta/2}{2 \sin \theta/2 \cos \theta/2},$$

or

$$\boxed{\tan \frac{\theta}{2} \equiv \frac{1 - \cos \theta}{\sin \theta}.} \tag{6–52}$$

In the same expression, multiplying by $2 \cos \theta/2$, we have

$$\tan \frac{\theta}{2} \equiv \frac{2 \sin \theta/2 \cos \theta/2}{2 \cos^2 \theta/2},$$

or

$$\boxed{\tan \frac{\theta}{2} \equiv \frac{\sin \theta}{1 + \cos \theta}.} \tag{6–53}$$

Some of the uses of the identities of this article will be more clearly understood by considering the following examples.

EXAMPLE 1. Compute the value of $\sin \pi/12$ and $\cos \pi/12$ from the functions of $\pi/6$.

Solution. We use Eq. (6–49) and obtain

$$\sin \frac{\pi}{12} = \sin \frac{1}{2} \cdot \frac{\pi}{6} = \sqrt{\frac{1 - \cos \pi/6}{2}} = \sqrt{\frac{1 - \sqrt{3}/2}{2}} = \frac{\sqrt{2 - \sqrt{3}}}{2}.$$

Also, by Eq. (6–51),

$$\cos \frac{\pi}{12} = \cos \frac{1}{2} \cdot \frac{\pi}{6} = \sqrt{\frac{1 + \cos \pi/6}{2}} = \sqrt{\frac{1 + \sqrt{3}/2}{2}} = \frac{\sqrt{2 + \sqrt{3}}}{2}.$$

Explain the difference between this result and that in Example 2, Article 6–9.

EXAMPLE 2. Express $\sin 2\theta$, $\cos 2\theta$, and $\tan 2\theta$ in terms of x if $x = \tan \theta$.

Solution. First let us find $\sin \theta$ and $\cos \theta$ in terms of x. Since

$$\sec \theta \equiv \pm\sqrt{1 + \tan^2 \theta} \equiv \pm\sqrt{1 + x^2},$$

$$\cos \theta \equiv \pm \frac{1}{\sqrt{1 + x^2}}.$$

Also,

$$\sin \theta \equiv \tan \theta \cos \theta \equiv \pm \frac{x}{\sqrt{1 + x^2}}.$$

Therefore,

$$\sin 2\theta \equiv 2 \sin \theta \cos \theta \equiv \frac{2x}{1 + x^2}.$$

A complete analysis, considering $P(\theta)$ in the first, second, third, and fourth quadrants, is necessary to show that the sign in the above example is correct. In addition, we have

$$\cos 2\theta \equiv \cos^2 \theta - \sin^2 \theta \equiv \frac{1 - x^2}{1 + x^2}$$

and

$$\tan 2\theta \equiv \frac{2 \tan \theta}{1 - \tan^2 \theta} \equiv \frac{2x}{1 - x^2}.$$

EXAMPLE 3. Reduce $\sin^4 \theta$ to an expression involving only functions of θ raised to the first power.

Solution. By Eq. (6–48), we have

$$\sin^2 \theta \equiv \frac{1 - \cos 2\theta}{2}.$$

Thus we notice that by doubling θ we have changed the exponent of the circular function from 2 to 1. Hence,

$$\sin^4 \theta \equiv (\sin^2 \theta)^2 \equiv \frac{(1 - \cos 2\theta)^2}{4} \equiv \frac{1 - 2\cos 2\theta + \cos^2 2\theta}{4},$$

and replacing

$$\cos^2 2\theta \qquad \text{by} \qquad \frac{1 + \cos 4\theta}{2}$$

(why is this possible?), we obtain

$$\sin^4 \theta \equiv \frac{3 - 4\cos 2\theta + \cos 4\theta}{8}.$$

This type of transformation is extremely useful in calculus.

PROBLEMS

1. Verify the identities for $\sin 2\theta$ and $\tan 2\theta$ for the value $\theta = \pi/3$.

2. Use the double-value identities to compute $\sin 4\pi/3$, $\cos 4\pi/3$, and $\tan 4\pi/3$ from the functions of $2\pi/3$.

3. Compute $\sin 7\pi/12$, $\cos 7\pi/12$, and $\tan 7\pi/12$ from the values of the functions of $7\pi/6$.

4. If $\sin \theta = \frac{3}{5}$ and $P(\theta)$ is in the first quadrant, find the exact value of the following.

(a) $\sin 2\theta$ (b) $\cos 2\theta$ (c) $\tan 2\theta$
(d) $\sin \theta/2$ (e) $\cos \theta/2$ (f) $\tan \theta/2$

5. If $\cos \theta = -\frac{5}{13}$ and $P(\theta)$ is in the second quadrant, find the exact value of the following.

(a) $\sin 2\theta$ (b) $\cos 2\theta$ (c) $\tan 2\theta$
(d) $\sin \theta/2$ (e) $\cos \theta/2$ (f) $\tan \theta/2$

6. Reduce $\sin^2 \theta$ to an expression involving only circular functions of θ, raised to the first power.

7. Reduce $\cos^4 \theta$ to an expression involving only circular functions of θ which are raised to the first power.

8. Derive identity (6–53) by using the identity $\sin \omega/2 \equiv \sin (\omega - \omega/2)$. [*Hint:* $\sin \omega/2 \equiv \sin \omega \cos \omega/2 - \cos \omega \sin \omega/2$ or $(1 + \cos \omega) \sin \omega/2 \equiv \sin \omega \cos \omega/2$.]

9. Derive identity (6–52) by using the identity

$$\cos \frac{\omega}{2} \equiv \cos \left(\omega - \frac{\omega}{2} \right).$$

10. Derive the identity

$$\tan \frac{\omega}{2} \equiv \pm \sqrt{\frac{1 - \cos \omega}{1 + \cos \omega}}.$$

11. Derive the identity $\tan \omega/2 \equiv \csc \omega - \cot \omega$.

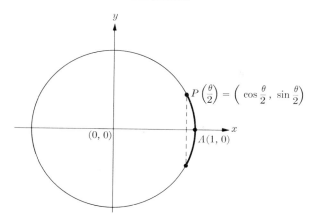

FIGURE 6–17

Prove the following identities.

12. $\sin 3\theta \equiv 3 \sin \theta - 4 \sin^3 \theta$

13. $\cos 3\theta \equiv 4 \cos^3 \theta - 3 \cos \theta$

14. $\sin \dfrac{\theta}{2} \cos \dfrac{\theta}{2} \equiv \dfrac{\sin \theta}{2}$

15. $\dfrac{1 - \cos 2\theta}{\sin 2\theta} \equiv \tan \theta$

16. $\left(\cos \dfrac{\theta}{2} - \sin \dfrac{\theta}{2} \right)^2 \equiv 1 - \sin \theta$

17. $\csc 2\theta - \cot 2\theta \equiv \tan \theta$

18. $\csc 2\theta + \cot 2\theta \equiv \cot \theta$

19. $\tan 3\theta \equiv \dfrac{3 \tan \theta - \tan^3 \theta}{1 - 3 \tan^2 \theta}$

20. $\dfrac{\tan \theta/2 + \cot \theta/2}{\cot \theta/2 - \tan \theta/2} \equiv \sec \theta$

21. $\dfrac{\sin 2\theta}{\sin \theta} - \dfrac{\cos 2\theta}{\cos \theta} \equiv \sec \theta$

22. $\dfrac{\sin 3\theta}{\sin \theta} - \dfrac{\cos 3\theta}{\cos \theta} \equiv 2$

23. $\dfrac{\sin 3\theta}{\cos \theta} + \dfrac{\cos 3\theta}{\sin \theta} \equiv 2 \cot 2\theta$

24. $\dfrac{2 \tan \theta}{1 + \tan^2 \theta} \equiv \sin 2\theta$

25. $\dfrac{\cot^2 \theta - 1}{\csc^2 \theta} \equiv \cos 2\theta$

26. In Fig. 6–17, A is the midpoint of an arc of the unit circle of length θ. Using this figure, where $0 < \theta < \pi$, and Eq. (6–18), show that

$$\sin \frac{\theta}{2} \equiv \sqrt{\frac{1 - \cos \theta}{2}} .$$

27. In the unit circle in Fig. 6–18, P_2 is the midpoint of the arc $\widehat{AP_1}$ whose length is θ, where $0 < \theta < \pi/2$. BP_1 is drawn parallel to OP_2, so that $\angle P_1 BA = \angle P_2 OA$. (Why?)

(a) Verify that $BP_1 = 2 \cos \theta/2$ and $P_1 A = 2 \sin \theta/2$. [Hint: $CP_2 = AD = P_1 A/2$, and $OC = OD = BP_1/2$.]

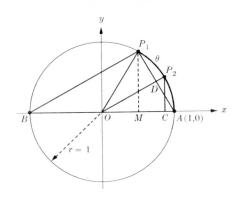

FIGURE 6–18

(b) Verify from the figure that $\sin \theta = 2 \sin \theta/2 \cos \theta/2$.

(c) Verify from the figure that

$$\sin \frac{\theta}{2} \equiv \sqrt{\frac{1 - \cos \theta}{2}}.$$

(d) Verify from the figure that

$$\cos \frac{\theta}{2} \equiv \sqrt{\frac{1 + \cos \theta}{2}}.$$

6–12 Conversions of sums and products. It is quite often necessary to convert a product of two circular functions into a sum of two functions, and vice versa. This can be done by using the identities (6–40) and (6–41). (The following identities are not as important as the previous ones in this chapter.) By adding the members of the two identities given by Eq. (6–40), we get

$$\sin (\alpha + \beta) + \sin (\alpha - \beta) \equiv 2 \sin \alpha \cos \beta,$$

or

$$\sin \alpha \cos \beta \equiv \tfrac{1}{2} [\sin (\alpha + \beta) + \sin (\alpha - \beta)]. \tag{6–54}$$

By subtracting the members of the two identities given in Eq. (6–40), we obtain

$$\cos \alpha \sin \beta \equiv \tfrac{1}{2} [\sin (\alpha + \beta) - \sin (\alpha - \beta)]. \tag{6–55}$$

Similarly, using Eq. (6–41), by adding and then subtracting, we obtain

$$\cos \alpha \cos \beta \equiv \tfrac{1}{2} [\cos (\alpha + \beta) + \cos (\alpha - \beta), \tag{6–56}$$

$$\sin \alpha \sin \beta \equiv \tfrac{1}{2} [\cos (\alpha - \beta) - \cos (\alpha + \beta)]. \tag{6–57}$$

As an example, the product $\cos 6\theta \cos 3\theta$ may be represented as a sum. Using Eq. (6–56) with $\alpha = 6\theta$ and $\beta = 3\theta$, we have

$$\cos 6\theta \cos 3\theta \equiv \tfrac{1}{2}(\cos 9\theta + \cos 3\theta).$$

The same four identities can also be used for transforming a sum into a product. Such a transformation is useful when logarithms are to be used, for products are more readily calculated by logarithms than are sums. For convenience, we change the notation by letting $\alpha + \beta = \theta$ and $\alpha - \beta = \omega$. Solving these equations for α and β, we obtain $\alpha = (\theta + \omega)/2$, and $\beta = (\theta - \omega)/2$. Substituting these values in the above identities and simplifying, we obtain

$$\sin \theta + \sin \omega \equiv 2 \sin \frac{\theta + \omega}{2} \cos \frac{\theta - \omega}{2}, \qquad (6\text{–}58)$$

$$\sin \theta - \sin \omega \equiv 2 \cos \frac{\theta + \omega}{2} \sin \frac{\theta - \omega}{2}, \qquad (6\text{–}59)$$

$$\cos \theta + \cos \omega \equiv 2 \cos \frac{\theta + \omega}{2} \cos \frac{\theta - \omega}{2}, \qquad (6\text{–}60)$$

$$\cos \theta - \cos \omega \equiv -2 \sin \frac{\theta + \omega}{2} \sin \frac{\theta - \omega}{2}. \qquad (6\text{–}61)$$

EXAMPLE. Express $\sin \theta + \sin 3\theta + \sin 5\theta + \sin 7\theta$ as a product.

Solution. By grouping the first two and the last two terms and using Eq. (6–58), we get

$$\sin \theta + \sin 3\theta + \sin 5\theta + \sin 7\theta$$

$$\equiv 2 \sin \frac{\theta + 3\theta}{2} \cos \frac{\theta - 3\theta}{2} + 2 \sin \frac{5\theta + 7\theta}{2} \cos \frac{5\theta - 7\theta}{2}$$

$$\equiv 2 \sin 2\theta \cos(-\theta) + 2 \sin 6\theta \cos(-\theta)$$

$$\equiv 2 \cos \theta (\sin 2\theta + \sin 6\theta) \qquad \text{(Why?)}$$

$$\equiv 2 \cos \theta (2 \sin 4\theta \cos 2\theta) \qquad \text{(Why?)}$$

$$\equiv 4 \cos \theta \cos 2\theta \sin 4\theta.$$

PROBLEMS

Express each of the following products as a sum.

1. $\sin 3\theta \cos 5\theta$
2. $4 \cos \pi/3 \cos \pi/6$
3. $\cos 7\theta \sin 5\theta$
4. $6 \sin 2\pi/3 \sin \pi/3$
5. $\sin 5\theta \cos 2\theta$
6. $\cos 2\theta \cos 6\theta$
7. $\cos \theta \sin \theta/2$
8. $2 \sin 7\theta \sin 2\theta$

Express each of the following sums as products.

9. $\sin \pi/9 + \sin 2\pi/9$
10. $\cos 2\theta - \cos \theta$
11. $\cos 7\pi/9 + \cos 2\pi/9$
12. $\sin \pi/4 - \sin \pi/5$

13. $\sin 8\theta + \sin 4\theta$

14. $\cos 4\theta - \cos 8\theta$

15. $\sin 5\theta/3 - \sin 5\theta/6$

16. $\cos 6\theta + \cos 7\theta$

Prove the following identities.

17. $\dfrac{\sin 5\theta - \sin 3\theta}{\cos 5\theta + \cos 3\theta} \equiv \tan \theta$

18. $\dfrac{\cos 6\theta + \cos 4\theta}{\sin 6\theta - \sin 4\theta} \equiv \cot \theta$

19. $\dfrac{\sin 8\theta + \sin 2\theta}{\cos 8\theta + \cos 2\theta} \equiv \tan 5\theta$

20. $\dfrac{\sin 3\theta - \sin \theta}{\cos^2 \theta - \sin^2 \theta} \equiv 2 \sin \theta$

21. $\dfrac{\sin \alpha - \sin \beta}{\cos \alpha + \cos \beta} \equiv \tan \dfrac{\alpha - \beta}{2}$

22. $\dfrac{\sin \alpha - \sin \beta}{\sin \alpha + \sin \beta} \equiv \dfrac{\tan \frac{1}{2}(\alpha - \beta)}{\tan \frac{1}{2}(\alpha + \beta)}$

23. $\dfrac{\sin \theta + \sin 3\theta + \sin 5\theta}{\cos \theta + \cos 3\theta + \cos 5\theta} \equiv \tan 3\theta$

24. $\sin\left(\dfrac{\pi}{4} - \theta\right) \sin\left(\dfrac{\pi}{4} + \theta\right) \equiv \dfrac{1}{2} \cos 2\theta$

6–13 Function values of any number. In several of the previous articles of this chapter we computed the values of the circular functions for certain numbers. We found $\cos \pi/3 = 0.5000$, an exact decimal value, while $\sin \pi/3 = \sqrt{3}/2$ and $\tan \pi/3 = \sqrt{3}$ could be approximated as decimal values to whatever accuracy we wished. Such approximations to exact values, expressed in radicals, can be obtained only in special cases.

To find the values of the functions for any given number θ, we might approximate $|\theta|$ along the arc of the unit circle from $(1, 0)$, and thus locate the position of the terminal point $P(\theta)$. By measuring the x- and y-coordinates of the point $P(\theta)$, we could find approximate values for the sine and cosine functions. Because of inaccuracies in drawing and measuring, such a method has definite limitations. The usual method for finding the values of the functions to a good degree of accuracy is based on calculus and is beyond the scope of this book.

We are able to find exact values of the functions for angles of any integral multiple of $\pi/60$, however, by a completely elementary process. Although this method is *not* an efficient way of obtaining the values for a table, it has sufficient mathematical interest to warrant this brief discussion. By combining the exact values of the functions for $\theta = \pi/6$, $\pi/5$, $\pi/4$, $\pi/3$, and $\pi/2$ (which we have already found) and using some of the relations of Article 6–9, we obtain our results.

Let us find exact values for $\sin \pi/60$ and $\cos \pi/60$. By applying the values found for $\cos \pi/5$ (Article 6–5) to Eqs. (6–49) and (6–50), we have

$$\sin \frac{\pi}{10} = \sqrt{\frac{1 - \cos \pi/5}{2}} = \sqrt{\frac{3 - \sqrt{5}}{8}}$$

and

$$\cos \frac{\pi}{10} = \sqrt{\frac{1 + \cos \pi/5}{2}} = \sqrt{\frac{5 + \sqrt{5}}{8}}.$$

Also, from Example 2 and Problem 2, Article 6–9, we have

$$\sin \frac{\pi}{12} = \frac{\sqrt{6} - \sqrt{2}}{4}$$

and

$$\cos \frac{\pi}{12} = \frac{\sqrt{6} + \sqrt{2}}{4}.$$

Since $\pi/10 - \pi/12 = \pi/60$, we have, by using Eq. (6–31),

$$\sin \frac{\pi}{60} = \sin \left(\frac{\pi}{10} - \frac{\pi}{12} \right)$$

$$= \sin \frac{\pi}{10} \cos \frac{\pi}{12} - \cos \frac{\pi}{10} \sin \frac{\pi}{12}$$

$$= \sqrt{\frac{3 - \sqrt{5}}{8}} \frac{\sqrt{6} + \sqrt{2}}{4} - \sqrt{\frac{5 + \sqrt{5}}{8}} \frac{\sqrt{6} - \sqrt{2}}{4}$$

$$= \sqrt{\frac{(3 - \sqrt{5})(8 + 4\sqrt{3})}{128}} - \sqrt{\frac{(5 + \sqrt{5})(8 - 4\sqrt{3})}{128}},$$

so that

$$\sin \frac{\pi}{60} = \frac{\sqrt{12 - 2\sqrt{15} - 4\sqrt{5} + 6\sqrt{3}} - \sqrt{20 - 2\sqrt{15} + 4\sqrt{5} - 10\sqrt{3}}}{8}.$$

$$(6\text{–}62)$$

In a similar way, using Eq. (6–21), we obtain

$$\cos \frac{\pi}{60} = \frac{\sqrt{20 + 2\sqrt{15} + 4\sqrt{5} + 10\sqrt{3}} + \sqrt{12 + 2\sqrt{15} - 4\sqrt{5} - 6\sqrt{3}}}{8}.$$

$$(6\text{–}63)$$

The values of the other functions can be found from these exact values. Of course, approximated decimal values can also be obtained to any degree of accuracy desired, but the actual computation is long.

The functional values of other numbers could be handled similarly. For example, $\pi/30 = \pi/5 - \pi/6$, $\pi/20 = \pi/4 - \pi/5$, $\pi/15 = \pi/6 - \pi/10$, and so on. The purpose of this discussion has been to demonstrate how a workable table could be constructed by a completely elementary process.

The special numbers which have been considered are included in tables of trigonometric function values, which can be used either to find the approximate value of the functions of any given member or to find the number when the value of some functional value of that number is given. Table I, in the Appendix, lists the values, approximated to four decimal places, of the sine, cosine, tangent, and cotangent of numbers at intervals of approximately 0.0029 for positive numbers up to $\pi/2 = 1.5708$. From these values, in the column headed radian (radian will be defined in Chapter 15), it is possible to find an approximate value for the functions of any real number.

Since the circular function of any number is the same as the cofunction of $\pi/2$ minus the number, Table I is constructed so that numbers from 0 to $\pi/4 = 0.7854$ are at the left, while numbers from 0.7854 to 1.5708 are at the right. Moreover, the circular functions listed at the top go with the numbers at the left, while those at the bottom go with the numbers at the right.

For example, opposite 0.4218, and in the column under sine, we find 0.4094, which is sin 0.4218. The value for sin 1.1926 = 0.9293, which we find in the column above sine, since 1.1926 is given at the right. We shall not interpolate between values, but merely choose the closest value until we discuss interpolation at the appropriate time.

EXAMPLE 1. Find cos 1.

Solution. Since 1, in the right-hand column, is the closest to the tabulated number 1.007, cos 1 is approximately equal to 0.5398 (read in cosine column from bottom).

EXAMPLE 2. Find cos 12.

Solution. By the method outlined in Article 6–10, we have cos 12 = cos $(7 \cdot 1.5708 + 1.0044)$ = sin 1.0044 (Eq. 6–37). Therefore, cos 12 = 0.8434.

EXAMPLE 3. Find the number θ between 0 and $\pi/2$ if sin $\theta = 0.6231$.

Solution. Since 0.6231 is closer to 0.6225 than any other number in the sine column, $\theta = 0.6720$. Because of the relation sin θ = sin $(\pi - \theta)$ and its periodicity, there are other possible values of θ, but none in the range required. For example, since $\theta = 0.6720$, we know

$$\sin (3.1416 - 0.6720) = \sin 2.496 = 0.6231.$$

Also,

$$\sin (6.2832 + 0.6720) = \sin 6.9552 = 0.6231,$$

and so on.

Problems

1. Establish Eq. (6–63).

2. Express $7\pi/60$, $2\pi/15$, and $3\pi/20$ by using combinations similar to those above that might be used to find the sines and cosines of such values.

3. Do the same for $11\pi/60$, $13\pi/60$, and $7\pi/30$.

4. If you have access to a computing machine, find the decimal approximation for $\sin \pi/60$ and $\cos \pi/60$, using Eqs. (6–42) and (6–43). Check your results with the values given in Table I.

5. Find the value of each of the following by using Table I.

(a) $\sin 0.4741$ (b) $\cos 0.3869$ (c) $\tan 1.15$

(d) $\sin 0.17$ (e) $\cos 3$ (f) $\tan 4$

(g) $\sin 30$ (h) $\cos 60$

6. Find the number θ between 0 and $\pi/2 = 1.5708$ using Table I if:

(a) $\sin \theta = 0.2979$,   (b) $\cos \theta = 0.3365$,

(c) $\tan \theta = 2.25$,   (d) $\sin \theta = 0.745$,

(e) $\cos \theta = 0.1423$,   (f) $\cot \theta = 10$.

6–14 Approximations of functional values for small numbers. With the use of the properties of order and our definition for the length of a circular arc (Definition 4–10), we are able to find the approximate value of the circular functions for small positive values of θ. By recalling the definition for $\sin \theta$ and $\tan \theta$ (Problem 16, Article 6–3), and restricting θ to a small *positive* value, we would expect the values of $\sin \theta$, $\tan \theta$, and θ to be approximately the same. We recall from Problem 9, Article 4–6, with Fig. 4–10, and Problem 19, Article 6–3, that if $0 < \theta < \pi/2$,

$$\sin \theta < \theta < \tan \theta. \qquad (6\text{–}64)$$

This inequality will enable us to find an approximation to the values of the sine or tangent of small values of θ.

By dividing each member of Eq. (6–64) by $\sin \theta$, we have

$$1 < \frac{\theta}{\sin \theta} < \sec \theta.$$

Considering the reciprocals, we get

$$\cos \theta < \frac{\sin \theta}{\theta} < 1, \qquad (6\text{–}65)*$$

---

* Consider inequality (6–65). As θ becomes smaller and smaller through positive values (approaches 0), $\cos \theta$ approaches 1. A similar argument may be given if θ is negative. Thus $\sin \theta/\theta$, as θ approaches 0, is always between 1 and a number approaching 1. Therefore, the ratio must approach 1. This is written

$$\lim_{\theta \to 0} \sin \theta/\theta = 1,$$

and is read: the limit of $\sin \theta/\theta$, as θ approaches zero, is one. This is an extremely important result in more advanced mathematics.

and since $\cos \theta = \sqrt{1 - \sin^2 \theta} > \sqrt{1 - \theta^2}$ (why?), we have

$$\sqrt{1 - \theta^2} < \frac{\sin \theta}{\theta} < 1$$

or

$$\theta\sqrt{1 - \theta^2} < \sin \theta < \theta. \tag{6-66}$$

This inequality can be used in connection with the sine function. Again, by dividing each member of Eq. (6–64) by $\tan \theta$, we have

$$\cos \theta < \frac{\theta}{\tan \theta} < 1 \tag{6-67}$$

or

$$\sqrt{1 - \theta^2} < \frac{\theta}{\tan \theta} < 1.$$

Using the reciprocal relation, this becomes

$$1 < \frac{\tan \theta}{\theta} < \frac{1}{\sqrt{1 - \theta^2}}, \tag{6-68}$$

or

$$\theta < \tan \theta < \frac{\theta}{\sqrt{1 - \theta^2}}. \tag{6-69}$$

Relations (6–66) and (6–69) give us bounds for $\sin \theta$ and $\tan \theta$.

EXAMPLE. Find an approximate value of $\sin \pi/60$.

Solution. Substituting in (6–66) for $\theta = \pi/60$, where $\pi = 3.1416$, we find

$$0.05229 < \sin \pi/60 < 0.05236.$$

Thus, correct to four decimal places, $\sin \pi/60 = 0.0523$. Notice the value listed in Table I.

It is also possible to find the value of $\cos \theta$, for small positive values of θ. Since $\cos \theta \equiv 1 - 2 \sin^2 (\theta/2)$, we have

$$\cos \theta > 1 - 2 \frac{\theta^2}{4},$$

and thus,

$$1 > \cos \theta > 1 - \frac{\theta^2}{2}. \tag{6-70}$$

Problems

1. Using $\pi = 3.1416$, find the best possible approximation for $\sin \pi/30$, $\cos \pi/30$, and $\tan \pi/30$, using the above inequalities.

2. Find approximations for $\cos \pi/60$ and $\tan \pi/60$. Compare these values with those given in Table I.

3. Using Eq. (6–68), show that

$$\lim_{\theta \to 0} \frac{\tan \theta}{\theta} = 1.$$

4. Using Eq. (6–65) or Eq. (6–67), prove the inequality for $0 < \theta < \pi/2$.

$$\cos \theta = \frac{\sin \theta}{\tan \theta} < 1.$$

5. Using the result of Problem 4, prove

$$\lim_{\theta \to 0} \frac{\sin \theta}{\tan \theta} = 1.$$

6. With the use of Eqs. (6–65) and (6–70), obtain the bounds for $\sin \theta$:

$$\theta(1 - \tfrac{1}{2}\theta^2) < \sin \theta < \theta.$$

This inequality does not involve a square root, and thus has advantages in certain cases.

7. Recall from plane geometry the expression for the perimeter P of a regular n-gon inscribed in a circle of radius r, $P = 2nr \sin (\pi/n)$, and

$$\lim_{n \to \infty} P = 2\pi r$$

(the limit of the perimeter of a regular n-gon as the number of sides increases indefinitely is the circumference, $2\pi r$). Set up a limit by eliminating P from these two expressions and, by substituting $\theta = \pi/n$, prove

$$\lim_{\theta \to 0} \frac{\sin \theta}{\theta} = 1.$$

CHAPTER 7

LINEAR AND QUADRATIC FUNCTIONS

7-1 The linear function. The circular functions considered in the last chapter were not defined by algebraic expressions but rather by rule and, in fact, cannot be expressed algebraically. Probably the simplest function defined in mathematics by means of a non-trivial algebraic expression, is the function defined by the equation, $y = mx + b$.

DEFINITION 7-1. *The function f, defined by the first degree equation*

$$f(x) = mx + b, \tag{7-1}$$

where m and b are constants is called a linear function.

The function derives its name from the fact that its graph is a straight line.* Moreover, any straight line other than $x = k$ (a straight line parallel to the y-axis) can be represented by such an equation with the appropriate m and b. We shall concern ourselves with the linear function's algebraic properties and its zeros, rather than the geometric properties.

We recall (Article 5–2) that the zero of a function is the x-coordinate or x-value for which y, the value of the function, is zero. Hence, we let $y = 0$, and we can find the zero of a linear function by solving the equation $mx + b = 0$ for x. In general, the zeros of a function are the *roots* or *solution* of the equation $f(x) = 0$. Before considering the solving of such a linear equation specifically, let us consider the problem of solving any equation.

Various methods are used in solving an equation. Any device that produces an *equivalent equation*, one which has the same roots, and only those roots, is permitted. Some procedures, such as squaring, may introduce new factors, and some, such as dividing, may lose some factors, so that extreme care should be exercised in using such procedures. Furthermore, it is always wise to check any purported solution, for the ultimate test of a number as a root of any equation is not how it is obtained, but whether it satisfies the equation. The following operations are called *permissible*, since they always result in equations which are equivalent to the original, that is, the new equation has exactly the same roots.

---

* The fact that $y = mx + b$ represents the equation of a straight line is proved in analytic geometry and will be assumed here.

1. The same number or algebraic expression may be added to or sub-tracted from both members of an equation.

2. Both members of an equation may be multiplied or divided by any nonzero number.

ILLUSTRATION 1. In the solving of $4x - 5 = x + 7$, 5 is added and x is subtracted from both members, giving $3x = 12$. Then, division by 3 yields $x = 4$.

It should be clear that any permissible operation is reversible.

In addition to the permissible operations mentioned, an operation such as squaring both members of an equation is sometimes used. This device, however, is not reversible. Although no root of the original equation will be lost by the process, certain values may be introduced which are roots of the new equation, but not of the original one. If this type of operation is employed, the roots of the final equation *must* be examined to determine whether they are roots of the original equation.

ILLUSTRATION 2. If in the equation $x - 1 = 3$, which has the root $x = 4$, both members are squared $(x - 1)^2 = 9$. If this equation is solved, one of its roots is -2, although it does not satisfy the original equation.*

ILLUSTRATION 3. In solving the equation $\sin^2 \theta - \frac{1}{2} \sin \theta = 0$ for values of θ between 0 and $\pi/2$, we find $\sin \theta = 0$ or $\frac{1}{2}$ and $\theta = 0$ or $\pi/6$. If we were to divide both members by $\sin \theta$, however, we would have only the value $\sin \theta = \frac{1}{2}$. The value $\sin \theta = 0$ would have been "lost."†

Now let us consider the solution of linear equations.

EXAMPLE 1. Solve the equation

$$\frac{2x + 5}{2} - \frac{5x}{x - 1} = x$$

for all possible values of x.

Solution. We first clear the equation of fractions by multiplying by the LCD, $2(x - 1)$,

$$(2x + 5)(x - 1) - (5x)(2) = (x)(2)(x - 1),$$

or

$$2x^2 + 3x - 5 - 10x = 2x^2 - 2x.$$

---

* Any equation which, because of some mathematical process, has acquired an extra root is sometimes called a *redundant equation.*

† Any equation which, because of some mathematical process, has fewer roots than its original is sometimes called a *defective equation.*

Combining similar terms, we have

$$-7x - 5 = -2x.$$

Adding $2x + 5$ to both members,

$$-5x = 5,$$

and dividing by -5,

$$x = -1.$$

This result should be verified by substituting $x = -1$ in the original equation.

EXAMPLE 2. Solve the equation $2 \cos \theta + 3 = 2$ for all values of θ between 0 and 2π.

Solution. Although this type of equation is not algebraic and therefore not linear, it is linear in the circular function of θ, and can be solved for $\cos \theta$ as though it were linear. The values of θ can then be found. Problem 6 of Article 6–13 was a simple example of this type.

$$2 \cos \theta + 3 = 2$$

$$2 \cos \theta = -1$$

$$\cos \theta = -\tfrac{1}{2}$$

Therefore $\theta = 2\pi/3$ or $4\pi/3$, since $P(\theta)$ must be in the second or third quadrant when its x-coordinate is negative.

EXAMPLE 3. Solve the equation

$$s = \frac{a - rl}{1 - r}$$

for r.

Solution. This equation, one in which some or all of the known quantities are represented by letters, is called a *literal* equation. Each step in the solution should be verified.

$$s = \frac{a - rl}{1 - r},$$

$$s(1 - r) = a - rl,$$

$$s - rs = a - rl,$$

$$rl - rs = a - s,$$

$$r(l - s) = a - s,$$

$$r = \frac{a - s}{l - s}, \quad \text{if } s \neq l.$$

PROBLEMS

Find the zeros of the linear functions f, defined by the following expressions for $f(x)$.

1. $2x + 4$
2. $-5x + 10$
3. $10 - 12x$
4. $6x - 9$
5. $8x + 24$
6. $5x - 17$

Solve the following linear equations and check.

7. $4x - 2 = 6x + 12$
8. $3x + 7 = 5x - 13$
9. $5 + 2(3 - x) = 4 + 2(x - 2) + 5x$
10. $x^2 - 7x + 10 = x^2 + 5x - 6$

11. $\dfrac{3x + 5}{12} - \dfrac{4 - x}{6} = \dfrac{x - 2}{3}$

12. $\dfrac{3x - 6}{5} = \dfrac{2x - 5}{10} + \dfrac{x - 4}{2}$

13. $\dfrac{3x + 2}{x - 1} - \dfrac{6}{5} = 0$

14. $\dfrac{2}{6x - 7} - \dfrac{5}{3x - 4} = 0$

Using Table I if necessary, find the values of θ between 0 and 2π which satisfy each of the following equations.

15. $2 \sin \theta - \sqrt{3} = 0$

16. $\dfrac{\cos \theta - 2}{3} = 3 - \dfrac{\cos \theta + 9}{3}$

17. $\dfrac{1 + \tan \theta}{1 - \tan \theta} = 2$

18. $\sin 3\theta = 2 - 3 \sin 3\theta$

19. $\dfrac{4 \cos (2\theta + \pi/6)}{5} = \dfrac{4 + \cos (2\theta + \pi/6)}{10}$

20. $\dfrac{1}{2 \tan (\theta + \pi)} = \dfrac{2}{\tan (\theta + \pi)} + 1$

Solve the following equations for the letters indicated.

21. $ax - bx = c$, for x
22. $ay + by = c + dy$, for y
23. $A = \frac{1}{2}bh$, for b
24. $A = \frac{1}{2}(b_1 + b_2)h$, for b_1
25. $l = a + (n - 1)d$, for d
26. $l = a + (n - 1)d$, for n

27. $S = \dfrac{a - rl}{1 - r}$, for l

28. $S = \dfrac{a - rl}{1 - r}$, for a

29. $S = \dfrac{n}{2}(a + l)$, for l

30. $S = v_0 t + \dfrac{1}{2} gt^2$, for v_0

31. $\dfrac{y}{\tan \theta_1} = \dfrac{a + y}{\tan \theta_2}$, for y

32. $\tan \theta_1 \left(\dfrac{x}{\tan \theta_2} + a \right) = x$, for x

In Problems 33 through 40 sketch the graph of the linear function $f \colon x \to y$, where $y = f(x)$ is given by the following expressions.

33. $f(x) = 2x - 7$
34. $f(x) = (x/3) + 5$
35. $f(x) = -4x + 8$
36. $f(x) = 6 - (x/2)$
37. $f(x) = 4$
38. $f(x) = 3x + 6$
39. $f(x) = 20x - 30$
40. $f(x) = -(x/50) + (1/100)$

In solving the following problems, *read the problem carefully*, let one of the unknown quantities be x, and express all other unknown quantities in terms of x. Find two expressions or quantities that are equal, equate these, and solve the resulting equation. Check *all* answers.

41. A man 42 years old has a son 12. In how many years will the father be twice as old as his son?

42. The tens digit of a number is 3 less than the units digit. If the number is divided by the sum of the digits, the quotient is 4 and the remainder 3. What is the original number? [*Hint:* If x equals the units digit, $x - 3$ is the tens digit, and the number may be written $10(x - 3) + x$.]

43. A man left $\frac{1}{2}$ of his estate to his wife, $\frac{1}{6}$ to his daughter, and the remainder, an amount of $15,000, to his son. How large was the entire estate?

44. A starts walking along a road at 3 mi/hr. Two hours later B starts in the same direction at 3.5 mi/hr. How far from the starting point will B overtake A? [*Hint:* Rate $\times$ time $=$ Distance.]

45. A can do a certain job in 3 hours, while the same job takes B 4 hours. How long will it take both of them working together? [*Hint:* If $x =$ number of hours for both to complete the work, $1/x$ will be the amount of the work done by both in 1 hour.]

46. If the larger of two integers, whose sum is 88, is divided by the smaller, the quotient is 5 and the remainder is 10. What are the two numbers?

7-2 Arithmetic progressions. Let us consider the linear function defined by the equation $f(x) = 2x - 1$, where the domain of the function consists of the positive integers. In this case the function assumes the values $1, 3, 5, \ldots, 2n - 1, \ldots$ Similarly, if the function whose defining equation is $y = 2^x$ has as its domain the positive integers, the corresponding functional values are $2, 4, 8, \ldots, 2^n, \ldots$. Both of these sets of functional values are examples of sequences. In general, a *sequence* is the range of some function whose domain is either all or a part of the set of positive integers. The functional value of the integer 1 is the first term of the sequence, of 2 the second term, of 3 the third term, and so on. In this way, the first, second, third, etc., values in the sequence are specifically determined. If the entire set of integers is considered, the sequence is *infinite;* but if only the first n positive integers make up the domain of the function, the sequence is *finite.* We are concerned in this article with one specific type of sequence.

DEFINITION 7-2. *An* arithmetic progression *is a sequence in which each term after the first is obtained by adding the same fixed number, called the common difference, to the preceding term.*

ALTERNATIVE DEFINITION 7-2. *An* arithmetic progression *is any sequence for which the "defining function" is linear.* (See Problem 33.)

ILLUSTRATION 1. The finite sequence 2, 5, 8, 11, 14 is an arithmetic progression with the common difference of 3. The function defining this sequence is $f : x \to 3x - 1$, with the domain $\{1, 2, 3, 4, 5\}$.

ILLUSTRATION 2. The infinite sequence 7, 2, -3, -8, -13, ... is an arithmetic progression with the common difference $-5 : f(x) = 12 - 5x$.

Let us use the following general notations for any arithmetic progression:

t_1, the first term,

d, the common difference,

n, the number of terms,

t_n, the last or nth term.

Thus, in Illustration 1, $t_1 = 2$, $d = 3$, $n = 5$, and $t_n = 3n - 1$, while for Illustration 2, $t_1 = 7$, $d = -5$, and $t_n = 12 - 5n$. Note that the nth term really represents the function which defines the sequence.

In general, the first n terms of an arithmetic progression may be represented by

$$t_1, \quad t_1 + d, \quad t_1 + 2d, \quad t_1 + 3d, \ldots, \quad t_1 + (n - 1)d.$$

The last value also gives us the expression for the nth term t_n, in terms of t_1, n, and d,

$$\boxed{t_n = t_1 + (n - 1)d.} \qquad (7\text{–}2)$$

EXAMPLE 1. Find the 25th term of the arithmetic progression 2, 5, 8, 11, ...

Solution. In this progression, since $t_1 = 2$ and $d = 3$, we have

$$t_{25} = t_1 + (n - 1)d = 2 + (24)3 = 74.$$

EXAMPLE 2. If the 6th term of an airthmetic progression is 27 and the 12th term is 48, find the first term.

Solution. We have the two relations,

$$t_6 = 27 = t_1 + 5d$$

and

$$t_{12} = 48 = t_1 + 11d.$$

Subtracting the respective members of the first equation from those of the second, we obtain $21 = 6d$, or

$$d = \tfrac{7}{2}.$$

Substituting this value in the first equation, we have

$$27 = t_1 + 5(\tfrac{7}{2}),$$

and we find

$$t_1 = 9\tfrac{1}{2}.$$

EXAMPLE 3. Find the arithmetic progression of 6 terms if the first is $\tfrac{2}{3}$ and the last is $7\tfrac{1}{3}$.

Solution. Using Eq. (7–2), we have

$$t_5 = \tfrac{22}{3} = \tfrac{2}{3} + 5d,$$

and solving,

$$d = \tfrac{4}{3}.$$

Therefore the required progression is

$$\tfrac{2}{3}, \quad 2, \quad \tfrac{10}{3}, \quad \tfrac{14}{3}, \quad 6, \quad \tfrac{22}{3}.$$

We are often interested in the sum of the general finite arithmetic progression. We let

$$S_n = t_1 + (t_1 + d) + (t_1 + 2d) + \cdots + [t_1 + (n - 1)d]. \qquad (7–3)$$

We may also write this expression in reverse order:

$$S_n = [t_1 + (n - 1)d] + [t_1 + (n - 2)d] + \cdots + (t_1 + d) + t_1.$$

If we add the respective members of these equations and group the corresponding terms,

$$2S_n = [2t_1 + (n - 1)d] + [2t_1 + (n - 1)d]$$
$$+ [2t_1 + (n - 1)d] + \cdots + [2t_1 + (n - 1)d].$$

Since there are n terms, $2t_1 + (n - 1)d$, on the right side of this equation, we have

$$2S_n = n[2t_1 + (n - 1)d],$$

or

$$\boxed{S_n = \frac{n[2t_1 + (n - 1)d]}{2}.} \qquad (7–4)^*$$

Recalling that $t_n = t_1 + (n - 1)d$, we may also write Eq. (7–4) as

$$\boxed{S_n = \frac{n(t_1 + t_n)}{2}.} \qquad (7–5)$$

---

* This relation can also be proved by mathematical induction. (See Problem 17, Article 12–1).

EXAMPLE 4. Find the sum of the first 30 terms of the arithmetic progression $-15, -13, -11, \ldots$

Solution. Since $t_1 = -15$, $d = 2$, and $n = 30$, we have

$$S_{30} = \frac{30[2(-15) + (30 - 1)2]}{2}$$

$$= \frac{30(-30 + 58)}{2} = 420.$$

EXAMPLE 5. The sum of the first 15 terms of an arithmetic progression is 270. Find the first term and the common difference if the 15th term is 39.

Solution. By using Eq. (7–5), we obtain

$$270 = \frac{15(t_1 + 39)}{2}.$$

Solving for t_1, we have

$$15t_1 + 585 = 540,$$
$$15t_1 = -45,$$
$$t_1 = -3.$$

Since $t_{15} = t_1 + (n - 1)d$,

$$39 = -3 + 14d,$$

or

$$d = 3.$$

PROBLEMS

Write the next three terms in each of the following arithmetic progressions, and find t_n and S_n.

1. $1, 4, 7, \ldots$ to 9 terms.
2. $27, 25, 23, \ldots$ to 30 terms.
3. $10, 7, 4, \ldots$ to 15 terms.
4. $-\frac{5}{4}, -\frac{1}{4}, \frac{3}{4}, \ldots$ to 8 terms.

In Problems 5 through 11, three of the elements t_1, t_n, d, n, and S_n of the arithmetic progression are given. Find the missing elements in each case.

5. $t_1 = 2$, $d = 4$, $n = 12$
6. $t_1 = 3$, $n = 4$, $t_n = 12$
7. $t_1 = -2$, $n = 14$, $S_n = 20$
8. $d = 3$, $n = 5$, $t_n = 14$
9. $d = \frac{1}{2}$, $n = 14$, $S_n = 30$
10. $t_1 = 4$, $d = 4$, $S_n = 40$
11. $t_1 = 6$, $d = 5$, $t_n = 36$

12. Find the value of k so that $8k + 4$, $6k - 2$, and $2k - 7$ will form an arithmetic progression.

13. What are the first three terms of an arithmetic progression whose 9th term is 16 and 40th term is 47?

14. The 18th and 52nd terms of an arithmetic progression are 3 and 173, respectively. Find the 25th term.

15. Find the sum of all the even integers from 12 to 864, inclusive.

16. Find the sum of all the odd integers from 27 to 495, inclusive.

*17. The terms between any two terms of an arithmetic progression are called the *arithmetic means* between these two terms. Insert four arithmetic means between −1 and 14.

18. Insert five arithmetic means between 14 and 86.

19. Insert three arithmetic means between −18 and 4.

*20. Insert one arithmetic mean between 24 and 68. Such a number is called the *arithmetic mean* of the two numbers.

21. Find the arithmetic mean of (a) 7 and −15, (b) $\frac{3}{5}$ and $\frac{5}{3}$.

*22. A *harmonic progression* is a sequence of numbers whose reciprocals form an arithmetic progression. Insert two harmonic means between 4 and 8.

23. For any sequence of numbers forming an arithmetic progression, show that the products formed by multiplying each term by any constant also form an arithmetic progression.

24. If a^2, b^2, and c^2 form an arithmetic progression, show that $a + b$, $c + a$, and $b + c$ form a harmonic progression.

25. How many numbers between 10 and 200 are exactly divisible by 7? Find their sum.

26. How many numbers between 25 and 400 are exactly divisible by 11? Find their sum.

27. If a clock strikes the appropriate number of times on each hour, how many times will it strike in one week?

28. A man accepts a position at the rate of $3600 a year with the understanding that he will receive an increase of $250 every six months. What will his salary be after working 15 years? How much will his entire earnings be?

29. The force of gravity causes a body to fall 16.1 feet during the first second, 48.3 the next second, 80.5 the third, and so on. How far will the body fall in 10 seconds?

30. A man bought a house at the beginning of 1945 for $10,000. If it increased $500 in value each year, how much was it worth at the end of 1959?

31. A piece of equipment cost a certain factory $29,000. If it depreciates in value 15% the first year, 13.5% the second, 12% the third, and so on, what will its value be at the end of 10 years, all percentages applying to the original cost?

32. A certain antique originally worth $1600 is evaluated at $5660 after 80 years. Find the value at the end of each ten-year period if the increase in value during each such period was $125 more than during the preceding ten years.

33. By using Eq. (7–2), prove that the two definitions of an arithmetic progression are equivalent.

7–3 The quadratic function. The second type of algebraic function usually considered, is one in which the defining equation is of the second degree.

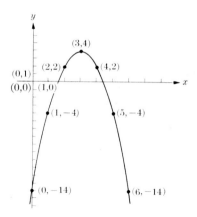

FIGURE 7–1

DEFINITION 7–3. *The function f, defined by the second degree equation*

$$f(x) = ax^2 + bx + c, \qquad (7\text{–}6)$$

where a, b, and c are constants, and a $\neq$ 0, is called a quadratic function.

The graph of such a function was briefly considered in Example 2, Article 5–2. Another example seems appropriate.

EXAMPLE 1.   Draw the graph of the quadratic function

$$q: x \to -2x^2 + 12x - 14.$$

Solution. The graph (Fig. 7–1) is drawn by tabulating a sufficient number of points whose coordinates satisfy the equation $y = -2x^2 + 12x - 14$.

x	0	1	2	3	4	5	6
y	-14	-4	2	4	2	-4	-14

Comparing this curve with that in Fig. 5–5, we see that both have the same general shape. The graph of any quadratic function is of this type and is called a *parabola*. Although we shall not prove it, when the coefficient of x^2 is positive, the curve opens upward, while the curve opens downward if the coefficient of x^2 is negative. Compare the two examples.

The graph of the general quadratic function may be sketched by the more direct process of expressing the quadratic function in terms of the square of a linear function. Consider

$$y = ax^2 + bx + c. \qquad (7\text{–}7)$$

Factoring out a, and grouping the x^2 and x terms together, we have

$$y = a\left[\left(x^2 + \frac{b}{a}\,x\right) + \frac{c}{a}\right].$$

Recalling Eq. (3–13), we must add $(b/2a)^2$ to $x^2 + (b/a)x$ in order to form a perfect square. Thus, adding and subtracting $b^2/4a^2$ within the bracket,

$$y = a\left[\left(x^2 + \frac{b}{a}\,x + \frac{b^2}{4a^2}\right) + \frac{c}{a} - \frac{b^2}{4a^2}\right],$$

and simplifying, we have

$$y = a\left[\left(x + \frac{b}{2a}\right)^2 + \frac{4ac - b^2}{4a^2}\right]. \qquad (7\text{–}8)$$

Since the squared quantity $(x + b/2a)^2 \geq 0$, the expression within the bracket has its least value when $x = -b/2a$. If $a > 0$, the function also has its least value at $x = -b/2a$. This least value of the function, $(4ac - b^2)/4a$, is called its *minimum*. If, however, $a < 0$, when $x = -b/2a$, the function has its greatest value, called its *maximum*, and is also equal to $(4ac - b^2)/4a$. In either case, the point

$$\left[\frac{-b}{2a}, \frac{4ac - b^2}{4a}\right]$$

is called the *vertex* of the parabola. With this point found, and an additional point or two, the graph can be sketched. It is usually simpler to complete the square in each case than to use the formulas in this discussion.

EXAMPLE 2. Find the vertex of the parabola represented by the equation $y = x^2 - x - 6$. Compare with Example 2, Article 5–2.

Solution. Grouping the first two terms on the right and completing the square, we obtain

$$y = (x^2 - x) - 6$$
$$= (x^2 - x + \tfrac{1}{4}) - 6 - \tfrac{1}{4}$$
$$= (x - \tfrac{1}{2})^2 - \tfrac{25}{4}.$$

The vertex is $(\tfrac{1}{2}, -\tfrac{25}{4})$. Since $a = 1$, which is positive, the minimum value of the function is $-\tfrac{25}{4}$, and this occurs when $x = \tfrac{1}{2}$. The graph of this function appears in Fig. 5–5.

PROBLEMS

For each of the following functions f, where $f(x)$ is given by the following expressions, find the maximum or minimum and draw the graph.

1. $x^2 + 6x + 5$
2. $x^2 + x - 6$
3. $2x^2 + 5x - 12$
4. $-2x^2 + 11x - 15$
5. $6x^2 - 17x + 5$
6. $-2x^2 + 5x + 8$
7. $x^2 + 6x + 11$
8. $-3x^2 + 5x - 4$

9. Find two numbers whose sum is 16 and whose product is a maximum. [*Hint:* Letting x be one number, and $16 - x$ the other, the product y can be expressed in terms of x, namely, $y = x(16 - x) = 16x - x^2$.

10. Divide 40 into two parts such that the sum of the squares of these parts is a minimum.

11. A man with 160 ft of fencing wishes to fence off an area in the shape of a rectangle. What should be the dimensions of the area if the enclosed space is to be as large as possible?

12. A man with 160 ft of fencing wishes to fence off an area in the shape of a rectangle. If one side of the area will not require fencing, what should be the dimensions to ensure the largest area possible?

7–4 Solution of the quadratic equation. We are now in a position to find the zeros of any quadratic function. Recalling the definition of the zeros of a function (Article 5–2), we are interested in finding the abscissas of the points where the graph $y = ax^2 + bx + c$ crosses or meets the x-axis. This may be found graphically by sketching the curve. For example, from Fig. 5–5, the zeros of $x^2 - x - 6$ are -2, and 3. Likewise, from Fig. 7–1, the zeros of $-2x^2 + 12x - 14$ are approximately 1.3 and 4.7. Such values can, of course, be checked by substituting in the original function, set equal to zero.

There are more accurate methods for finding the zeros of the function $f: x \rightarrow ax^2 + bx + c$. In finding its zeros or, equivalently, in solving the equation

$$ax^2 + bx + c = 0 \qquad (a \neq 0), \qquad (7\text{–}9)$$

we may be able to factor the left member. This method, known as the *factoring method*, depends upon the fact that either factor is zero if the product is zero (Theorem 2–5).

EXAMPLE 1.   Solve the quadratic equation $x^2 - 7x + 10 = 0$ by factoring.

Solution. Since $x^2 - 7x + 10 \equiv (x - 5)(x - 2)$, [see Eq. (3–14)], the equation may be written

$$(x - 5)(x - 2) = 0.$$

We wish to find a value such that when it is substituted for x in the member on the left, the product is zero. Such may be found by solving either of

$$x - 5 = 0 \quad \text{and} \quad x - 2 = 0.$$

For these, we find $x = 5$ or $x = 2$, either of which is a root of the original equation. All answers should be checked.

EXAMPLE 2.   Solve the equation $2 \sin^2 \theta + \sin \theta - 1 = 0$, for all possible values of θ between 0 and 2π.

Solution. As Example 2 in Article 7–1, this equation is not algebraic, but may be considered as a quadratic equation in $\sin \theta$. Factoring the left-hand member, we get

$$2 \sin^2 \theta + \sin \theta - 1 \equiv (2 \sin \theta - 1)(\sin \theta + 1).$$

Thus, we have the two equations

$$2 \sin \theta - 1 = 0 \quad \text{and} \quad \sin \theta + 1 = 0$$

to solve for $\sin \theta$, and we obtain

$$\sin \theta = \tfrac{1}{2} \quad \text{or} \quad -1.$$

Since $\sin \theta$ is positive in the first or second quadrant, there are two values of θ between 0 and 2π for which $\sin \theta = \tfrac{1}{2}$. Therefore,

$$\theta = \pi/6, \quad 5\pi/6, \quad \text{or} \quad 3\pi/2.$$

PROBLEMS

1–8. From the graphs of the functions listed in Problems 1 through 8 Article 7–3, give the roots of the corresponding equations. Check these by substituting the results into the original equations.

Solve Problems 9 through 26 by factoring and check by substitution. In the equations involving circular functions, give all roots between 0 and 2π.

9. $9x^2 - 16 = 0$

10. $2x^2 - 5x - 12 = 0$

11. $4 \sin^2 \theta = 1$

12. $4 \cos^2 \theta = 3$

13. $6x^2 - 5x = 50$

14. $2x^2 - 2 = x - 4x$

15. $1 - \cos^2 \theta = \cos^2 \theta$

16. $\tan \theta (2 \sin \theta - \sqrt{3}) = 0$

17. $3x^2 - x = 10$

18. $4x^2 - 12x + 9 = 0$

19. $2 \cot \theta \cos \theta - \cot \theta = 0$

20. $2 \tan^2 \theta + \tan \theta = 0$

21. $x^2 + 2ax = b^2 - a^2$

22. $8x^2 + 14ax + 3a^2 = 0$

23. $2 \sin^2 \theta - \sin \theta = 1$

24. $2 \cos^2 \theta + 3 \cos \theta + 1 = 0$

25. $\dfrac{x - 2}{x + 3} - 3 = \dfrac{4(x + 3)}{x - 2}$

26. $(x - 2)(x + 3) = 6$

The quadratic expression in an equation may be difficult to factor. Moreover, in many cases factors may not exist. As a result, the most useful method of solving any quadratic equation is *by the quadratic formula*. We obtain this formula by completing the square, as was done in finding the vertex of the parabola.

THEOREM 7–1. *The two roots of any quadratic equation,*

$$ax^2 + bx + c = 0 \qquad (a \neq 0), \tag{7–9}$$

are

$$x = \frac{-b \pm \sqrt{b^2 - 4ac}}{2a}. \tag{7–10}$$

Proof. If we divide by the coefficient of x^2 in Eq. (7–9) and transpose the constant term to the right side of the equation, we have

$$x^2 + \frac{b}{a}x = -\frac{c}{a}.$$

We may complete the square of the left member by adding $b^2/4a^2$ to both sides of the equation,

$$x^2 + \frac{b}{a}x + \frac{b^2}{4a^2} = \frac{b^2}{4a^2} - \frac{c}{a},$$

or

$$\left(x + \frac{b}{2a}\right)^2 = \frac{b^2 - 4ac}{4a^2}.$$

If we extract the square root, this becomes

$$x + \frac{b}{2a} = \frac{\pm\sqrt{b^2 - 4ac}}{2a},$$

or

$$x = \frac{-b \pm \sqrt{b^2 - 4ac}}{2a}.$$

The use of the plus and then the minus sign gives the two roots of the quadratic equation $ax^2 + bx + c = 0$, which completes the proof. The reader should verify that each of these roots is actually a solution by substituting them in Eq. (7–9).

Although any quadratic equation can be solved by the *method of completing the square* used to obtain this formula, direct substitution into Eq. (7–10) is more frequently employed because of its efficiency. Consider the following examples.

EXAMPLE 3. Solve the quadratic equation $4x^2 + 5x = 21$.

Solution. Transposing all the members to the left side to put the equation in the form $ax^2 + bx + c = 0$, and comparing the two, we have $a = 4$, $b = 5$, and $c = -21$. Substituting these values into Eq. (7–10), we have

$$x = \frac{-5 \pm \sqrt{(5)^2 - 4(4)(-21)}}{2(4)}.$$

Simplification yields

$$x = \frac{-5 \pm \sqrt{25 + 336}}{8} = \frac{-5 \pm \sqrt{361}}{8} = \frac{-5 \pm 19}{8}.$$

Therefore, choosing the plus and then the minus sign, we obtain

$$x = \tfrac{7}{4} \qquad \text{or} \qquad -3.$$

Both answers should be checked by substituting them in the original equation. The fact that the number under the radical sign is a perfect square guarantees that the roots are rational. Thus the equation could have been solved by the method of factoring. Specifically,

$$4x^2 + 5x - 21 \equiv (4x - 7)(x + 3).$$

EXAMPLE 4. Solve $\cos^2 \theta + 5 \sin \theta + 2 = 0$ for all values of θ between 0 and 2π.

Solution. Since $\cos^2 \theta$ may be expressed as $1 - \sin^2 \theta$, it is possible to rewrite this equation entirely in terms of $\sin \theta$. Thus,

$$1 - \sin^2 \theta + 5 \sin \theta + 2 = 0,$$
$$\sin^2 \theta - 5 \sin \theta - 3 = 0.$$

Regarding the variable as $\sin \theta$, and using Eq. (7–10), we find $a = 1$, $b = -5$, and $c = -3$. Therefore,

$$\sin \theta = \frac{5 \pm \sqrt{25 + 12}}{2} = \frac{5 \pm 6.0828}{2},$$

or

$$\sin \theta = 5.5414 \qquad \text{or} \qquad -0.5414.$$

Since $|\sin \theta| \leq 1$, we consider only the value -0.5414, which results in a value for θ between π and $3\pi/2$ and another between $3\pi/2$ and 2π. Using Table I, we find $\sin \alpha = 0.5414$ gives $\alpha = 0.5721$. Therefore,

$$\theta = 3.1416 + .5721 = 3.7137$$

or $$6.2832 - .5721 = 5.7111.$$

The general procedure in solving any quadratic equation is:
1. Try to solve the equation by the method of factoring.
2. If this method fails, either because the factors are not immediately evident or because they actually do not exist as rational factors, use the quadratic formula.

PROBLEMS

Solve the equations of Problems 1 through 19 by using the quadratic formula. If the equations involve circular functions, find all values between 0 and 2π. Check all answers.

1. $2x^2 + 5x - 12 = 0$

2. $4x^2 - 2x = 7$

3. $x^2 + x - 1 = 0$

4. $2x^2 + x - 12 = 0$

5. $\tan^2 \theta - 3 \sec \theta + 3 = 0$
   [*Hint:* $\tan^2 \theta \equiv \sec^2 \theta - 1$]

6. $2 \cos^2 \theta + 3 \sin \theta = 0$

7. $x^2 - (a + b)x + ab = 0$

8. $6x^2 + 17x + 12 = 0$

9. $(a - b)x^2 + (b - c)x + (c - a) = 0$

10. $4 \sin^2 \theta - 3 \cos \theta - 2 = 0$

11. $3 \sec^2 \theta + \tan \theta - 5 = 0$

12. $x^2 - 2x + 1 = 4a^2$

13. $\dfrac{x - 1}{x^2 - 9} - \dfrac{3x + 5}{x + 3} = \dfrac{x + 3}{x - 3}$

14. $\cot 2\theta = 2 + \tan 2\theta$

15. $4 \sin^2 2\theta + 2 \cos 2\theta = 3$

16. $6ax^2 - 2bx + 3b = 9ax$

17. $s = v_0 x - gx^2/2$

18. $\tan 2\theta + 5 = 3 \sec^2 2\theta$

19. $\dfrac{1}{x^2 + 3x + 2} - \dfrac{1}{1 - x} = \dfrac{2}{x^2 - 1}$

20. The product of two consecutive positive integers is 72. Find the integers.

21. The sum of a number and its reciprocal is 34/15. Find the number.

22. A man traveling 40 miles finds that by traveling one more mile per hour, he would make the journey in 2 hr less time. How many miles per hour did he actually travel?

23. If $(6 - x)$, $(13 - x)$, and $(14 - x)$ are the lengths of the sides of a right triangle, find the value of x.

24. By how much must a radius of 24 in be reduced in order to decrease the area of a circle by 49π in^2?

25. A rectangular flower bed 30 yards long by 24 yards wide has a walk of uniform width around it. If the area of the path is one-fourth that of the flower bed, find the width of the path.

26. Working together, two men can do a job in 20 days. Working alone, however, it would take one man 9 days longer than it would take the other to complete the job. How long would it take each separately?

7–5 Inequalities. Since most of the inequalities discussed in this book involve either first or second degree algebraic expressions, it seems appropriate to consider them in this chapter. The student should review the order axioms and basic theorems in Article 4–1.

A statement that one mathematical expression is greater than or less than another is called an *inequality*. As is true for equations (Article 1–6), there are two general types of inequalities in mathematics, the conditional inequality, corresponding to the conditional equation, and the absolute inequality, corresponding to the identity.

DEFINITION 7–4. *An inequality is called an* absolute inequality *if it is true for all permissible values of the variables involved.*

Although frequently an inequality may be true for an entire set of values, if it is not true for every permissible value, the inequality is not absolute.

DEFINITION 7–5. *An inequality is called a* conditional inequality *if it is not true for all permissible values of the variables involved.*

ILLUSTRATION. The inequality $a^2 + b^2 + 1 > 0$ is an absolute inequality. The expression $-4 < 3$ is also of this type. But $2x - 6 > 0$ is a conditional inequality, since it is true only for values of x greater than 3. Also, $\sin \theta < 0$ is conditional, for this is true only if $P(\theta)$ lies in the third or fourth quadrants.

As is true in dealing with equations, there are certain important properties to be remembered in working with inequalities. The proofs of the theorems below follow directly from the axioms and theorems in Article 4–1.

THEOREM 7–2. *The sense of an inequality is not changed if both members are increased or decreased by the same number.*

Proof. This is a direct result of Axiom O3, where c may be either positive or negative. The usefulness of this property lies in the fact that a term may be transposed from one member of an inequality to the other member by changing the sign of the term without changing the sense of the inequality.

THEOREM 7–3. *The sense of an inequality is not changed if both members are multiplied or divided by the same* positive *number.*

This is a restatement of Axiom O4.

THEOREM 7–4. *The sense of an inequality is reversed if both members are multiplied or divided by the same* negative *number.*

This is a restatement of Theorem 4–3.

Since we wish to confine our discussion to inequalities in one variable, we are interested in those inequalities which may be written $f(x) > 0$

or $f(x) < 0$. First let us consider conditional inequalities. To solve such an inequality, *we must find the set of values of x for which the inequality is true.* When $f(x)$ is linear or quadratic, this set may be found by either an algebraic or graphical method.

EXAMPLE 1. Solve

$$\frac{x}{3} - 2 < \frac{5x + 9}{2}$$

both algebraically and graphically.

Algebraic solution. Multiplying both members by 6, we have

$$2x - 12 < 15x + 27.$$

Transposing and collecting terms, we obtain

$$-13x < 39.$$

If we divide by -13,

$$x > -3,$$

so that the solution is $\{x | x > -3\}$.

Graphical solution. If we transpose all terms to the left side of the inequality, we have

$$\frac{x}{3} - 2 - \frac{5x + 9}{2} < 0.$$

Denoting this left member by $f(x)$, we get

$$f(x) \equiv \frac{2x - 12 - 15x - 27}{6} \equiv \frac{-13x - 39}{6}.$$

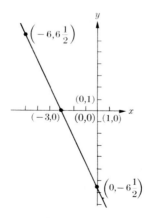

FIGURE 7–2

From the graph of $y = f(x)$ in Fig. 7–2, which can easily be drawn from the table below, it is clear that the inequality is satisfied for $x > -3$, since for these values of x, $y = f(x)$ is below the x-axis, that is, $f(x) < 0$. The graphical method is more frequently used for quadratic inequalities.

x	0	-3	-6
y	$-6\frac{1}{2}$	0	$6\frac{1}{2}$

EXAMPLE 2. For what values of x does the inequality $x^2 - x - 6 > 0$ hold?

Solution. If we factor the expression, we have

$$x^2 - x - 6 \equiv (x - 3)(x + 2).$$

Since the product of two terms will be positive only if both are positive or both negative (Problem 10, Article 4–1), $x - 3$ and $x + 2$ must both be greater than zero or both less than zero. We see that

$$\begin{Bmatrix} x - 3 > 0 \\ \text{and} \\ x + 2 > 0 \end{Bmatrix} \quad \text{or} \quad \begin{Bmatrix} x > 3 \\ \text{and} \\ x > -2 \end{Bmatrix} \text{ will both be true if } x > 3,$$

and

$$\begin{Bmatrix} x - 3 < 0 \\ \text{and} \\ x + 2 < 0 \end{Bmatrix} \quad \text{or} \quad \begin{Bmatrix} x < 3 \\ \text{and} \\ x < -2 \end{Bmatrix} \text{ will both be true if } x < -2.$$

Thus the solution for the inequality is

$$\{x \,|\, x > 3 \text{ or } x < -2\}.$$

This may be checked graphically by Fig. 5–5. It is often helpful to test some value in the set for which the inequality holds. Although this will not guarantee the proper complete solution, it is usually a helpful check of the work.

EXAMPLE 3. For what values of x does the inequality $-2x^2 + 12x - 14 > 0$ hold?

Solution. Since the left member is not factorable rationally, we use the graphical method. In Fig. 7–1 we have the graph of the function

$$y = f(x) = -2x^2 + 12x - 14,$$

whose zeros we may approximate as 1.6 and 4.4. Thus the inequality holds for the set

$$\{x \mid 1.6 < x < 4.4\}.$$

Should we wish to determine the zeros more accurately, we could use the quadratic formula for the equation $-2x^2 + 12x - 14 = 0$, or the equivalent equation $x^2 - 6x + 7 = 0$.

$$x = \frac{6 \pm \sqrt{36 - 28}}{2} = \frac{6 \pm 2\sqrt{2}}{2} = 3 \pm \sqrt{2}.$$

Hence,

$$x = 4.414 \quad \text{or} \quad 1.586,$$

and as a result the solution would be written

$$\{x \mid 1.586 < x < 4.414\}.$$

EXAMPLE 4. Determine the values of θ, such that $0 \leq \theta < 2\pi$, which satisfy the inequality $2 \cos^2 \theta + \sin \theta < 2$.

Solution. Since $\cos^2 \theta \equiv 1 - \sin^2 \theta$, we may express the members of the inequality as functions of $\sin \theta$,

$$2(1 - \sin^2 \theta) + \sin \theta < 2,$$

and simplifying, we have

$$2 - 2 \sin^2 \theta + \sin \theta - 2 < 0,$$

or

$$\sin \theta (1 - 2 \sin \theta) < 0.$$

Since the product of two quantities will be negative if one is negative while the other is positive (Problem 11, Article 4–1), we may have

either
$$\begin{Bmatrix} \sin \theta < 0 \\ \text{and} \\ 1 - 2 \sin \theta > 0 \end{Bmatrix}, \quad \text{which gives} \quad \begin{Bmatrix} \sin \theta < 0 \\ \text{and} \\ \sin \theta < \frac{1}{2} \end{Bmatrix},$$

or
$$\begin{Bmatrix} \sin \theta > 0 \\ \text{and} \\ 1 - 2 \sin \theta < 0 \end{Bmatrix}, \quad \text{which gives} \quad \begin{Bmatrix} \sin \theta > 0 \\ \text{and} \\ \sin \theta > \frac{1}{2} \end{Bmatrix}.$$

The first set is satisfied if $\sin \theta < 0$, while the second is satisfied if $\sin \theta > \frac{1}{2}$. The solution set is

$$\left\{ \theta \,\middle|\, \frac{\pi}{6} < \theta < \frac{5\pi}{6} \text{ or } \pi < \theta < 2\pi \right\}.$$

PROBLEMS

Find the values of x for which the following inequalities are satisfied. Use either the algebraic or graphical method.

1. $3x - 27 > 0$ 2. $2x - 12 < 0$
3. $2x + 5 > 4x - 9$ 4. $5x - 3 < 8x - 12$
5. $x^2 + 2x > 99$ 6. $2x^2 + 3x < 14$
7. $6x^2 + x < 1$ 8. $6x^2 - x > 35$
9. $x^2 + 2x > 12$ 10. $x^2 + 2x + 4 > 0$

11. $x^4 + x^2 < 0$ 12. $\dfrac{x - 2}{x - 5} > 0$

13. $\dfrac{1}{x} < \dfrac{1}{5}$ 14. $\dfrac{1}{x - 2} < \dfrac{1}{3}$

15. $|x - 4| < 1$ 16. $|x - 3| > 2$
   [*Hint:* Problem 9, Article 4–2.]   [*Hint:* Problem 13, Article 4–2.]

17. $|2x - 3| \leq 4$ 18. $\left|\dfrac{x}{3} - 7\right| \leq 5$

19. $\left|\dfrac{x}{4} + 6\right| \geq \dfrac{1}{2}$ 20. $|5x + 1| \geq 4$

Find the values of θ for which each of the following inequalities holds. Limit the answers to values of θ, such that $0 \leq \theta < 2\pi$.

21. $2 \sin^2 \theta < 1$ 22. $4 \cos^2 \theta > 1$
23. $\sin^2 \theta > \sin \theta$ 24. $\cos^2 \theta < \cos \theta$

25. $\sin \theta + \sin \dfrac{\theta}{2} < 0$ [*Hint:* Recall Problem 14, Article 6–11.]

26. $\sin \theta + \cos \dfrac{\theta}{2} > 0$ 27. $2 \cos^2 \theta + \sin \theta > 1$

28. $2 \sin^2 \theta + \cos \theta > 2$ 29. $\tan^2 \theta + \sec \theta + 1 \geq 0$
30. $\sqrt{3} \sin^2 \theta + 2\sqrt{3} > 5 \sin \theta$ 31. $\sin \theta > \cos \theta$

Absolute inequalities, of course, will also satisfy the properties mentioned in this section as well as those in Article 4–1. The usual problem in dealing with absolute inequalities is to establish the validity of the given inequality for all permissible values. Since we must start with a valid inequality in any proof, it is often convenient to assume tentatively the proposition we are proving and reduce it to a simpler inequality which is known to be valid. Then the actual proof will consist of retracing the steps. The method is illustrated below.

EXAMPLE 5. Prove that for all real values of x, $x^2 + 1 \geq 2x$.

Solution. We wish to find an inequality known to be true. By subtracting $2x$ from both members of

$$x^2 + 1 \geq 2x, \tag{7–11}$$

we have

$$x^2 - 2x + 1 \geq 0, \tag{7–12}$$

which is known to be true, since $x^2 - 2x + 1 \equiv (x - 1)^2$ (Problem 12, Article 4–1). Our proof therefore starts with inequality (7–12). Since

$$x^2 - 2x + 1 \geq 0,$$

for all real values of x, by adding $2x$ to both members, we obtain the desired result,

$$x^2 + 1 \geq 2x.$$

EXAMPLE 6. Prove that the sum of any *positive* number and its reciprocal is greater than or equal to 2.

Solution. If we let x be any positive number, we wish to prove

$$x + \frac{1}{x} \geq 2. \tag{7–13}$$

Although this is not an absolute inequality, we shall use one to establish it. If we divide both members of Eq. (7–11) by x, which is positive, we get the required inequality.

We may also be interested in proving that certain absolute inequalities hold when they involve the circular functions.

EXAMPLE 7. Prove the absolute inequality $3 \sin \theta + 4 \cos \theta \leq 5$.

Solution. Recalling Example 5, Article 6–9, we have

$$3 \sin \theta + 4 \cos \theta = 5 \sin (\theta + \theta_1) \leq 5,$$

since $\sin \alpha \leq 1$ for all α.

PROBLEMS

Prove each of the following inequalities. The letters in Problems 1 through 10 represent unequal positive numbers, and θ, α, and β represent any real number. Tell which are conditional and which are absolute inequalities.

1. $a^2 + b^2 > 2ab$

2. $\dfrac{a}{b} + \dfrac{b}{a} > 2$

3. $\dfrac{x + y}{2} > \sqrt{xy}$

4. $\dfrac{a + b}{2} > \dfrac{2ab}{a + b}$

5. $\dfrac{x^2}{y} + \dfrac{y^2}{x} > x + y$

6. $x^3 + y^3 > x^2 y + xy^2$

7. $x^2 + y^2 + z^2 < (x + y + z)^2$

8. $a^2 + 2a + 2 > 0$

9. $|a + b| \leq |a| + |b|$

10. $|a - b| \geq |a| - |b|$

11. $|\sin \theta| + |\csc \theta| \geq 2$

12. $|\cos \theta| + |\sec \theta| \geq 2$

13. $|\cos^4 \theta - \sin^4 \theta| \leq 1$

14. $|\sin (\alpha + \beta) \cos (\alpha - \beta)| \leq 1$

15. $\sin \theta + \cos \theta \leq \sqrt{2}$

16. $\sin^2 \theta + \cot^2 \theta \geq 2 \cos \theta$

17. $12 \sin \theta - 5 \cos \theta \leq 13$

18. $4 \sin \theta + 3 \cos \theta \leq 6$

7–6 Relations between zeros and coefficients of the quadratic function.
In addition to Eq. (7–10), which gives the zeros of the quadratic function
$f : x \rightarrow ax^2 + bx + c$ in terms of the coefficients, there are other relations
between the zeros and the coefficients. By letting r_1 and r_2 be the zeros
of $ax^2 + bx + c$, where

$$r_1 = \frac{-b + \sqrt{b^2 - 4ac}}{2a}, \qquad r_2 = \frac{-b - \sqrt{b^2 - 4ac}}{2a}, \qquad (7\text{–}14)$$

we have the sum of the two zeros,

$$r_1 + r_2 = -\frac{b}{a}. \qquad (7\text{–}15)$$

Likewise, we have the product

$$r_1 \cdot r_2 = \frac{(-b)^2 - (\sqrt{b^2 - 4ac})^2}{4a^2}$$

$$= \frac{b^2 - (b^2 - 4ac)}{4a^2},$$

or

$$r_1 \cdot r_2 = \frac{c}{a}. \qquad (7\text{–}16)$$

Since the zeros of the function $f : x \rightarrow ax^2 + bx + c$ and the roots of the
equation formed by setting the functional value $f(x)$ equal to zero are the
same, Eqs. (7–15) and (7–16) are useful in forming such an equation.
The following theorem will clarify this remark.

THEOREM 7–5. *If any quadratic equation $ax^2 + bx + c = 0$ is written*

$$x^2 + \frac{b}{a} x + \frac{c}{a} = 0, \qquad (7\text{–}17)$$

*so that the coefficient of x^2 is unity, (1) the sum of its roots is equal to the
negative of the coefficient of x, and (2) the product of its roots is equal to
the constant term.*

Proof. We establish this result by comparing the coefficient of x with Eq. (7–15), and the constant term with Eq. (7–16).

EXAMPLE 1. Without obtaining the zeros, find the sum and product of the zeros of $f: x \to 3x^2 - 4x + 8$.

Solution. Since $a = 3$, $b = -4$, and $c = 8$, the sum is $-(-4/3) = \frac{4}{3}$, and the product is $\frac{8}{3}$.

EXAMPLE 2. Write a quadratic equation whose roots are $3 + \sqrt{2}$ and $3 - \sqrt{2}$.

Solution. Since $(3 + \sqrt{2}) + (3 - \sqrt{2}) = 6$, and $(3 + \sqrt{2})(3 - \sqrt{2}) = 9 - 2 = 7$, an equation of this type is

$$x^2 - 6x + 7 = 0.$$

EXAMPLE 3. Without solving, form a quadratic equation whose roots are the squares of the roots of $2x^2 + x - 6 = 0$.

Solution. By letting r_1 and r_2 be the roots of the given equation, we have

$$r_1 + r_2 = -\tfrac{1}{2}, \qquad r_1 r_2 = -3.$$

Since $(r_1 + r_2)^2 \equiv r_1^2 + 2r_1 r_2 + r_2^2$, the sum of the roots for the new equation will be

$$r_1^2 + r_2^2 \equiv (r_1 + r_2)^2 - 2r_1 r_2 = \tfrac{1}{4} + 6 = \tfrac{25}{4},$$

and the product will be

$$(r_1 r_2)^2 = 9.$$

Therefore the required equation is

$$x^2 - \tfrac{25}{4}x + 9 = 0$$

or, clearing fractions,

$$4x^2 - 25x + 36 = 0.$$

The expression $b^2 - 4ac$, under the radical in Eq. (7–14), is another quantity which, in terms of the coefficients, is important in considering the nature of the zeros of the function. If this expression, called the *discriminant*, is negative, no real square root will exist. The zeros will be *imaginary*. Such numbers will be considered in Chapter 16. If $b^2 - 4ac$ is equal to zero, $r_1 = r_2$ and the zeros are equal; while if $b^2 - 4ac$ is positive, the zeros are real and unequal. Since the zeros of the function $f: x \to ax^2 + bx + c$ and the roots of the equation $ax^2 + bx + c = 0$ are the same, we have immediately the following theorem.

THEOREM 7–6. *Consider the quadratic equation $ax^2 + bx + c = 0$.*

1. *If $b^2 - 4ac < 0$, the roots are imaginary.*
2. *If $b^2 - 4ac = 0$, the roots are equal.*
3. *If $b^2 - 4ac > 0$, the roots are real and unequal.*

If we wished to emphasize the graph of $y = f(x) = ax^2 + bx + c$, rather than the roots of $ax^2 + bx + c = 0$, we could give the following theorem:

THEOREM 7–7. *Consider the quadratic function $f(x) = ax^2 + bx + c$.*

1. *If $b^2 - 4ac < 0$, the graph of the parabola does not touch or cross the x-axis.*
2. *If $b^2 - 4ac = 0$, the graph of the parabola has its vertex on the x-axis.*
3. *If $b^2 - 4ac > 0$, the graph of the parabola intersects the x-axis in two real points.*

EXAMPLE 4. Without solving equations, determine the nature of the zeros of $f: x \to 2x^2 - 9x - 35$.

Solution. Since $a = 2$, $b = -9$, and $c = -35$, $b^2 - 4ac = (-9)^2 - 4(2)(-35) = 81 + 280 = 361$. Since $361 > 0$, the zeros are real and unequal. Moreover, since $b^2 - 4ac = 361$, a perfect square, the zeros will be rational. Is this always true when $b^2 - 4ac$ is a perfect square?

EXAMPLE 5. On the same coordinate axis, sketch graphs of

(a) $y = x^2 - 6x + 5$,
(b) $y = x^2 - 6x + 9$,
(c) $y = x^2 - 6x + 13$.

Check the results by finding $b^2 - 4ac$ in each case.

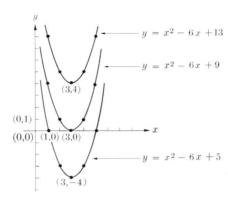

FIGURE 7–3

Solution. The graphs of each are shown in Fig. 7–3. These are consistent with the values for $b^2 - 4ac$, since we have

(a) $b^2 - 4ac = (-6)^2 - 4(1)(5) = 16,$
(b) $b^2 - 4ac = (-6)^2 - 4(1)(9) = 0,$
(c) $b^2 - 4ac = (-6)^2 - 4(1)(13) = -16.$

PROBLEMS

1. Without solving, find the sum and product of the zeros of the functions given in Problems 1 through 8, Article 7–3.

Find quadratic equations with integral coefficients having the following given numbers as roots.

2. $2, -3$
3. $-5, 4$
4. $\frac{2}{3}, -2$
5. $-\frac{3}{4}, \frac{2}{3}$
6. $+\sqrt{3}, -\sqrt{3}$
7. $2 + \sqrt{3}, 2 - \sqrt{3}$
8. $\dfrac{-1 + \sqrt{5}}{2}, \dfrac{-1 - \sqrt{5}}{2}$
9. $\dfrac{-3 + \sqrt{7}}{4}, \dfrac{-3 - \sqrt{7}}{4}$

10. Find a quadratic equation whose roots are the squares of the roots of $4x^2 + 8x - 5 = 0$.

11. Find a quadratic equation whose roots are the reciprocals of the roots of $4x^2 + 8x - 5 = 0$.

$$\left[Hint: \quad \frac{1}{r_1} + \frac{1}{r_2} = \frac{r_1 + r_2}{r_1 r_2}. \right]$$

12. Find a quadratic equation whose roots are the squares of the roots of $3x^2 - 5x - 2 = 0$.

13. Find a quadratic equation whose roots are the reciprocals of the roots of $3x^2 - 5x - 2 = 0$.

14. Find a quadratic equation whose roots are twice the roots of $4x^2 + 8x - 5 = 0$.

15. Find a quadratic equation whose roots are one-third the roots of $4x^2 + 8x - 5 = 0$.

16. Find a quadratic equation whose roots are three times the roots of $3x^2 - 5x - 2 = 0$.

17. Find a quadratic equation whose roots are half the roots of $3x^2 - 5x - 2 = 0$.

Find the value of k so that the equation:

18. $4x^2 + kx + 6 = 0$ has one root $= -2$.
19. $2x^2 + kx - 15 = 0$ has one root $= 3$.
20. $3x^2 + kx - 2 = 0$ has roots whose sum is equal to 6.
21. $5x^2 - 8x + k = 0$ has roots whose product is equal to $\frac{1}{5}$.
22. $4x^2 + 20x + k = 0$ has equal roots.
23. $3x^2 - 7x + k = 0$ has equal roots.
24. $2x^2 + (4 - k)x - 17 = 0$ has roots numerically equal but opposite in sign.

25. $3x^2 - 5x + 8 = kx$ has roots numerically equal but opposite in sign.
26. $3x^2 - 7x + 6 = k$ has one root equal to zero.
27. $4x^2 + 20x + k = 0$ has one root equal to zero.

Find the range of values of k so that the equation:

28. $3x^2 - 4kx + k = 0$ will have real roots.
29. $2x^2 + 3kx - 9 = 0$ will have real roots.
30. $x^2 + (k - 2)x + 4 = 0$ will have real roots.
31. $2x^2 - kx + 8 = 0$ will have imaginary roots.
32. $kx^2 + 4\sqrt{3}x + k = 1$ will have imaginary roots.

Find the range of values of k or value of k so that the graph of the function where y equals:

33. $3x^2 - 9x + k$ will touch (have its vertex on) the x-axis.
34. $x^2 + 2kx + \frac{3}{4} - k$ will not intersect the x-axis.
35. $4x^2 + 4\sqrt{2}kx + k + 3$ will intersect the x-axis in two real points.
36. Show that there are no real values of x and y such that

$$\frac{1}{x} + \frac{1}{y} = \frac{1}{x + y}.$$

7–7 Equations in quadratic form. In the last few articles, we have discussed the quadratic function and quadratic equations. In the problems we solved, those involving the circular functions were not specifically quadratic equations, but what might be termed equations in quadratic form. Generally, any equation which can be written in the form

$$av^2 + bv + c = 0 \qquad (a \neq 0), \tag{7–18}$$

where v is expressed in terms of another variable, is called an *equation in quadratic form*. The methods developed in the last articles apply equally to any equation of this type.

EXAMPLE 1. Solve $9x^4 - 37x^2 + 4 = 0$.

Solution. Letting $v = x^2$, and substituting, we have

$$9v^2 - 37v + 4 = 0,$$

or

$$(9v - 1)(v - 4) = 0.$$

Thus,

$$v = x^2 = \tfrac{1}{9} \quad \text{or} \quad 4,$$

and

$$x = \pm\tfrac{1}{3}, \quad \pm 2.$$

EXAMPLE 2. Solve $(x^2 - 5x)^2 + (x^2 - 5x) - 30 = 0$.

Solution. With $v = x^2 - 5x$, we wish to solve

$$v^2 + v - 30 = 0,$$

a quadratic equation in v, whose roots are

$$v = 5 \quad \text{or} \quad -6.$$

Hence, we must solve

$$x^2 - 5x - 5 = 0 \quad \text{and} \quad x^2 - 5x + 6 = 0.$$

Our solution is $x = (5 \pm 3\sqrt{5})/2$, 3, and 2.

PROBLEMS

Solve the following equations for x.

1. $x^4 - 11x^2 + 28 = 0$

2. $9x^4 + 5x^2 - 4 = 0$

3. $x^{-4} - 13x^{-2} + 36 = 0$

4. $x^{-4} - 8x^{-2} + 15 = 0$

5. $x^6 + 7x^3 - 8 = 0$

6. $8x^{-6} + 7x^{-3} = 1$

7. $x^{2/3} + 2x^{1/3} - 8 = 0$

8. $x + x^{1/2} = 20$

9. $(x^2 - 7x)^2 + 9(x^2 - 7x) - 10 = 0$

10. $(x^2 + 2x)^2 + (x^2 + 2x) = 12$

11. $\dfrac{2 + x}{2 - x} + \dfrac{2 - x}{2 + x} = 2$

12. $\left(x + \dfrac{1}{x}\right)^2 - 2\left(x + \dfrac{1}{x}\right) + 1 = 0$

13. $3(x + 3) + \sqrt{x + 3} = 2$

14. $2x - 9\sqrt{x + 2} + 14 = 0$

15. $2x^2 - 5x + 10 = 7\sqrt{2x^2 - 5x}$

16. $x^2 - x - 4 = \sqrt{x^2 - x - 2}$

7–8 Equations involving radicals. The last four problems of Article 7–7 contain radicals. Fortunately, they are of a special form, and it is possible to solve them by the method prescribed. Many equations involving radicals are not solvable by this method, and the radical or radicals must first be eliminated. Then the usual methods may be used. Extreme care must be taken, however, to substitute all possible roots in the original equation, since the method of eliminating radicals involves raising both members of an equality to some power. This process (recall Illustration 2, Article 7–1) may introduce roots of the final equation which are not roots of the original one.

EXAMPLE 1. Solve $\sqrt{2x + 5} = 3$.

Solution. In an equation involving one radical, we must first eliminate the radical by squaring both members of the equation,

$$2x + 5 = 9.$$

Solving, we find
$$x = 2.$$

By substituting, we find that $x = 2$ does satisfy the original equation
$$\sqrt{2(2) + 5} = \sqrt{9} = 3,$$

so that $x = 2$ is the only root of the original equation.

EXAMPLE 2. Solve $\sqrt{1 - 5x} + \sqrt{1 - x} = 2$.

Solution. With two radicals, it is simpler to transpose one to the opposite side before squaring. Thus,
$$\sqrt{1 - 5x} = 2 - \sqrt{1 - x}.$$

Squaring, we find
$$1 - 5x = 4 - 4\sqrt{1 - x} + 1 - x,$$

and we have
$$-4x - 4 = -4\sqrt{1 - x}$$

or
$$1 + x = \sqrt{1 - x}.$$

Squaring again, we obtain
$$1 + 2x + x^2 = 1 - x,$$
$$x^2 = -3x,$$
$$x = 0, -3.$$

Therefore, no numbers other than 0 or -3 are roots of the original equation. By substitution, we find that 0 satisfies the original equation, but -3 does not. Therefore, $x = 0$ is the only solution.

EXAMPLE 3. Solve $3 \sin \theta + 4 \cos \theta = 5$ for all values of θ between 0 and 2π.

Solution. Although this is not an algebraic equation, it may be solved by the method discussed in this article. In order to express $\cos \theta$ in terms of $\sin \theta$, we recall that $\cos \theta \equiv \pm\sqrt{1 - \sin^2 \theta}$. Thus,
$$\pm 4\sqrt{1 - \sin^2 \theta} = 5 - 3 \sin \theta.$$

Squaring and solving for $\sin \theta$, we have
$$16 - 16 \sin^2 \theta = 25 - 30 \sin \theta + 9 \sin^2 \theta,$$
$$25 \sin^2 \theta - 30 \sin \theta + 9 = 0,$$
$$(5 \sin \theta - 3)^2 = 0,$$
$$\sin \theta = \tfrac{3}{5}.$$

Therefore $\theta = 0.6464$ or $3.1416 - 0.6464 = 2.4952$. By substituting our results in the original equation, we find $\theta = 0.6464$ is the only solution.

PROBLEMS

Solve and check the following equations.

1. $\sqrt{2x+5} = 4$ 2. $\sqrt{6x-3} = 7$

3. $\sqrt{8x-7} - x = 0$ 4. $\sqrt{3x+1} + 1 = x$

5. $\sqrt{3x+1} = \sqrt{x} + 3$ 6. $2\sqrt{4x+5} = \sqrt{8-x} - 1$

7. $\sqrt{11-x} - \sqrt{x+6} = 3$ 8. $\sqrt{3-x} - \sqrt{2+x} = 3$

9. $\sqrt{2x + \sqrt{2x+4}} = 4$ 10. $\sqrt{2x + \sqrt{7+x}} = 3$

Find and check the values of θ between 0 and 2π which satisfy the following equations.

11. $4 \sin \theta + 3 \cos \theta = 2$ 12. $\cos \theta - 2 = \sqrt{3} \sin \theta$

13. $\sin \theta + \cos \theta = 1$ 14. $12 \cos \theta - 5 \sin \theta = 13$

15. $5 \tan \theta - \sqrt{2} \sec \theta + 3 = 0$ 16. $\tan \theta + \sec \theta = 1$

7–9 Variation. Many applications in physical and social science make use of a functional dependence known as *proportion* or *variation*. Often the relations are linear or quadratic (although this is by no means always the case). For example, Ohm's law for an electrical circuit states that the current *varies directly* as the electromotive force, and *varies inversely* as the resistance. Thus the current is a function of both the electromotive force and the resistance. We may write this functional equation

$$I = k \cdot \frac{E}{R},$$

where k is called the *proportionality constant*. Let us define the three different common types of variation.

DEFINITION 7–6. *If the two variables x and y are so related (no matter how their values change) that the quotient of y divided by x, called the ratio of y to x, is constant, then y is said to* vary directly *as x. This relationship may be written $y/x = k$, or*

$$\boxed{y = kx.} \qquad (7\text{–}19)$$

DEFINITION 7–7. *If the two variables, x and y, are so related (no matter how their values change) that the product of y and x is constant, then y is said to* vary inversely *as x. This relationship may be written $yx = k$, or*

$$\boxed{y = \frac{k}{x}.} \qquad (7\text{–}20)$$

DEFINITION 7–8. *If the variable z varies directly as x when y is held constant, and varies directly as y when x is held constant, then z is said to vary* jointly *as x and y, and is written*

$$z = kxy.$$ (7–21)

EXAMPLE 1. Express z as a specific functional equation of x and y if z varies directly as x and inversely as the square of y, and $z = 18$ when $x = 3$ and $y = 2$.

Solution. The given proportion may be written

$$z = k\,\frac{x}{y^2}.$$

Substituting the values for x, y, and z, we have $18 = k(\frac{3}{4})$, and $k = 24$. Therefore the functional equation may be written

$$z = \frac{24x}{y^2}.$$

EXAMPLE 2. At constant temperature, the resistance of a wire varies directly as its length and inversely as the square of its diameter. If a piece of wire 0.1 in. in diameter and 50 ft long has a resistance of 0.1 ohm, what is the resistance of a piece of wire of the same material, 2000 ft long, 0.2 in. in diameter?

Solution. Letting R, L, and d represent the resistance, the length, and the diameter, respectively, of the wire, we have $R = kL/d^2$. By substitution, $0.1 = k(50)/(0.1)^2$, or $k = (0.1)^3/50$. Thus,

$$R = \frac{(0.1)^3}{50} \cdot \frac{L}{d^2}.$$

Therefore,

$$R = \frac{(0.1)^3}{50} \cdot \frac{(2000)}{(0.2)^2} = \frac{(0.001)(2000)}{50(0.04)} = 1 \text{ ohm.}$$

Note that all the measurements need not be expressed in the same unit, although we must be consistent for each variable.

EXAMPLE 3. If y varies inversely as the square of x, how is y affected if x is increased 25%?

Solution. We have $y = k/x^2$. If $x = x_1$, then $y = k/x_1^2$. But $x = 5x_1/4$.

Thus,

$$y = \frac{k}{(5x_1/4)^2} = \frac{16}{25} \cdot \frac{k}{x_1^2} = 0.64 \frac{k}{x_1^2}.$$

Therefore y is 0.64 of its original value.

PROBLEMS

In Problems 1 through 8, express the functional equation as a single algebraic equation, giving the specific value of k if possible.

1. The variable z varies directly as x and inversely as y.

2. The variable z varies directly as x and inversely as the square of y.

3. The variable z varies jointly as x and y, and $z = 72$ when $x = 4$ and $y = 3$.

4. The variable z varies inversely as x, and $z = 8$ when $x = 16$.

5. The area of a circle varies directly as the square of the diameter.

6. The area of any triangle varies jointly as the product of the base and altitude.

7. The area of an equilateral triangle varies directly as the square of one side. (Compare Problem 14, Article 5–1.)

8. The distance a falling body travels (neglecting air resistance) varies as the square of the time traveled, and a body starting from rest falls 64 feet in 2 seconds.

9. (a) If $y = f(x)$ varies directly with x, and the point $(3, 2)$ is on its graph, find the specific equation for y in terms of x. (b) Give the coordinates of another point on the graph.

10. (a) If $y = f(x)$ varies inversely with x, and the point $(3, 2)$ is on its graph, find the specific equation for y in terms of x. (b) Give the coordinates of another point on the graph.

11. If z varies jointly as x^2 and y, and $z = 24$ when $x = 2$ and $y = 3$, find the value of z when $x = 3$ and $y = 5$.

12. If z varies directly as x and inversely as y, and if $z = 5$ when $x = 2$ and $y = 3$, find z when $x = 4$ and $y = 2$.

13. The surface area of a sphere varies directly as the square of the radius. If the surface is 36π in^2 when the radius is 3 in, what is the surface area when the radius is 12 in?

14. With the information in Problem 8, (a) find the distance the body has fallen in 5 sec, (b) find the distance the body fell during the fifth second.

15. The kinetic energy K varies jointly as the mass m and the square of the velocity v. If K is 36 ergs when m is 8 gm and v is 3 cm/sec, find K if $m = 4$ gm and $v = 6$ cm/sec.

16. The vibrating frequency, or pitch, of a vibrating string varies directly as the square root of the tension of the string. If a string vibrates 216 times/sec due to a tension of 3 pounds, find its rate of vibration caused by a tension of 12 pounds.

17. The intensity of light varies inversely as the square of the distance from its source. How much farther from the light must an object be moved to receive one-fourth the amount of light it now receives if it is now 2 ft from the light?

18. If z varies directly as the square of x and inversely as y, what effect on z does doubling x and tripling y have?

19. The gravitational attraction F between two bodies varies jointly as their masses m_1 and m_2 and inversely as the square of the distance d between them. What is the effect on the gravitational attraction between two bodies if the masses are each doubled and the distance between them is halved?

20. The stiffness of a beam varies jointly as its breadth and depth and inversely as the square of the length. (a) Find the change in stiffness if each of the three dimensions is increased 10%. (b) Find the change in the length that is necessary to increase the stiffness 20% if the breadth and depth are unaltered.

21. Draw the graph of $y = kx$ for $k > 0$. Note that on the graph y increases as x increases. [*Hint:* Use units of k length on the y-axis.]

22. Draw $y = k/x$ for $k > 0$. Note that y decreases as x increases.

23. (a) If $y = f(x)$ varies directly as x, show that

$$\frac{f(x_1)}{f(x_2)} = \frac{x_1}{x_2}.$$

(b) If $y = f(x)$ varies inversely as x, show that

$$\frac{f(x_1)}{f(x_2)} = \frac{x_2}{x_1}.$$

24. The law of divine proportion, according to early Egyptians and Greeks, states, "the most beautiful division of a line segment into two parts is such that the ratio of the longer part to the total length is equal to the ratio of the length of the shorter part to that of the longer part."

(a) If we consider the length of the line to be one unit and call t the length of the longer of the two parts, find t.

(b) What is the proportionality constant for this ratio?*

7–10 Solution of two linear equations. We recall the general definition of a function (Definition 5–1) $f: P \rightarrow Z$, which associated with each element of P exactly one element of Z. If we consider the elements of P as the set of all ordered pairs of real numbers and Z the set of all real numbers, we might write this function

$$\boxed{f: (x, y) \rightarrow z,} \qquad (7\text{–}22)$$

where the correspondence is from an ordered pair to a real number. This is frequently done, where z is expressed algebraically in terms of x and y.†

---

* Recall Eq. (6–19), Article 6–5.

† In many books this is referred to as a function of two variables and is written $z = f(x, y)$.

Our special interest is the linear case where z is equal to a first degree expression of this type, namely, $z = ax + by + c$. As a simple generalization of Eq. (7–1), our main concern is to find "the zeros" of this function. In a manner analogous to that in Article 7–1, we set $z = 0$, and wish to find the set of ordered pairs (x, y) such that $ax + by + c = 0$. This set

$$\{(x, y)|ax + by + c = 0\} \tag{7–23}$$

is called the *solution set*, while any particular member of this set is a solution to the equation

$$ax + by + c = 0. \tag{7–24}$$

In Article 7–1, we sketched the graph of equations such as $ax + by + c = 0$* (Problems 33 through 40) by solving for y and obtaining an equivalent equation in the form $y = mx + b$,† which represented a straight line. There are, clearly, infinitely many solutions to the equation $ax + by + c = 0$, for there are infinitely many points (x, y) which lie on the line. Any arbitrary value of x will determine a corresponding value of y. For example, the linear equation $3x - 2y - 5 = 0$ has one solution $(3, 2)$ since $x = 3$, $y = 2$ satisfies the equation. Another is $(1, -1)$, another $(-1, -4)$, and so on. In this case the solution set is

$$\{(x, y)|3x - 2y - 5 = 0\}.$$

We are frequently interested in the solution not of one equation but of a pair of linear equations in x and y, such as

$$\boxed{\begin{aligned} a_1x + b_1y &= c_1, \\ a_2x + b_2y &= c_2. \end{aligned}} \tag{7–25}‡$$

Thus, we are interested in finding any ordered pairs (x, y) whose values satisfy both equations. If we put our problem in the context of sets by letting $A = \{(x, y)|a_1x + b_1y = c_1\}$ and $B = \{(x, y)|a_2x + b_2y = c_2\}$, we wish to find the intersection of A and B, namely, $A \cap B = \{(x, y)|a_1x + b_1y = c_1 \text{ and } a_2x + b_2y = c_2\}$. From a geometrical point of view, the graph of each of the equations in (7–25) is a straight line,

---

* If $b = 0$, $x = -c/a$ is a straight line parallel to the y-axis. If $b \neq 0$, $by = -ax + c$ or $y = -(a/b)x + c/b$.

† The two b's are not the same in Eq. (7–1) and Eq. (7–24). The reader should differentiate between them.

‡ Since it is often more convenient to write the constant term as the right member of such an equation, we have chosen to write these equations in this form.

FIGURE 7-4   FIGURE 7-5

FIGURE 7-6

and hence we must find the coordinates of the points (x, y) which lie on both lines. Since, in general, two straight lines intersect in one point, their solution usually consists of one element. By drawing a graph of each line, we can approximate the coordinates of the point of intersection.

EXAMPLE 1. Solve graphically the pair of equations

$$x + 2y = 4 \quad \text{and} \quad 3x - 2y = -12.$$

Solution. The graph of each of these straight lines is shown in Fig. 7-4. It appears that the two lines intersect at the point $(-2, 3)$. This is actually the case as may be verified by direct substitution, so that the solution is, $x = -2$, $y = 3$, where the ordered pair is $(-2, 3)$. If we consider $A = \{(x, y)|x + 2y = 4\}$ and $B = \{(x, y)|3x - 2y = -12\}$, then the solution set is $A \cap B = \{(-2, 3)\}$, which contains the one element $(-2, 3)$.

We should remark that two parallel lines such as $x + 2y = 4$ and $x + 2y = 8$, when plotted, will not intersect. (Fig. 7-5.) The fact that the equations of two such lines have no points of intersection is, of course, apparent from the equations, since there can be no pair of numbers such that the first number plus twice the second is equal to 4 and also 8. If we consider the intersection of $\{(x, y)|x + 2y = 4\}$ and $\{(x, y)|x + 2y = 8\}$, the result is the null set $\emptyset$. Two equations of this type are called *inconsistent.*

If two lines such as $x + 2y = 4$ and $3x + 6y = 12$ coincide when their graphs are plotted (Fig. 7–6), any pair of values (x, y) which satisfies one equation will also satisfy the other. Any two equations of this type have an infinite number of solutions and are said to be *dependent*.

In summary, the two equations (7–25) either

(1) have a unique solution, when their graphs are two straight lines which intersect in one point;

(2) have no solution, when their graphs are two parallel but not co-incident straight lines;

(3) have infinitely many solutions, when their graphs are two straight lines which are parallel and coincide.

Since the graphical method of solution is only approximate, we must also consider some exact method. One of the variables may be eliminated by a proper combination of the two equations (or equations equivalent to them), and the resulting equation may be solved in terms of the other variable. The eliminated variable may then be found by substitution.

EXAMPLE 2. Solve algebraically the two equations of Example 1.

Solution. Since the coefficients of y are equal, but opposite in sign, the members of the first equation may be added to those of the second, and thereby the y is eliminated.

$$\begin{aligned} x + 2y &= 4 \\ 3x - 2y &= -12 \\ \hline 4x &= -8 \end{aligned}$$

Solving this equation in one variable, we have $x = -2$. When this value is substituted in either of the two original equations, we find $y = 3$. Therefore the required solution is $x = -2$, $y = 3$ or $(-2, 3)$. We might have found y by multiplying each member of the first equation by -3, adding the members of the resulting equation, $-3x - 6y = -12$, to those of the second equation, $3x - 2y = -12$, and finding $-8y = -24$, or $y = 3$.

EXAMPLE 3. Solve the pair of two general equations (7–25) for x and y in terms of the coefficients.

Solution. If we multiply each member of the first equation by b_2, and of the second by b_1, we have

$$a_1 b_2 x + b_1 b_2 y = c_1 b_2,$$
$$a_2 b_1 x + b_1 b_2 y = c_2 b_1.$$

Subtracting the members of the second from those of the first, we obtain

$$a_1 b_2 x - a_2 b_1 x = c_1 b_2 - c_2 b_1.$$

Solving this equation for x, we find

$$(a_1 b_2 - a_2 b_1)x = c_1 b_2 - c_2 b_1,$$

$$x = \frac{c_1 b_2 - c_2 b_1}{a_1 b_2 - a_2 b_1} \qquad (a_1 b_2 - a_2 b_1 \neq 0).$$

By multiplying each member of the first equation by a_2, of the second by a_1, and so on, we find

$$y = \frac{a_1 c_2 - a_2 c_1}{a_1 b_2 - a_2 b_1} \qquad (a_1 b_2 - a_2 b_1 \neq 0).$$

Although not used in this form, these values for x and y can be considered a *solution by formula*.

Problems

Solve the following pairs of linear equations algebraically. The graphical method might be used as an approximate check. If circular functions are involved, find all possible values between 0 and 2π.

1. $2x - y = 5$, $x - 3y = 5$.
2. $3x - 2y = -14$, $2x + 3y = 8$.
3. $4x + 3y = 27$, $2x - 5y + 19 = 0$.
4. $2x - 5y + 43 = 0$, $6x - y + 31 = 0$.
5. $3x + 4 = 4y$, $9x + 2y = 9$.
6. $6x + 9y = 7$, $3x - 6y + 14 = 0$.
†7. $4 \sin \alpha + \cos \beta = 3$, $6 \sin \alpha - 2 \cos \beta = 1$.
8. $\sqrt{3} \sin \alpha - \cos \beta = 1$, $\sin \alpha - 3\sqrt{3} \cos \beta = -\sqrt{3}$.
9. $2 \sec \alpha - 4 \tan \beta = 0$, $\sec \alpha + \tan \beta = \sqrt{3}$.
10. $\dfrac{2}{x} + \dfrac{3}{y} = 2$, $\quad \dfrac{4}{x} - \dfrac{9}{y} + 1 = 0$.
11. $\dfrac{15}{x} + \dfrac{4}{y} = 1$, $\quad \dfrac{5}{x} - \dfrac{12}{y} = 7$.
12. $\dfrac{15}{2x} - \dfrac{16}{3y} = \dfrac{23}{6}$, $\quad \dfrac{4}{3x} + \dfrac{7}{2y} + \dfrac{31}{72} = 0$.
13. $ax + by = a^2 + 2ab + b^2$, $bx - ay = b^2 + 2ab - a^2$.
14. $ax - by = a^2 - b^2$, $bx + ay = 2ab$.
*15. $\tan k_1 = \dfrac{y}{x}$, $\quad \tan k_2 = \dfrac{y + a}{x}$.

---

† Although Problems 7 through 12 are not linear, they may be solved by the method discussed in this article.

*16. $\tan k_1 = \dfrac{a}{y}$, $\quad \tan k_2 = \dfrac{a}{y+x}$.

*17. Solve the pair of equations

$$x = x' \cos \alpha - y' \sin \alpha,$$
$$y = x' \sin \alpha + y' \cos \alpha$$

for x' and y' in terms of x and y.

Find $A \cap B$ in Problems 18 through 20 if:

18. $A = \{(x, y)|3x - 4y = -7\}$, $B = \{(x, y)|x + y = 7\}$.
19. $A = \{(x, y)|x + y = 1\}$, $B = \{(x, y)|2x + 3y = 4\}$.
20. $A = \{(x, y)|3x + y = 5\}$, $B = \{(x, y)|6x + 2y = 7\}$.
21. Sketch the graph of $\{(x, y)|x - y = 3$ and $x + 2y > 4\}$.
22. Sketch the graph of $\{(x, y)|x + 2y = 6$ and $x - y < 3\}$.
23. Sketch the graph of
(a) $A = \{(x, y)|2x + y > 3\}$, $\quad$ (b) $B = \{(x, y)|x - y > 6\}$.
(c) Show algebraically that

$$A \cap B = \{(x, y)|x > 3 \text{ and } 3 - 2x < y < x - 6\}.$$

(d) Sketch the graph of $A \cap B$.

24. Sketch the graph of
$$A = \{(x, y)|x > 0, y > 0, x + 3y < 15, \text{ and } 2x + y < 10\}.$$
25. Sketch the graph of $|x| + |y| = 1$.
26. Sketch the graph of $|x - 4| + |y - 3| = 2$.
27. Sketch the graph of $4|x| + 3|y| = 12$.
28. The sum of the digits of a two-digit number is 9. If the digits are reversed, the new number is 9 less than the original number. Find the two numbers.
29. A certain fraction has the value $\frac{3}{4}$. If its numerator is decreased by 7 and its denominator increased by 4, the resulting fraction has the value $\frac{1}{2}$. Find the original fraction.
30. The sum of the two nonright angles in a right triangle is, of course, 90°. If twice the first is 40° more than 3 times the second, find the angles.
31. With the wind, an airplane travels 1120 miles in 7 hours. Against the wind, however, it takes 8 hours. Find the rate of the plane in still air and the velocity of the wind.
32. The sum of the reciprocals of two numbers is 9. Twice the reciprocal of the first is 12 less than 4 times the reciprocal of the second. Find the numbers.
33. A and B, working together, can do a job in $6\frac{2}{3}$ hours. A became ill after 3 hours of working with B, and B finished the job, continuing to work alone in $8\frac{1}{4}$ more hours. How long would it take each working alone to do the job?
34. Find α and β, values between 0 and $\pi/2$, so that

$$2 \sin (\alpha + \beta) = 2 \cos (\alpha - \beta) = \sqrt{3}.$$

35. Find the coordinates of the vertices of the triangle formed by the lines

$$x - y = -3, \quad 3x + 4y = 5, \quad 6x + y = 17.$$

36. Check the coordinates found in Problem 35 in the equations.

37. Show that the lines

$$2x - y = 4, \qquad x + 3y = 6,$$
$$2x - y = 8, \qquad x + 3y = -1$$

form a parallelogram, and find its vertices.

38. We recall that $y = mx + b$ represents an equation of any straight line (not parallel to the y-axis). Find the values of m and b so that $y = mx + b$ passes through $(-3, 1)$ and $(1, 9)$. (If a point lies on a line, its coordinates satisfy the equation.) If these values for m and b are substituted in the equation $y = mx + b$, we have found an equation of the straight line which passes through two given points.

39. By the method of Problem 38, find an equation of the straight line that passes through (a) $(2, 3)$ and $(-1, 4)$, (b) $(-4, 2)$ and $(6, -1)$.

40. Find the linear relation between the centigrade temperature C and the Fahrenheit temperature F of any body. [*Hint:* $F = mC + b$. Also $F = 32$ when $C = 0$, and $F = 212$ when $C = 100$.]

7–11 Algebraic solution of three linear equations. Any equation of the form

$$ax + by + cz = d, \tag{7–26}$$

where a, b, c, and d are constants and a, b, and c are not all equal to zero, is called a *linear equation in three variables*. A solution of such an equation is any set of three numbers x, y, and z that satisfies the equation. As was the case for Eq. (7–24), there are an infinite number of solutions for one equation of this type.

Although we shall not prove it in this book, the geometric interpretation of Eq. (7–26) is a plane in a three-dimensional rectangular coordinate system.* Two nonparallel planes intersect in a straight line, and this line intersects a third plane, parallel to neither of the first two, in a point. In general, then, three planes have one point in common. Algebraically, this may be interpreted by the fact that the system of equations

$$\begin{aligned} a_1 x + b_1 y + c_1 z &= d_1, \\ a_2 x + b_2 y + c_2 z &= d_2, \\ a_3 x + b_3 y + c_3 z &= d_3 \end{aligned} \tag{7–27}$$

has a single solution for x, y, and z.

---

* A three-dimensional rectangular coordinate system is a generalization of the one- and two-dimensional systems discussed in Articles 4–2 and 4–4. For example, each point in the space has three coordinates and is denoted (x, y, z), an ordered triple, and so on. (Recall Problem 15, Article 4–4.)

To solve such a system, we follow a method which is a generalization of that used to solve the pair of equations (7–25). We choose a pair from the three equations and eliminate one of the variables from the pair, obtaining an equation in two variables. Repeating this procedure for another pair of the equations, we obtain a second equation in the same two variables. We now solve the two resulting equations for the two variables and, by substitution in any one of the original equations, find the complete solution. Let us illustrate.

EXAMPLE. Solve the system of equations

$$2x - y + z = 8,$$
$$x + 2y + 3z = 9,$$
$$4x + y - 2z = 1.$$

Solution. Let us eliminate z by combining the first two equations, and then by combining the first and third. Multiply each member of the first equation by -3 and add the result, member by member, to the second equation.

$$
\begin{array}{r}
-6x + 3y - 3z = -24 \\
\underline{x + 2y + 3z = 9} \\
-5x + 5y = -15
\end{array}
$$

or $x - y = 3$.

Multiply each member of the first equation by 2 and add the result, member by member, to the third equation.

$$
\begin{array}{r}
4x - 2y + 2z = 16 \\
\underline{4x + y - 2z = 1} \\
8x - y = 17
\end{array}
$$

We now solve the two resulting equations. Give the reasons for each step.

$$
\begin{array}{r}
8x - y = 17 \\
\underline{x - y = 3} \\
7x = 14
\end{array}
$$

Therefore, $x = 2$ and $y = -1$. Substituting these values in the first of the original equations, we have

$$2(2) - (-1) + z = 8,$$
$$z = 3.$$

Therefore the complete solution is $x = 2$, $y = -1$, $z = 3$ and may be written $(2, -1, 3)$. All solutions should be checked.

PROBLEMS

Solve each system of equations.

1. $x + 3y - z = 4$,
$3x - 2y + 4z = 11$,
$2x + y + 3z = 13$.

2. $3x - y - 2z = -13$,
$5x + 3y - z = 4$,
$2x - 7y + 3z = -36$.

3. $2x - y + 3z = 19$,
$5x - 2y + 4z = 33$,
$3x + 3y - z = 2$.

4. $6x + 4y - z = 13$,
$5x - 2y + 7z = 18$,
$x + y - 8z = -35$.

5. $3x + 5y + 2z = 0$,
$12x - 15y + 4z = 12$,
$6x + 25y - 8z = -12$.

6. $7x - 3y + 4z = 18$,
$13x + 6y + 8z = 30$,
$11x - 9y - 12z = 16$.

7. $2x + 3y = 28$,
$3y + 4z = 46$,
$4z + 5x = 53$.

8. $x - 3y = -11$,
$2y - 5z = 26$,
$3z - 7x = 2$.

9. $\dfrac{3}{x} - \dfrac{4}{y} + \dfrac{6}{z} = 1$,

$\dfrac{9}{x} + \dfrac{8}{y} - \dfrac{12}{z} = 3$,

$\dfrac{9}{x} - \dfrac{4}{y} + \dfrac{12}{z} = 4$.

10. $x + y + z = a + b + c$,
$bx - ay + cz = b^2$,
$ax - ay + cz = ab$.

11. If three given sets of ordered triples are given

$$A = \{(x, y, z)|x - 2y + 3z = 4\},$$
$$B = \{(x, y, z)|2x - y + z = -1\}, \quad \text{and}$$
$$C = \{(x, y, z)|4x + y + 2z = 4\},$$

find $(A \cap B) \cap C$.

12. The sum of the digits of a three-digit number is 13. If the tens and hundreds digits are interchanged, the new number is 90 less than the original, and if the units and hundreds digits are interchanged, the resulting number is 99 less than the original. Find the original number.

13. Twenty-five coins, whose value is \$2.75, are made up of nickels, dimes, and quarters. If the nickels were dimes, the dimes were quarters, and the quarters nickels, the total value would be \$3.75. How many coins of each type are there?

14. We recall that the sum of the angles of any triangle is 180°. What are the three angles if the sum of two is equal to the third angle, but the difference of these two is only two-thirds of the third angle?

15. If the general equation (4–10) of the circle is expanded, it can be written in the form $x^2 + y^2 + Ax + By + C = 0$. Recalling that the coordinate of any point on the circle must satisfy its equation, find the values of A, B, and C and, thereby, the circle which passes through the points $(1, 1)$, $(-2, 3)$, $(3, 4)$.

16. If A, B, and C work together on a job, it will take $1\frac{1}{3}$ hours. If only A and B work, it would take $1\frac{5}{7}$ hours, but if B and C work, it would take $2\frac{2}{5}$ hours. How long would it take each man, working alone, to complete the job?

17. We recall from the footnote in this section that $ax + by + cz = d$ represents the equation of a plane in a three-dimensional coordinate system. At least one of the coefficients is not zero. We can divide by this coefficient, and, for example, the equivalent equation might be in the form $x = ey + fz + g$. Find an equation of the plane that passes through the three points $(4, 1, 2)$, $(3, 2, 1)$, and $(-6, -1, -2)$.

18. Find an equation of the plane that passes through the three points $(1, -5, -2)$, $(0, 5, 2)$ and $(3, 2, -1)$.

7–12 Solution of one linear and one quadratic equation. In Articles 7–10 and 7–11 we discussed systems of linear equations. These systems may be generalized either by considering more variables than two or three, or by considering functions of higher degree than the linear ones. The solutions of such systems, if they exist, are often difficult to obtain. We shall consider one simple but useful generalization in two variables, namely, the case in which one equation is linear and one is of the second degree, or quadratic. Such a system, in general, might be written

$$ax^2 + bxy + cy^2 + dx + ey + f = 0,$$
$$gx + hy + k = 0, \qquad\qquad (7\text{–}28)$$

where a, b, c, d, e, f, g, h, and k are constants, a, b, and c not all zero, and g and h not both zero. If each of the equations (conditions) in Eq. (7–28) is considered as defining a set of points, whose coordinates satisfy the equation, again, as in Article 7–10, the intersection of these two sets has for its elements, the points of intersection of the two curves representing these equations.

It is possible to solve such a system either graphically or algebraically, as in the case of two linear equations. The graph of the quadratic equation may best be plotted by solving for one variable in terms of the others, before the table of values is obtained. The points of intersection of the graphs of the quadratic equation and the linear equation may be approximated and their coordinates taken as solutions, since the points lie on both curves.

The simplest algebraic method is carried out by eliminating one of the variables. More specifically, we solve the linear equation for one variable in terms of the other, substitute this value in the quadratic equation, and solve the resulting quadratic equation in one variable. With these results substituted in the original linear equation, we obtain our complete solution.

Since this system reduces to the problem of solving one quadratic equation, we shall have two real, distinct ordered pairs, one real ordered pair, or no real ordered pair. (Recall Article 7–6.)

EXAMPLE 1. Solve the system of equations

$$x^2 - 5x - y + 4 = 0,$$
$$x - 4y = 1.$$

Algebraic solution. Although we are able to eliminate x or y, we choose to solve the linear equation for y in terms of x, and substitute this value in the quadratic, since this approach appears to be simpler.

$$4y = x - 1$$

or

$$y = \frac{x - 1}{4}.$$

Therefore,

$$x^2 - 5x - \left(\frac{x - 1}{4}\right) + 4 = 0,$$

$$4x^2 - 20x - x + 1 + 16 = 0,$$

$$4x^2 - 21x + 17 = 0,$$

$$(4x - 17)(x - 1) = 0.$$

Thus $x = 1$ or $\frac{17}{4}$. Substitution of these values in the linear equation gives the corresponding values $y = 0, \frac{13}{16}$. The two solutions are $x = 1$, $y = 0$, and $x = \frac{17}{4}$, $y = \frac{13}{16}$ or $(1, 0)$ and $(\frac{17}{4}, \frac{13}{16})$.

Graphical solution. The given equations represent the parabola and straight line whose graphs are shown in Fig. 7–7. The intersections of the two curves show the solutions found by the algebraic method.

EXAMPLE 2. Solve the system of equations

$$x^2 - 2y^2 + 3x - 4y + 20 = 0,$$
$$2x - y = 1.$$

*Solution.** Although we are able to eliminate x or y, we choose to solve the linear equation for y and thus work with x, since the work appears to be simpler. Substituting $y = 2x - 1$ in the first equation, we have

$$x^2 - 2(2x - 1)^2 + 3x - 4(2x - 1) + 20 = 0.$$

---

* A graphical solution involves the plotting of $x^2 - 2y^2 + 3x - 4y + 20 = 0$. Problems of this kind will be discussed in Article 10–2.

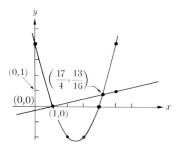

FIGURE 7–7

Simplifying, we obtain

$$x^2 - 8x^2 + 8x - 2 + 3x - 8x + 4 + 20 = 0,$$
$$-7x^2 + 3x + 22 = 0,$$
$$7x^2 - 3x - 22 = 0,$$
$$(7x + 11)(x - 2) = 0.$$

Therefore,

$$x = 2, \qquad -\tfrac{11}{7}.$$

Substitution of these values in the linear equation yields the corresponding values $y = 3, -\tfrac{29}{7}$. The two solutions are then $x = 2$, $y = 3$, and $x = -\tfrac{11}{7}$, $y = -\tfrac{29}{7}$ or $(2, 3)$ and $(-\tfrac{11}{7}, -\tfrac{29}{7})$.

PROBLEMS

Solve each of the systems in Problems 1 through 6 both graphically and algebraically.

1. $y = 4x^2,$
   $y = 8x.$

2. $x - 2y = 10,$
   $y = x^2 + 2x - 15.$

3. $y^2 = 4x,$
   $x - y = -4.$

4. $(x - 2)^2 + (y - 3)^2 = 4,$
   $x + y + 3 = 0.$

5. $(x - 2)^2 + (y - 3)^2 = 4,$
   $x + y = 4.$

6. $xy = 1,$
   $x + y = 2.$

[*Hint:* Recall Article 4–6 for the graph of this quadratic equation.]

For each of the Problems 7 through 10, find $A \cap B$ if

7. $A = \{(x, y)|y^2 + 2xy - 3x^2 + 7 = 0\},$
   $B = \{(x, y)|x - 3y + 1 = 0\}.$

8. $A = \{(x, y)|x^2 + y^2 - 2x = 1\},$
   $B = \{(x, y)|2x + y - 5 = 0\}.$

9. $A = \{(x, y)|3xy + 6x = 4y\},$
   $B = \{(x, y)|2y - 3x - 4 = 0\}.$

10. $A = \{(x, y)|4x^2 + 3xy - 2y^2 - x - y + 1 = 0\}$,
     $B = \{(x, y)|x - 2y + 3 = 0\}$.

11. The circle $x^2 + y^2 = a^2$ and the straight line $y = mx + b$ will intersect in two points, be tangent, or not intersect, depending upon whether the solutions of this system of equations are real and distinct, real and equal, or imaginary. Find the value of b in terms of a and m so that the straight line will be tangent to the circle.

12. Find the dimensions of a rectangle if its diagonal is 17 inches and its perimeter is 46 inches.

13. The product of a two-digit number and the number obtained by reversing its digits is 736. If the difference of the two numbers is 9, find the numbers.

14. A and B, working together, can complete a certain job in $7\frac{1}{2}$ hours. Working alone, A would take 8 hours longer than B to do the job. How long would it take each working alone?

15. The sum of two numbers is 11, while the sum of their reciprocals is $\frac{11}{28}$. Find the numbers.

CHAPTER 8

DETERMINANTS

In mathematics it is frequently convenient to consider square or rectangular arrays of numbers such as

$$\left\|\begin{array}{ccc} a_1 & b_1 & c_1 \\ a_2 & b_2 & c_2 \end{array}\right\|. \qquad (8\text{--}1)$$

This rectangular array of numbers is called a *matrix*. The numbers $a_1, b_1, \ldots, c_2$ are called the *elements* of the matrix. The horizontal lines of numbers are called *rows*, while the vertical lines of numbers are called *columns*. In general, if a rectangular array has m rows and n columns, we call it an m by n matrix. We shall be interested only in square matrices ($m = n$), since any further study is beyond the scope of this book. Such an n by n matrix is said to be of *order n*.

8–1 Determinants of orders two and three. With each *square* matrix we associate a real number called the *determinant* of the matrix. We are thus defining a function, *Det*, where the elements of the domain are square matrices, and the range is the set of real numbers R. For a matrix of order 2, this number or determinant is defined to be the product of the elements in the upper left and lower right corners minus the product of the lower left and upper right elements. This determinant is symbolized as

$$D = \left|\begin{array}{cc} a_1 & b_1 \\ a_2 & b_2 \end{array}\right| = a_1 b_2 - a_2 b_1. \qquad (8\text{--}2)$$

ILLUSTRATION.

(a) $\quad D = \left|\begin{array}{cc} 3 & 2 \\ 5 & 4 \end{array}\right| = (12) - (10) = 2,$

(b) $\quad D = \left|\begin{array}{cc} -1 & -4 \\ 2 & -3 \end{array}\right| = (-1)(-3) - 2(-4) = 11.$

PROBLEMS

Evaluate the determinants in Problems 1 through 6.

1. $\left|\begin{array}{cc} 3 & 4 \\ 5 & 6 \end{array}\right|$

2. $\left|\begin{array}{cc} 6 & -1 \\ 3 & -2 \end{array}\right|$

3. $\left|\begin{array}{cc} -2 & 3 \\ -5 & 6 \end{array}\right|$

4. $\begin{vmatrix} 8 & 0 \\ 1 & 2 \end{vmatrix}$ 5. $\begin{vmatrix} \sin\theta & \cos\theta \\ -\cos\theta & \sin\theta \end{vmatrix}$ 6. $\begin{vmatrix} \sec\theta & \tan\theta \\ \tan\theta & \sec\theta \end{vmatrix}$

*7. From Example 3, Article 7–10, show that the solution of the system of equations

$$a_1 x + b_1 y = c_1, \qquad a_2 x + b_2 y = c_2$$

may be written in terms of determinants as

$$x = \frac{\begin{vmatrix} c_1 & b_1 \\ c_2 & b_2 \end{vmatrix}}{\begin{vmatrix} a_1 & b_1 \\ a_2 & b_2 \end{vmatrix}}, \qquad y = \frac{\begin{vmatrix} a_1 & c_1 \\ a_2 & c_2 \end{vmatrix}}{\begin{vmatrix} a_1 & b_1 \\ a_2 & b_2 \end{vmatrix}}. \tag{8–3}$$

8. Using Eqs. (8–3), solve Problems 1, 3, 5 of Article 7–10.

9. Using Eqs. (8–3), solve Problems 2, 4, 6 of Article 7–10.

10. Solve for x: $\begin{vmatrix} 3 & 2 \\ x & 4 \end{vmatrix} = 0.$

11. Solve for x: $\begin{vmatrix} 2x & 3 \\ -5 & -4 \end{vmatrix} = 7x.$

12. Prove the identity $\begin{vmatrix} x-2 & 3 \\ x-2 & 5 \end{vmatrix} \equiv 2(x-2).$

13. Prove the identity $\begin{vmatrix} a-b & 0 \\ 1 & c-d \end{vmatrix} \equiv (a-b)(c-d).$

14. For what values of x is $\begin{vmatrix} x & 5 \\ 125 & x \end{vmatrix} > 0?$

15. What can be said about the nature of the roots of

$$ax^2 + bx + c = 0$$

if

$$\begin{vmatrix} b & 4a \\ c & b \end{vmatrix} > 0, \qquad = 0, \qquad < 0?$$

Let us now consider the square matrix of order three,

$$M = \begin{Vmatrix} a_1 & b_1 & c_1 \\ a_2 & b_2 & c_2 \\ a_3 & b_3 & c_3 \end{Vmatrix}. \tag{8–4}$$

For each element in such a matrix there exists a matrix of order 2, obtained by deleting the row and column in which the element lies. The second order determinant associated with the matrix obtained in this way is called the *minor* of the element under consideration. For example, denoting the minor of any element by the corresponding capital letter, we have

$$A_1 = \begin{vmatrix} b_2 & c_2 \\ b_3 & c_3 \end{vmatrix}, \qquad B_3 = \begin{vmatrix} a_1 & c_1 \\ a_2 & c_2 \end{vmatrix}, \qquad C_2 = \begin{vmatrix} a_1 & b_1 \\ a_3 & b_3 \end{vmatrix}.$$

We now define the determinant of the third order matrix in Eq. (8–4) by

$$D = \begin{vmatrix} a_1 & b_1 & c_1 \\ a_2 & b_2 & c_2 \\ a_3 & b_3 & c_3 \end{vmatrix} = a_1 A_1 - b_1 B_1 + c_1 C_1. \tag{8–5}$$

EXAMPLE 1. Find the determinant of the matrix

$$\begin{Vmatrix} 2 & -1 & 3 \\ 3 & -2 & 1 \\ 4 & -3 & 2 \end{Vmatrix}.$$

Solution.

$$\begin{vmatrix} 2 & -1 & 3 \\ 3 & -2 & 1 \\ 4 & -3 & 2 \end{vmatrix} = 2 \begin{vmatrix} -2 & 1 \\ -3 & 2 \end{vmatrix} - (-1) \begin{vmatrix} 3 & 1 \\ 4 & 2 \end{vmatrix} + 3 \begin{vmatrix} 3 & -2 \\ 4 & -3 \end{vmatrix}$$

$$= 2(-4 + 3) + 1(6 - 4) + 3(-9 + 8)$$

$$= -2 + 2 - 3$$

$$= -3.$$

EXAMPLE 2. Express D, Eq. (8–5), in terms of the elements only.

Solution.

$$D = \begin{vmatrix} a_1 & b_1 & c_1 \\ a_2 & b_2 & c_2 \\ a_3 & b_3 & c_3 \end{vmatrix} = a_1 \begin{vmatrix} b_2 & c_2 \\ b_3 & c_3 \end{vmatrix} - b_1 \begin{vmatrix} a_2 & c_2 \\ a_3 & c_3 \end{vmatrix} + c_1 \begin{vmatrix} a_2 & b_2 \\ a_3 & b_3 \end{vmatrix}$$

$$= a_1(b_2 c_3 - b_3 c_2) - b_1(a_2 c_3 - a_3 c_2) + c_1(a_2 b_3 - a_3 b_2)$$

$$= a_1 b_2 c_3 + a_2 b_3 c_1 + a_3 b_1 c_2 - a_1 b_3 c_2 - a_2 b_1 c_3 - a_3 b_2 c_1. \tag{8–6}$$

PROBLEMS

Evaluate each of the determinants in Problems 1 through 4.

1. $\begin{vmatrix} 1 & 2 & 3 \\ -2 & -1 & -2 \\ 3 & 1 & 4 \end{vmatrix}$ 2. $\begin{vmatrix} -1 & 2 & -3 \\ 2 & -1 & -4 \\ 3 & -2 & 1 \end{vmatrix}$

3. $\begin{vmatrix} 2 & 1 & 3 \\ -1 & 4 & 7 \\ 4 & 2 & 6 \end{vmatrix}$ 4. $\begin{vmatrix} 1 & -1 & 1 \\ 4 & 2 & 10 \\ 2 & 2 & 6 \end{vmatrix}$

Verify the following, using the value in Eq. (8–6).

*5. $D = -a_2 A_2 + b_2 B_2 - c_2 C_2$ *6. $D = a_3 A_3 - b_3 B_3 + c_3 C_3$

7. $D = a_1 A_1 - a_2 A_2 + a_3 A_3$ 8. $D = -b_1 B_1 + b_2 B_2 - b_3 B_3$

9. $D = c_1 C_1 - c_2 C_2 + c_3 C_3$

[*Note:* The third order determinant D could have been defined equally well by the equation given in Problems 5, 6, 7, 8, or 9. The definition (Eq. 8–5) gives the expansion of D by minors according to the elements of the first row. Problems 5 and 6 give the expansion by minors according to the elements of the second and third rows, respectively. Problems 7, 8, and 9 give the expansion by minors according to columns.]

10. Using the results of Problems 5 through 9, and Eq. (8–5), prove the following statement: The determinant of order three may be expressed as the sum of three products formed by multiplying each element of any row (or column) by its minor, where each such product has assigned to it a plus or minus sign, depending upon whether the sum of the number of the row and the number of the column in which each element is located is even or odd.

11. Evaluate Problems 1 through 4 by expansion by minors according to some row or column other than the first.

*12. Show that

$$\begin{vmatrix} x_1 & y_1 & 1 \\ x_2 & y_2 & 1 \\ x_3 & y_3 & 1 \end{vmatrix} = \begin{vmatrix} x_1 & y_1 \\ x_2 & y_2 \end{vmatrix} - \begin{vmatrix} x_1 & y_1 \\ x_3 & y_3 \end{vmatrix} + \begin{vmatrix} x_2 & y_2 \\ x_3 & y_3 \end{vmatrix}.$$

*13. Using Fig. 8–1 and recalling that the area of a trapezoid is $\frac{1}{2}(b_1 + b_2)h$, where b_1 and b_2 are its bases and h its altitude, show that the area K of the triangle ABC in terms of the coordinates of its vertices is

$$K = \text{area of } ADEC + CEFB - ADFB$$

$$= \frac{1}{2} \begin{vmatrix} x_1 & y_1 & 1 \\ x_2 & y_2 & 1 \\ x_3 & y_3 & 1 \end{vmatrix}. \qquad [\textit{Hint: Use Problem 12.}] \qquad (8\text{–}7)$$

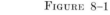

FIGURE 8–1   FIGURE 8–2

14. Find the area of the triangle whose vertices are the points (a) $(2, 3)$, $(5, 4)$, and $(4, 7)$; (b) $(-4, 2)$, $(-2, -3)$, and $(3, -1)$.

15. Find the area of the triangle the coordinates of whose vertices are (x, y), $(2, 3)$, and $(5, -1)$. (See Fig. 8–2.)

*16. The condition that the area of the triangle described in Problem 15 is equal to zero is equivalent to the fact that the point (x, y) lies on the line through $(2, 3)$ and $(5, -1)$. Using this fact, find the equation of the straight line through $(2, 3)$ and $(5, -1)$.

17. Find the equation of the straight line through $(-2, -4)$ and $(3, 5)$, using the method of this section.

18. Two nonparallel straight lines in the plane always intersect in one point. The condition that three such lines,

$$a_1 x + b_1 y = c_1, \qquad a_2 x + b_2 y = c_2, \qquad a_3 x + b_3 y = c_3,$$

pass through the same point is that the determinant of the matrix

$$\begin{Vmatrix} a_1 & b_1 & c_1 \\ a_2 & b_2 & c_2 \\ a_3 & b_3 & c_3 \end{Vmatrix}$$

is equal to zero. Assuming that such is the case, show that the three straight lines $x - 2y = -3$, $3x - y = 1$, $5x - 2y = 1$ pass through the same point.

19. Show that the system of equations $3x - 2y + 11 = 0$, $x - y + 5 = 0$, $2x + y = 2$ has a common solution, and find it.

20. Find the value of x if

(a) $\begin{vmatrix} 1 & 2 & 5 \\ 1 & x & 5 \\ 3 & -1 & 2 \end{vmatrix} = 0,$

(b) $\begin{vmatrix} 1 & 2 & -3 \\ 1 & x & -3 \\ 1 & 4 & -x \end{vmatrix} = 0.$

8–2 Determinants of order n. As might be expected, there exist determinants of any finite order. To consider them and their general properties, it will be convenient to use a different notation for the matrix and its elements. Let us denote the matrix by M and any element by the symbol a_{ij} (read "a sub i-j"), where i denotes the number of the row and j the number of the column in which the particular element appears. The notation for determinants used here was introduced by the English mathematician A. Cayley (1821–1895). According to this notation, Eq. (8–6) is written

$$D = \begin{vmatrix} a_{11} & a_{12} & a_{13} \\ a_{21} & a_{22} & a_{23} \\ a_{31} & a_{32} & a_{33} \end{vmatrix}$$

$$= a_{11}(a_{22}a_{33} - a_{23}a_{32}) - a_{12}(a_{21}a_{33} - a_{23}a_{31}) + a_{13}(a_{21}a_{32} - a_{22}a_{31})$$

$$= a_{11}a_{22}a_{33} + a_{12}a_{23}a_{31} + a_{13}a_{21}a_{32} - a_{11}a_{23}a_{32} - a_{12}a_{21}a_{33} - a_{13}a_{22}a_{31}. \quad (8\text{–}8)$$

It should be clear from this expression that each of the six products consists of one and only one element from each row and each column. Each of these products has been ordered by placing the first subscripts in natural numerical order. With the exception of the first term, the second subscripts are not in natural order. Let us consider the number of *inversions* of the second subscripts, that is, the number of times a greater integer precedes a smaller one.

	Second subscripts			*Number of inversions*
	1	2	3	0
Positive products	2	3	1	2
	3	1	2	2
	1	3	2	1
Negative products	2	1	3	1
	3	2	1	3

From this table, we see that the positive products have an even number of inversions, while the negative products have an odd number. Thus the correct sign for any term can be expressed $(-1)^k$, where k is the number of inversions. It is by means of a direct generalization of this study that we define the nth order determinant of the n square matrix. The expression

$$D = \begin{vmatrix} a_{11} & a_{12} & a_{13} & \ldots & a_{1n} \\ a_{21} & a_{22} & a_{23} & \ldots & a_{2n} \\ a_{31} & a_{32} & a_{33} & \ldots & a_{3n} \\ \vdots & & & & \vdots \\ a_{n1} & a_{n2} & a_{n3} & \ldots & a_{nn} \end{vmatrix} \quad (8\text{–}9)$$

is the *nth order determinant* associated with an n by n matrix. Thus, we define a function $Det: M \rightarrow D$, where M is an n by n matrix and D is given by Eq. (8–9). The value of D is equal to the algebraic sum of all possible products formed by taking one and only one element from each row and each column. The sign of each product is chosen as $(-1)^k$, where k is the number of inversions of the second subscripts when the factors are so arranged that their first subscripts are in natural numerical order.

In any possible product of n elements with the first subscripts in natural order, the second subscript in the first element may be any one of n numbers, the subscript for the second element any one of the remaining $n - 1$ numbers, and so on, so that there are $n!^* = n(n - 1)(n - 2) \cdots 2 \cdot 1$ terms in the expansion of D. For example, we recall that there are $3! = 6$ terms in the expansion of the third order determinant. There are $4! = 24$ in the fourth, and $5! = 120$ terms in the expansion of the fifth order determinant. Because of the large number of terms in the expansion of a determinant, our definition is clearly not a convenient way to find the value of the determinant. Before we consider a practical method of evaluation, we shall prove some of the elementary properties of determinants.

THEOREM 8–1.   *If the corresponding rows and columns of a matrix are interchanged, its determinant remains unchanged.*

For example,

$$\begin{vmatrix} a_{11} & a_{12} & a_{13} \\ a_{21} & a_{22} & a_{23} \\ a_{31} & a_{32} & a_{33} \end{vmatrix} = \begin{vmatrix} a_{11} & a_{21} & a_{31} \\ a_{12} & a_{22} & a_{32} \\ a_{13} & a_{23} & a_{33} \end{vmatrix}$$

Proof. We recall that for each element our notation indicated the row by the first subscript, and the column by the second subscript. If we now consider the determinant associated with a new matrix M' whose rows and columns are respectively the corresponding columns and rows of M, every term of D' (the determinant associated with M') will again have one element from each row and each column. If the second subscripts are placed in their numerical natural order, the number of inversions of the first subscripts will determine the sign of any particular term. Thus the interchange of rows and columns serves only to change the notation, and the result for each term is the same. Consequently, D' is identical to D.

As a direct result of Theorem 8–1, in any further property of determinants the words "row" and "column" may be interchanged throughout.

---

* The symbol $n!$ (read "factorial n") denotes the product of the positive integers from 1 to n. Specifically, $1! = 1$, $2! = 2$, $3! = 6$, and so on. This symbol will be used in later chapters.

THEOREM 8–2. *If any two columns (rows) of a determinant are interchanged, the sign of the determinant is changed.*

Proof. Let us first consider the interchange of two adjacent columns. In the expansion of the new determinant, the first subscripts will remain the same, but the second subscripts—those representing the columns—will be interchanged, and as a result the number of inversions in each term will be increased or decreased by one. Thus the sign of every term, and consequently the value of the determinants, will be changed.

Now suppose we wish to interchange the j and k columns (where for convenience $j < k$) and there are m columns between them. This may be done by moving the jth column to the position just to the left of the kth column (m interchanges), interchanging these two adjacent columns (1 interchange), and moving the kth column back to the original position of the jth column (m interchanges). Since the total number of interchanges, $2m + 1$, is odd, and each requires a change in sign, we again have our required result.

THEOREM 8–3. *If two columns (rows) of a matrix are identical, its determinant is zero.*

Proof. If D is the value of the determinant, with the two identical columns interchanged, the value becomes $-D$, by Theorem 8–2. But since the two columns were identical, the determinant has not changed. Thus, $D = -D$, that is $D = 0$.

THEOREM 8–4. *If each element of a column (row) in a determinant is multiplied by the same number m, the value of the determinant is multiplied by m.*

For example,

$$\begin{vmatrix} a_{11} & ma_{12} & a_{13} \\ a_{21} & ma_{22} & a_{23} \\ a_{31} & ma_{32} & a_{33} \end{vmatrix} = m \begin{vmatrix} a_{11} & a_{12} & a_{13} \\ a_{21} & a_{22} & a_{23} \\ a_{31} & a_{32} & a_{33} \end{vmatrix}.$$

Proof. This property follows directly from the definition. If each element of a column is multiplied by m, each term in the expansion of the determinant will have m as a factor.

As a direct result of Theorem 8–4, we have the following corollary.

COROLLARY 8–4. *Any quantity that is a factor of each element in a column (row) is actually a factor of the expansion of the determinant.*

THEOREM 8–5. *If three matrices M_1, M_2, and M_3 have corresponding elements equal except for one column (row) in which the elements of M_1 are the sums of the corresponding elements of M_2 and M_3, then $D_1 = D_2 + D_3$, where D_i is the determinant associated with M_i.*

For example,

$$\begin{vmatrix} a_{11} + a'_{11} & a_{12} & a_{13} \\ a_{21} + a'_{21} & a_{22} & a_{23} \\ a_{31} + a'_{31} & a_{32} & a_{33} \end{vmatrix} = \begin{vmatrix} a_{11} & a_{12} & a_{13} \\ a_{21} & a_{22} & a_{23} \\ a_{31} & a_{32} & a_{33} \end{vmatrix} + \begin{vmatrix} a'_{11} & a_{12} & a_{13} \\ a'_{21} & a_{22} & a_{23} \\ a'_{31} & a_{32} & a_{33} \end{vmatrix}.$$

Proof. Every term in the expansion of D_1 contains one and only one of these sums, each of which may be expressed as two terms. The expansions of D_2 and D_3 are the direct result.

THEOREM 8–6. *If each element of any column (row) of a matrix is multiplied by the same number m and added to the corresponding element of another column, the associated determinant remains unchanged.*

For example,

$$\begin{vmatrix} a_{11} & a_{12} & a_{13} \\ a_{21} & a_{22} & a_{23} \\ a_{31} & a_{32} & a_{33} \end{vmatrix} = \begin{vmatrix} a_{11} + ma_{13} & a_{12} & a_{13} \\ a_{21} + ma_{23} & a_{22} & a_{23} \\ a_{31} + ma_{33} & a_{32} & a_{33} \end{vmatrix}.$$

Proof. This follows directly by using Theorems 8–5, 8–4, and 8–3 in considering the determinant on the right.

Many of these properties will be useful in the evaluation of the nth order determinant. Methods for such evaluation will be given in the next article.

PROBLEMS

1. Explain why the following two determinants are equal. Verify this fact by actual evaluation.

$$\begin{vmatrix} 2 & 4 & 1 \\ 3 & 2 & -1 \\ -1 & 3 & 2 \end{vmatrix} \qquad \begin{vmatrix} 2 & 3 & -1 \\ 4 & 2 & 3 \\ 1 & -1 & 2 \end{vmatrix}$$

2. Show by actual expansion that the sign of the determinant

$$\begin{vmatrix} 3 & -1 & 2 \\ 2 & 4 & 5 \\ -1 & 3 & 2 \end{vmatrix}$$

is changed if the first and third row are interchanged.

Without evaluating, state why each of the determinants in Problems 3 and 4 is zero. Check by evaluating.

3.
$\begin{vmatrix} 2 & -3 & 2 \\ 1 & 2 & 1 \\ 6 & 4 & 6 \end{vmatrix}$
4.
$\begin{vmatrix} 3 & 1 & -2 \\ 2 & 7 & 3 \\ 6 & 2 & -4 \end{vmatrix}$

5. Evaluate the following determinant by factoring out the common terms from any row or column and then expanding. Check by expanding directly.

$$\begin{vmatrix} 3 & 3 & 5 \\ 6 & 16 & 8 \\ -12 & 6 & 10 \end{vmatrix}$$

6. Use Theorem 8–5 to express the sum of the two determinants as a single determinant. Check the work by evaluating all three.

$$\begin{vmatrix} 3 & 1 & -2 \\ 2 & 3 & 5 \\ -1 & 4 & 3 \end{vmatrix} + \begin{vmatrix} -2 & 1 & -2 \\ -1 & 3 & 5 \\ 2 & 4 & 3 \end{vmatrix}$$

7. In the following determinant, multiply each of the elements in the second row by 3, and form a new determinant by adding these results to the corresponding elements of the first row. Show by direct expansion that the value of the original determinant is unchanged.

$$\begin{vmatrix} 2 & 5 & -6 \\ -1 & 2 & 4 \\ 3 & 1 & 5 \end{vmatrix}$$

8. In the determinant of Problem 7, multiply each of the elements in the third column by 2 and subtract the products from the corresponding elements in the first column, forming a new determinant. Show by direct evaluation that the value of the original determinant is unchanged.

9. Determine the roots of the equation

$$\begin{vmatrix} 1 & 1 & 1 \\ x & a & b \\ x^2 & a^2 & b^2 \end{vmatrix} = 0.$$

[*Hint:* If $x = a$, the first two columns are equal.]

10. Determine the roots of the equation

$$\begin{vmatrix} 1 & a & a^2 & a^3 \\ 1 & b & b^2 & b^3 \\ 1 & c & c^2 & c^3 \\ 1 & x & x^2 & x^3 \end{vmatrix} = 0.$$

11. Find the roots of the equation

$$\begin{vmatrix} 3 & 1 & 9 \\ 2x & 2 & 6 \\ x^2 & 3 & 3 \end{vmatrix} = 0$$

by using Theorems 8–3 and 8–4, and check by expanding the determinant.

12. Prove that

$$2 \begin{vmatrix} a_1 & b_1 & c_1 \\ a_2 & b_2 & c_2 \\ a_3 & b_3 & c_3 \end{vmatrix} = \begin{vmatrix} b_1 + c_1 & c_1 + a_1 & a_1 + b_1 \\ b_2 + c_2 & c_2 + a_2 & a_2 + b_2 \\ b_3 + c_3 & c_3 + a_3 & a_3 + b_3 \end{vmatrix}.$$

8–3 Expansion of a determinant by minors. The statement in Problem 10 of the second set of problems in Article 8–1 may be considered the method for the expansion of a third order determinant by minors. The method holds true in general. The *minor* of an element of a square matrix of order n is the $(n-1)$st order determinant obtained by deleting the row and column in which this element lies. The minor of a_{ij} will be denoted by A_{ij}. We wish to prove the following theorem for the nth order determinant given in Eq. (8–9).

THEOREM 8–7. *The determinant is the algebraic sum of the products obtained by multiplying each element of a column (row) by its minor. The sign of each such product is $(-1)^{i+j}$, where the element is in the ith row and jth column.*

For example,

$$\begin{vmatrix} a_{11} & a_{12} & a_{13} & a_{14} \\ a_{21} & a_{22} & a_{23} & a_{24} \\ a_{31} & a_{32} & a_{33} & a_{34} \\ a_{41} & a_{42} & a_{43} & a_{44} \end{vmatrix} = -a_{12} \begin{vmatrix} a_{21} & a_{23} & a_{24} \\ a_{31} & a_{33} & a_{34} \\ a_{41} & a_{43} & a_{44} \end{vmatrix} + a_{22} \begin{vmatrix} a_{11} & a_{13} & a_{14} \\ a_{31} & a_{33} & a_{34} \\ a_{41} & a_{43} & a_{44} \end{vmatrix}$$

$$-a_{32} \begin{vmatrix} a_{11} & a_{13} & a_{14} \\ a_{21} & a_{23} & a_{24} \\ a_{41} & a_{43} & a_{44} \end{vmatrix} + a_{42} \begin{vmatrix} a_{11} & a_{13} & a_{14} \\ a_{21} & a_{23} & a_{24} \\ a_{31} & a_{33} & a_{34} \end{vmatrix}$$

is the expansion of the fourth order determinant by the second column.

Proof. The theorem is proved by noting two facts. Consider first the product $a_{11}A_{11}$. In this product, consisting of all the terms with a_{11} as a factor, all the signs of each term are correct, since the number of inversions in A_{11} is not changed by prefixing a_{11}.

Now consider any element a_{ij}. It may be moved to the original position of a_{11} by first moving the ith row to the first row, requiring $i - 1$ interchanges of rows, and then moving the jth column to the position of the first column, requiring an additional $j - 1$ interchange of columns. This process will produce $i - 1 + j - 1 = i + j - 2$ changes in sign. If D' is the new determinant, its relation to D is expressed by

$$D' = (-1)^{i+j-2}D = (-1)^{i+j}D.$$

Thus the terms of the expansion with a_{ij} as a factor are

$$(-1)^{i+j}a_{ij}A_{ij},$$

where A_{ij} is the original minor of a_{ij} in D. Thus D may be expanded by means of any column (row) as indicated in the theorem.

We are now prepared to evaluate any determinant. In the following examples, note the use of the foregoing theorems.

EXAMPLE 1. Find the value of the determinant

$$D = \begin{vmatrix} -4 & 2 & 5 & 6 \\ 2 & 1 & 0 & 3 \\ 7 & 2 & -3 & 2 \\ 4 & -1 & 7 & 5 \end{vmatrix}.$$

Solution. Since $a_{23} = 0$, it will simplify the work to expand by either the second row or third column. Since the elements in the third column are larger than the second row, we shall choose the second row. Thus,

$$D = -2\begin{vmatrix} 2 & 5 & 6 \\ 2 & -3 & 2 \\ -1 & 7 & 5 \end{vmatrix} + 1\begin{vmatrix} -4 & 5 & 6 \\ 7 & -3 & 2 \\ 4 & 7 & 5 \end{vmatrix} + 3\begin{vmatrix} -4 & 2 & 5 \\ 7 & 2 & -3 \\ 4 & -1 & 7 \end{vmatrix}.$$

Expanding each of the third order determinants, we get

$$\begin{vmatrix} 2 & 5 & 6 \\ 2 & -3 & 2 \\ -1 & 7 & 5 \end{vmatrix} = 2(-15 - 14) - 5(10 + 2) + 6(14 - 3)$$

$$= -58 - 60 + 66 = -52.$$

$$\begin{vmatrix} -4 & 5 & 6 \\ 7 & -3 & 2 \\ 4 & 7 & 5 \end{vmatrix} = -4(-15 - 14) - 5(35 - 8) + 6(49 + 12)$$

$$= 116 - 135 + 366 = 347.$$

$$\begin{vmatrix} -4 & 2 & 5 \\ 7 & 2 & -3 \\ 4 & -1 & 7 \end{vmatrix} = -4(14 - 3) - 2(49 + 12) + 5(-7 - 8)$$

$$= -44 - 122 - 75 = -241.$$

Using these values, we have

$$D = -2(-52) + 347 + 3(-241) = -272.$$

We note in this example that the work was shortened by the fact that one of the elements was zero. By making use of Theorem 8–6, we may introduce other zeros and shorten the work still further. Let us consider another example.

EXAMPLE 2. Find the value of the determinant

$$D = \begin{vmatrix} 3 & -2 & -1 & 2 \\ 4 & 1 & 2 & -3 \\ -9 & -5 & 7 & -8 \\ 1 & 5 & 3 & -2 \end{vmatrix}.$$

Solution. We look for an element equal to 1 or -1, and work with the row or column containing the ± 1. Let us select the -1 in the first row. By using Theorem 8–6, we are able to introduce zeros in the first row. In turn we (1) multiply the elements of the third column by 3 and add the products to the corresponding elements of the first column, (2) multiply the elements of the third column by -2 and add the products to the corresponding elements of the second column, and (3) multiply the elements of the third column by 2 and add the products to the corresponding elements of the fourth column. Therefore,

$$D = \begin{vmatrix} 0 & 0 & -1 & 0 \\ 10 & -3 & 2 & 1 \\ 12 & -19 & 7 & 6 \\ 10 & -1 & 3 & 4 \end{vmatrix}.$$

Now, expanding by the first row as in Example 1, we have

$$D = -1 \begin{vmatrix} 10 & -3 & 1 \\ 12 & -19 & 6 \\ 10 & -1 & 4 \end{vmatrix}.$$

We may again introduce zeros to simplify the work. In this third order determinant, (1) multiply the elements of the first row by -6 and add the products to the corresponding elements of the second row, (2) multiply the elements of the first row by -4 and add the products to the corresponding elements of the third row. This results in

$$D = -1 \begin{vmatrix} 10 & -3 & 1 \\ -48 & -1 & 0 \\ -30 & 11 & 0 \end{vmatrix},$$

which, expanded by the last column, gives

$$D = -1\{1[(-48)(11) - (-30)(-1)]\} = -1(-528 - 30) = 558.$$

If there is no element equal to 1 or -1 in any column or row, we are usually able to introduce such an element by using Theorem 8–6 and continuing as above. Although the introduction of a 1 is not necessary, the process eliminates the possibilities of fractions if there were none initially.

PROBLEMS

Evaluate each of the following determinants.

1. $\begin{vmatrix} 1 & -2 & 2 & -3 \\ 0 & 5 & 0 & -2 \\ 2 & 4 & -6 & 2 \\ 3 & -4 & 1 & -2 \end{vmatrix}$

2. $\begin{vmatrix} 2 & 4 & 3 & -5 \\ 3 & 0 & 2 & -1 \\ -2 & 3 & 1 & 6 \\ 1 & -4 & 2 & 8 \end{vmatrix}$

3. $\begin{vmatrix} 4 & 2 & 4 & 8 \\ 7 & 5 & 2 & 4 \\ -7 & 2 & 3 & -8 \\ 6 & 4 & 5 & 6 \end{vmatrix}$

4. $\begin{vmatrix} 3 & 2 & -1 & 4 \\ 4 & -3 & 5 & -2 \\ 6 & -1 & 4 & 7 \\ 5 & -2 & 8 & 3 \end{vmatrix}$

5. $\begin{vmatrix} 3 & -1 & 2 & 6 \\ 2 & 3 & 5 & 4 \\ 4 & -2 & 2 & 7 \\ -3 & 2 & -1 & -3 \end{vmatrix}$

6. $\begin{vmatrix} 1 & 1 & 1 & 1 \\ 1 & 2 & 3 & 4 \\ 1 & 3 & 6 & 10 \\ 1 & 4 & 10 & 20 \end{vmatrix}$

8-4 Solution of a system of linear equations by determinants. In Articles 7–10 and 7–11 we discussed the solution of systems of linear equations in two and three unknowns. Systems of linear equations involving any number of unknowns, with the proper number of equations, may be expressed in terms of determinants. In considering the general case with n linear equations in n unknowns,

$$\begin{aligned}
a_{11}x_1 + a_{12}x_2 + \cdots + a_{1n}x_n &= k_1, \\
a_{21}x_1 + a_{22}x_2 + \cdots + a_{2n}x_n &= k_2, \\
&\vdots \\
a_{n1}x_1 + a_{n2}x_2 + \cdots + a_{nn}x_n &= k_n,
\end{aligned} \tag{8-10}$$

we are able to prove a theorem which is known as Cramer's Rule, in honor of the Swiss mathematician Gabriel Cramer (1704–1752).

THEOREM 8-8. *If D is the determinant of the coefficients of the unknowns, the product of D and any one of the unknowns is equal to the determinant D_i, obtained from D by substituting the constant terms in place of the coefficients of that unknown and leaving the other elements unchanged.*

Proof. Since

$$D = \begin{vmatrix} a_{11} & a_{12} & \ldots & a_{1n} \\ a_{21} & a_{22} & \ldots & a_{2n} \\ \vdots & & & \\ a_{n1} & a_{n2} & \ldots & a_{nn} \end{vmatrix},$$

by Theorem 8–4,

$$Dx_1 = \begin{vmatrix} a_{11}x_1 & a_{12} & \ldots & a_{1n} \\ a_{21}x_1 & a_{22} & \ldots & a_{2n} \\ \vdots & & & \\ a_{n1}x_1 & a_{n2} & \ldots & a_{nn} \end{vmatrix}.$$

If we now multiply each element of the second column by x_2, of the third by x_3, and so on, and add all these products to the corresponding elements in the first column, we have, by Theorem 8–6,

$$\begin{aligned}
Dx_1 &= \begin{vmatrix} a_{11}x_1 + a_{12}x_2 + \cdots + a_{1n}x_n & a_{12} & \ldots & a_{1n} \\ a_{21}x_1 + a_{22}x_2 + \cdots + a_{2n}x_n & a_{22} & \ldots & a_{2n} \\ \vdots & & & \\ a_{n1}x_1 + a_{n2}x_2 + \cdots + a_{nn}x_n & a_{n2} & \ldots & a_{nn} \end{vmatrix} \\
&= \begin{vmatrix} k_1 & a_{12} & \ldots & a_{1n} \\ k_2 & a_{22} & \ldots & a_{2n} \\ \vdots & & & \\ k_n & a_{n2} & \ldots & a_{nn} \end{vmatrix} = D_1.
\end{aligned}$$

In this way, we find

$$Dx_1 = D_1, \qquad Dx_2 = D_2, \qquad \ldots, \qquad Dx_n = D_n, \tag{8-11}$$

where D_i is obtained from D by substituting $k_1, k_2, \ldots, k_n$ for the elements $a_{1i}, a_{2i}, \ldots, a_{ni}$ of the ith column of D.

If $D \neq 0$,* the unique solution of Eqs. (8–10) is obtained from Eqs. (8–11) by division:

$$x_1 = \frac{D_1}{D}, \qquad x_2 = \frac{D_2}{D}, \qquad \cdots, \qquad x_n = \frac{D_n}{D}. \qquad (8\text{–}12)$$

It is clear that this set of values satisfies the system given in Eqs. (8–10), and therefore is a solution. For example, the first equation is satisfied, since

$$k_1 D - a_{11} D_1 - a_{12} D_2 - \cdots - a_{1n} D_n$$

is the expansion of

$$\begin{vmatrix} k_1 & a_{11} & a_{12} \ldots a_{1n} \\ k_1 & a_{11} & a_{12} \ldots a_{1n} \\ k_2 & a_{21} & a_{22} \ldots a_{2n} \\ \vdots & & \\ k_n & a_{n1} & a_{n2} \ldots a_{nn} \end{vmatrix} \qquad (8\text{–}13)$$

by the first row. But this determinant is zero, since the first two rows are identical. The other equations are similarly satisfied.

PROBLEMS

1. Solve the systems of equations given in Problems 1, 3, 5, and 7 of Article 7–11 by the method of this article.

2. Solve the systems of equations given in Problems 2, 4, 6, and 8 of Article 7–11 by the method of this article.

Solve the following systems of equations by determinants.

3. $x + y + z + w = -4$
   $x + 2y + 3z + 4w = 0$
   $x + 3y + 6z + 10w = 9$
   $x + 4y + 10z + 20w = 24$

4. $x + 2y - z = 8$
   $y + 3z - w = 3$
   $z + 4w - x = -20$
   $w + 5x - y = 9$

5. One of the well-known methods (used in numerical analysis with high-speed computing machines) of finding the nth degree expression† which passes through

---

* If $D = 0$, solutions may or may not exist. A complete discussion is beyond the scope of this book.

† Here we mean an nth degree polynomial, which will be discussed in the next chapter. [See Eq. (9–1). Recall the definition in Article 3–3.]

$n + 1$ distinct points makes use of determinants. Explain why the determinant,

$$\begin{vmatrix} f(x) & 1 & x & x^2 \\ f(x_1) & 1 & x_1 & x_1^2 \\ f(x_2) & 1 & x_2 & x_2^2 \\ f(x_3) & 1 & x_3 & x_3^2 \end{vmatrix},$$

set equal to zero, can be considered as the defining equation of the function f, where the expression for $f(x)$ is second degree and is satisfied by the coordinates of three points. [*Hint:* If $x = x_1$, $f(x) = f(x_1)$, so that the first two rows are identical, and so on.]

6. Explain Problem 16, Article 8–1, in the light of Problem 5 above.

7. By expanding the determinant, simplify the expression,

$$\begin{vmatrix} f(x) & 1 & x & x^2 \\ 1 & 1 & 1 & 1 \\ 2 & 1 & 2 & 4 \\ 11 & 1 & -1 & 1 \end{vmatrix} = 0,$$

and thus find the specific quadratic function of the form $f(x) = ax^2 + bx + c$ which passes through $(1, 1)$, $(2, 2)$, and $(-1, 11)$.

CHAPTER 9

POLYNOMIAL FUNCTIONS

In Chapter 7 we considered the first and second degree functions. We wish to generalize this type of function. Any function whose defining equation can be expressed in the form

$$f(x) = a_0x^n + a_1x^{n-1} + a_2x^{n-2} + \cdots + a_{n-1}x + a_n, \qquad (9\text{--}1)$$

where $a_0 \neq 0$, n is a positive integer or zero, and a_i $(i = 0, 1, 2, \ldots n)$ are constants, is called a *rational integral function* or a *polynomial of the nth degree in* x. (Compare the definition in Article 3–3.) Unless otherwise stated, $f(x)$ will denote such a function in this chapter.

9–1 Certain theorems. There are several theorems of considerable importance in the study of the polynomial function which must now be established, not only to facilitate graphing the function but also to help solve polynomial equations.

THEOREM 9–1. *(The Remainder Theorem) If a polynomial $f(x)$ is divided by $x - r$, where r is any constant, until a constant remainder independent of x is obtained, this remainder is equal to $f(r)$.*

Proof. Let $q(x)$ denote the quotient when $f(x)$ is divided by $x - r$, and let R denote the constant remainder. Then $f(x)$ may be expressed [recall Eqs. (3–8) and (3–9) of Article 3–3] by the identity

$$f(x) \equiv (x - r) \cdot q(x) + R, \qquad (9\text{--}2)$$

where clearly $q(x)$ is of degree $n - 1$, since we assume $f(x)$ is of degree n. Since this identity is true for all values of x, it is true for $x = r$. Therefore,

$$f(r) = (r - r) \cdot q(r) + R = 0 \cdot q(r) + R$$

or

$$f(r) = R. \qquad (9\text{--}3)$$

ILLUSTRATION 1. Let $f(x) = 5x^3 - 14x + 3$, and $r = 2$. Then, as was shown in Example 3, Article 3–3, $R = 15$. By substituting $r = 2$ for x in $f(x)$, we have $f(2) = 5(2)^3 - 14(2) + 3 = 40 - 28 + 3 = 15$, which is in accord with the Remainder Theorem.

Because of this theorem, the method of synthetic division described in Article 3–3 is most useful in finding the value of $f(x)$ for different values of

x. It has advantages over direct substitution that are especially evident either when n is large or when r is other than a small integer.

THEOREM 9–2. (*The Factor Theorem*) *If* $f(r) = R$ *is zero, that is, r is a zero of* $f(x)$, *then* $(x - r)$ *is a factor of* $f(x)$.

Proof. Since r is a zero of $f(x)$, that is $R = 0$, we have

$$f(x) \equiv (x - r) \cdot q(x) + 0.$$

Thus $(x - r)$ is a factor.

THEOREM 9–3. (*Converse of the Factor Theorem*) *If* $(x - r)$ *is a factor of* $f(x)$, *then* $f(r) = R = 0$, *and r is a zero of* $f(x)$.

Proof. Since $x - r$ is a factor of $f(x)$,

$$f(x) \equiv (x - r) \cdot q(x),$$

where $q(x)$ is the quotient of $f(x)/(x - r)$. Therefore,

$$f(r) = (r - r) \cdot q(r) = 0 \cdot q(r) = 0,$$

which states that r is a zero of $f(x)$.

ILLUSTRATION 2. The quantity $x - 3$ is a factor of $f(x) \equiv x^3 - 27$, since $f(3) = (3)^3 - 27 = 0$.

ILLUSTRATION 3. The functional equation $f(x) = x^3 - 6x^2 + 3x + 10$ is exactly divisible by $x - 2$, since $f(2) = 0$. The fact that $f(2) = 0$ is shown by synthetic division.

$$
\begin{array}{rrrr|r}
1 & -6 & 3 & 10 & 2 \\
 & 2 & -8 & -10 & \\
\hline
1 & -4 & -5 & 0 &
\end{array}
$$

PROBLEMS

By using synthetic division, find the remainder, and check by direct substitution, when

1. $3x^2 - 2x - 4$ is divided by $x - 3$
2. $x^3 + 4x - 7$ is divided by $x - 3$
3. $x^3 - 2x^2 + 9$ is divided by $x + 2$
4. $x^4 - 2x^3 - 3x^2 - 4x - 8$ is divided by (a) $x - 2$, (b) $x + 1$
5. $2x^4 - 3x^3 - 20x^2 - 6$ is divided by (a) $x - 4$, (b) $x + 3$
6. $x^3 + 3x^2 - 2x - 5$ is divided by (a) $x + 2$, (b) $x + 3$

By using the Factor Theorem, determine whether the first quantity is a factor of the second in Problems 7 through 12.

7. $x - 2$, $x^4 + 3x^3 - 5x^2 + 2x - 24$
8. $x + 3$, $x^3 - 4x^2 - 18x + 9$
9. $x - 3$, $x^4 - 5x^3 + 8x^2 + 15x - 2$
10. $x - 5$, $x^3 + 2x^2 - 25x - 50$
11. $2x + 3$, $2x^4 + 5x^3 + 3x^2 + 8x + 12$
12. $3x + 1$, $9x^3 + 6x^2 + 4x + 2$
13. Show that $x - y$ is a factor of $x^5 - y^5$, $x^6 - y^6$, $x^7 - y^7$, and $x^8 - y^8$. By using synthetic division, find the quotient in each case.
14. Show that $x + y$ is a factor of $x^5 + y^5$ and $x^7 + y^7$. By using synthetic division, find the quotient in each case.

One of the more important theorems in connection with the zeros of a polynomial function may be expressed in terms of synthetic division.

THEOREM 9–4. *In the synthetic division of*

$$f(x) = a_0 x^n + a_1 x^{n-1} + a_2 x^{n-2} + \cdots + a_{n-1} x + a_n \quad by \quad x - r,$$

where $a_0 > 0$,

1. *if $r > 0$ and all the numbers in the third row are positive, then r is an upper bound for the positive zeros of $f(x)$.*
2. *if $r < 0$ and the signs of the numbers in the third row alternate in sign, then r is a lower bound for the negative zeros of $f(x)$.*

Proof. Because of the process of synthetic division, in either (1) or (2) a numerical increase in r will numerically increase all the numbers in the third row except the first. Thus, if r were to be increased numerically, the final number in the third row would be numerically increased, so that the remainder would never be zero for any numerical increase in r.

EXAMPLE. Find an upper and lower bound for the zeros of $f(x) = x^4 + 3x^3 - 9x^2 + 3x - 10$.

Solution. By using synthetic division, we have

$$
\begin{array}{rrrrr|r}
1 & 3 & -9 & 3 & -10 & \underline{3} \\
  & 3 & 18 & 27 & 90 & . \\
\hline
1 & 6 & 9 & 30 & 80 &
\end{array}
$$

Since all the numbers in the third row are positive, 3 is an upper bound for the zeros of $f(x)$.

Again,

$$
\begin{array}{rrrrr|r}
1 & 3 & -9 & 3 & -10 & \underline{\,-6\,} \\
 & -6 & 18 & -54 & 306 & .\\
\hline
1 & -3 & 9 & -51 & 296 &
\end{array}
$$

Since the signs in the third row alternate, there is no zero less than -6.

The next theorem, unfortunately, has no elementary proof but, because of its importance, will be assumed.

THEOREM 9–5. (*Fundamental Theorem of Algebra*) *Every polynomial function whose defining equation is*

$$f(x) = a_0x^n + a_1x^{n-1} + a_2x^{n-2} + \cdots + a_{n-1}x + a_n,$$

$n \geq 1$, $a_0 \neq 0$, *has at least one (real or imaginary)* zero.*

This theorem was first proved by the German mathematician Karl Friedrich Gauss, at the age of 22. It enables us to prove a theorem on the number of zeros of a polynomial function.

THEOREM 9–6. *Every polynomial function whose defining equation is*

$$f(x) = a_0x^n + a_1x^{n-1} + a_2x^{n-2} + \cdots + a_{n-1}x + a_n, \qquad a_0 \neq 0$$

has exactly n zeros.

Proof. Since, by Theorem 9–5, $f(x)$ has at least one zero, r_1, Theorem 9–2 implies that $(x - r_1)$ is a factor of $f(x)$. Thus,

$$f(x) \equiv (x - r_1) \cdot q_1(x), \tag{9–4}$$

where $q_1(x)$ is the quotient of $f(x)$ by $(x - r_1)$. Again, $q_1(x)$ has a zero r_2, so that

$$q_1(x) \equiv (x - r_2) \cdot q_2(x),$$

where $q_2(x)$ is the quotient of $q_1(x)$ by $(x - r_2)$. Therefore, we may write

$$f(x) \equiv (x - r_1) \cdot (x - r_2) \cdot q_2(x). \tag{9–5}$$

Since we know that each new quotient is of one degree less than the preceding quotient, we can continue the process until we finally have

$$f(x) \equiv (x - r_1)(x - r_2) \cdots (x - r_n) \cdot q_n(x), \tag{9–6}$$

---

* Imaginary numbers are discussed in some detail in Chapter 16.

where, since there are n factors $(x - r_i)$, $q_n(x)$ must be the constant a_0; hence

$$f(x) \equiv a_0(x - r_1)(x - r_2) \cdots (x - r_n), \qquad (9\text{-}7)$$

where each r_i is a zero of $f(x)$.

Let r be any number. Since Eq. (9-7) is an identity, it is true for all values of x. Thus,

$$f(r) \equiv a_0(r - r_1)(r - r_2) \cdots (r - r_n).$$

If $r \neq r_i$ for any i, none of the factors $(r - r_i)$ is zero. Since $a_0 \neq 0$, $f(r) \neq 0$, and r is not a zero of $f(x)$. Therefore there are *exactly n zeros*, and the theorem is proved.

ILLUSTRATION 4. The function $(x - 3)^2(x - 1)(x + 2)^3$ is a polynomial of the sixth degree. Its six zeros are 3, 3, 1, -2, -2, -2. Note that any zero which occurs m times is considered as m zeros.

PROBLEMS

Find by inspection the zeros of each of the following functions, and give the multiplicity of each.

1. $(x - 2)(x - 3)^2(x + 4)^3$ 2. $(x + 1)^4(x - 2)^5$
3. $(x + 7)(2x - 3)^3$ 4. $(x^2 - 4x + 4)(x^2 + 3x - 10)$
5. $(3x + 5)(x^2 - 6x + 9)^2$

Find an upper bound and a lower bound for the zeros of the following functions.

6. $x^3 - 3x^2 - 2x + 15$ 7. $x^3 + 2x^2 - 7x - 8$
8. $x^4 - 2x^3 - 7x^2 + 10x + 10$ 9. $x^4 - x^3 - x^2 - 2x - 6$
10. $x^4 - 4x^3 + x^2 + 6x + 2$ 11. $x^4 - 5x^2 + 6x - 9$
12. $x^3 - 8x + 5$ 13. $x^3 + 16x - 29$
14. $x^5 + 5x^2 - 7$ 15. $x^5 - 3x^3 + 24$

9-2 Graphing of polynomial functions. One of the methods of finding the real zeros of a function was mentioned in connection with the graphs in Article 5-2. It is quite possible to use this method for any polynomial function. Since, by using synthetic division, we can easily obtain the values of the function for any value of the variable, a table of values can be constructed and the graph may be sketched. Care must be taken in joining the plotted points. We recall that the real zeros of a function f are the abscissas of the points where the graph of $y = f(x)$ crosses or touches the x-axis.

EXAMPLE 1. Draw the graph of $y = f(x) = x^4 - 2x^3 - 7x^2 + 10x + 10$, and verify that it has one real zero between -3 and -2, one between -1 and 0, and two between 2 and 3.

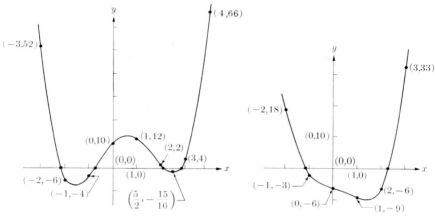

FIGURE 9–1   FIGURE 9–2

Solution. First construct the table of values shown below. For any arbitrary x, the corresponding value of the function is found by synthetic division. Usually it is wise to use all integral values of x between an upper and lower bound. (Why?) In addition, fractional values may be necessary to ascertain the shape of the curve. The values from the table have been plotted as points and the graph drawn in Fig. 9–1. Note that the scales on the two axes are conveniently *not* the same. From the figure it is clear that the zeros are located as suggested in the statement of the example.

x	-3	-2	-1	0	1	2	$2\frac{1}{2}$	3	4
y	52	-6	-4	10	12	2	$-\frac{15}{16}$	4	66

In Example 1 the fourth degree function has four real zeros. This is not always the case, for some of the zeros may be imaginary. An imaginary zero of a function cannot be approximated from its graph.

EXAMPLE 2. Draw the graph of the function whose defining equation is $y = f(x) = x^4 - x^3 - x^2 - 2x - 6$, and approximate its real zeros.

Solution. Again the table of values is constructed, the points are plotted, and the graph is drawn (Fig. 9–2).

x	-2	-1	0	1	2	3
y	18	-3	-6	-9	-6	33

Although the function is of the fourth degree, its graph crosses the x-axis only twice. These two real zeros are between -2 and -1, and between 2 and 3, while the other two are imaginary.

There is, unfortunately, no simple method for approximating the imaginary zeros of a general polynomial function.

PROBLEMS

Draw the graphs of the function defined by each of the following equations, and thus verify the statement given in Problems 1 through 4.

1. $f(x) = x^3 - x^2 - 2x + 1$ has one zero between -2 and -1, 0 and 1, and 1 and 2.

2. $f(x) = x^3 - 3x + 1$ has one zero between -2 and -1, 0 and 1, and 1 and 2.

3. $f(x) = x^4 - 2x^2 + 12x - 17$ has one zero between -3 and -2, and one between 1 and 2.

4. $f(x) = x^4 - 4x^3 + x^2 + 6x + 2$ has two zeros between 2 and 3, and two between -1 and 0.

Draw the graphs of the following functional equations, showing the location of all the real zeros.

5. $f(x) = x^4 - 20x^2 + 48x - 32$
6. $f(x) = x^3 + x^2 - 3x - 4$
7. $f(x) = 4x^3 + 8x^2 - 11x + 3$
8. $f(x) = x^4 - 2x^3 + 3x^2 + x + 6$
9. $f(x) = x^5 - 3x^3 + 9x^2 - 8x + 11$
10. $f(x) = -x^4 + 2x^2 + 8x + 3$

9–3 General remarks on zeros and roots. We recall that the zeros of any function are identical with the roots of the equation formed by equating the function to zero. Consequently, all our previous remarks about the zeros of the polynomial function apply also to the roots of the associated equation.

In Chapter 7 we found specific methods for solving any polynomial equation

$$a_0 x^n + a_1 x^{n-1} + a_2 x^{n-2} + \cdots + a_{n-1} x + a_n = 0 \qquad (a_0 \neq 0)$$

when $n = 1$ (linear equation) and $n = 2$ (quadratic equation). There are also formulas for solving this type of equation when $n = 3$ and 4, but these are beyond the scope of this book. Tartaglia was the first to obtain formulas for the solution of the general cubic equation. These were published in 1545 by Cardan and are known as *Cardan's formulas*. Shortly thereafter Ferrari obtained formulas for the solution of the general quartic or fourth degree equation. For equations when $n \geq 5$, it has been proved that, in general, no algebraic formulas for the roots in terms of the coefficients exist. Many attempts were made to obtain general formulas, but finally, in 1824, N. H. Abel (1802–1829), a Norwegian, proved that in the general case no such formulas exist. Later, E. Galois (1811–1832), a Frenchman, was able to show that such formulas did exist under certain conditions.

It is comparatively simple, however, to find all the rational roots of a polynomial equation and approximate any irrational roots. Imaginary roots will be discussed briefly in Chapter 16.

9–4 Rational roots. With regard to the rational roots of an equation with integral coefficients, we have the following theorem.

THEOREM 9–7. *If the rational number p/q, a fraction in lowest terms, is a root of the equation*

$$a_0 x^n + a_1 x^{n-1} + a_2 x^{n-2} + \cdots + a_{n-1} x + a_n = 0, \qquad (9\text{–}8)$$

where a_i $(i = 0, 1, 2, \ldots, n)$ are integral coefficients, then p is an exact divisor of a_n and q is an exact divisor of a_0.

Proof. Since p/q is a root of Eq. (9–8), we have

$$a_0 \left(\frac{p}{q}\right)^n + a_1 \left(\frac{p}{q}\right)^{n-1} + a_2 \left(\frac{p}{q}\right)^{n-2} + \cdots + a_{n-1} \left(\frac{p}{q}\right) + a_n = 0.$$

Multiplying each term of this equation by q^n, we get

$$a_0 p^n + a_1 p^{n-1} q + a_2 p^{n-2} q^2 + \cdots + a_{n-1} p q^{n-1} + a_n q^n = 0. \qquad (9\text{–}9)$$

If we transpose $a_n q^n$ to the right side and divide both members by p,

$$a_0 p^{n-1} + a_1 p^{n-2} q + a_2 p^{n-3} q^2 + \cdots + a_{n-1} q^{n-1} = \frac{-a_n q^n}{p}.$$

Since each a_i, p, and q is an integer, the left member, and therefore the right member, is an integer. Also, p and q have no common factor, so that p does not divide q^n. Thus p is an exact divisor of a_n.

If, in Eq. (9–9), we take the term $a_0 p^n$ to the opposite side of the equation and divide both members by q, we get

$$a_1 p^{n-1} + a_2 p^{n-2} q + \cdots + a_{n-1} p q^{n-2} + a_n q^{n-1} = \frac{-a_0 p^n}{q}.$$

By the same type of argument, we have the fact that q is an exact divisor of a_0.

A direct corollary of this is clearly the following theorem.

THEOREM 9–8. *Any rational root of the equation*

$$x^n + a_1 x^{n-1} + a_2 x^{n-2} + \cdots + a_{n-1} x + a_n = 0, \qquad (9\text{–}10)$$

where each a_i is an integral coefficient, must be an integer which is an exact divisor of the constant term a_n.

We are now prepared to find all the rational roots of any polynomial equation of the type given by Eq. (9–8).

EXAMPLE 1. Solve the equation

$$x^4 - x^3 - 7x^2 - 14x - 24 = 0$$

by first finding the rational roots.

Solution. In examining the equation for possible rational roots, we find by Theorem 9–8 that they are ± 1, ± 2, ± 3, ± 4, ± 6, ± 8, ± 12, and ± 24. By synthetic division we find that 1, 2, and 3 are not roots. For $x = 4$,

$$
\begin{array}{rrrrr|l}
1 & -1 & -7 & -14 & -24 & \underline{\,4\,} \\
  & 4 & 12 & 20 & 24 & \\
\hline
1 & 3 & 5 & 6 & 0 &
\end{array}
$$

Putting this result in algebraic form (Eq. 3–9), we get

$$x^4 - x^3 - 7x^2 - 14x - 24 \equiv (x^3 + 3x^2 + 5x + 6)(x - 4).$$

Since $x - 4$ is a factor of the original equation, $x = 4$ is one root, and our problem reduces to finding the roots of the depressed equation $x^3 + 3x^2 + 5x + 6 = 0$. Since all the signs in this equation are plus, there are no positive roots. (Why?) By using synthetic division, we find -1 is not a root but $x = -2$ is a root.

$$
\begin{array}{rrrr|l}
1 & 3 & 5 & 6 & \underline{-2} \\
  & -2 & -2 & -6 & \\
\hline
1 & 1 & 3 & 0 &
\end{array}
$$

The new depressed equation is $x^2 + x + 3 = 0$. Solving this by the quadratic formula (Eq. 7–10), we have $x = (-1 \pm \sqrt{-11})/2$, so that our complete solution is

$$x = 4, \qquad -2, \qquad \frac{-1 \pm \sqrt{-11}}{2},$$

with the last two roots imaginary.

EXAMPLE 2. Solve for the exact roots of

$$4x^5 - 16x^4 + 17x^3 - 19x^2 + 13x - 3 = 0.$$

Solution. Since the signs of the terms alternate, this equation has no negative roots. (Why?) Its possible rational roots are 1, 3, $\frac{1}{2}$, $\frac{3}{2}$, $\frac{1}{4}$, and $\frac{3}{4}$.

By using synthetic division, we find that 1 is not a root but $\frac{1}{2}$ is.

4	−16	17	−19	13	−3	$\frac{1}{2}$
	2	−7	5	−7	3	
4	−14	10	−14	6	0	

Since the depressed equation has a common factor of 2 in each term, it may be divided out, reducing to $2x^4 - 7x^3 + 5x^2 - 7x + 3 = 0$. Again we find that $\frac{1}{2}$ is a root, so that it is a double root of the original equation.

2	−7	5	−7	3	$\frac{1}{2}$
	1	−3	1	−3	
2	−6	2	−6	0	

Again, factoring out the common 2, we find that the new depressed equation becomes $x^3 - 3x^2 + x - 3 = 0$. The only possible remaining rational root is the integer 3. (Why?)

1	−3	1	−3	3
	3	0	3	
1	0	1	0	

We see that 3 is a root, and the solution of the depressed equation $x^2 + 1 = 0$ gives the final two imaginary roots $\pm\sqrt{-1}$. Thus the complete solution is $x = \frac{1}{2}, \frac{1}{2}, 3, \pm\sqrt{-1}$.

PROBLEMS

Find the exact roots of the following equations.
1. $2x^3 - 3x^2 - 11x + 6 = 0$
2. $x^3 - 6x^2 + 11x - 6 = 0$
3. $x^4 - 16x^3 + 86x^2 - 176x + 105 = 0$
4. $x^3 + x^2 - 24x + 36 = 0$
5. $x^4 - x^3 - 19x^2 + 49x - 30 = 0$
6. $x^4 - 4x^3 + 4x - 1 = 0$
7. $4x^4 + 8x^3 - 7x^2 - 21x - 9 = 0$
8. $2x^4 + 5x^3 - 11x^2 - 20x + 12 = 0$
9. $x^4 - 4x^3 + 6x^2 - 4x + 1 = 0$

10. $10x^4 - 13x^3 + 17x^2 - 26x - 6 = 0$
11. $8x^5 - 12x^4 + 14x^3 - 13x^2 + 6x - 1 = 0$
12. $12x^3 - 52x^2 + 61x - 15 = 0$

Solve each of the following for all positive values of θ less than 2π.

13. $4 \sin^4 \theta - 12 \sin \theta \cos^2 \theta - 7 \cos^2 \theta + 9 \sin \theta + 5 = 0$. [*Hint:* Use the identity $\cos^2 \theta \equiv 1 - \sin^2 \theta$ and then simplify by letting $x = \sin \theta$.]
14. $4 \sin^4 \theta - 4 \sin \theta \cos^2 \theta - 11 \cos^2 \theta + 3 \sin \theta + 8 = 0$
15. $3 \tan \theta \sec^2 \theta + 3 \sec^2 \theta - 4 \tan \theta - 4 = 0$

9–5 Irrational roots. There are several well-known approximation methods* for solving polynomial equations for irrational roots. We shall consider the most elementary method. In Article 9–2 we noticed that any simple root of $f(x) = 0$ could theoretically be isolated. If the function is relatively simple, this can be done with little work. If $f(a)$ and $f(b)$ are opposite in sign, there is at least one value of x between a and b where $f(x) = 0$. It is this basic idea that will be used in the following example.

EXAMPLE 1. Find the approximate value of the largest positive root of $x^3 - x^2 - 3x + 1 = 0$.

Solution. By first plotting the graph of the function $y = x^3 - x^2 - 3x + 1$, as shown in Fig. 9–3, we note that the root which we wish to approximate is between 2 and 3. If we divide this interval into ten equal parts and successively use synthetic division for the values $x = 2.1, 2.2, 2.3, \ldots, 2.9, 3$, we find $f(2.1) = -0.45$, while $f(2.2) = 0.21$, so that the root lies between 2.1 and 2.2. If we repeat this process for the values 2.11, 2.12, 2.13, \ldots, 2.19, 2.2, we find $f(2.17) = -0.0006$ but $f(2.18) = 0.0678$. We are thus led to believe that $x = 2.17$ represents the root correct to two decimal places. In fact, $f(2.171) = 0.00621$, which indicates that $x = 2.170$ is correct to three decimal places. This process may, of course, be continued indefinitely.

The amount of work involved in approximating such a root may be greatly reduced by the method of *linear interpolation*. We found that the root in question lay between 2.1 and 2.2. This section of the curve appears in Fig. 9–4, with the location of the two points whose abscissas are 2.1 and 2.2. If we assume that the curve approximates a straight line

---

* Methods such as Graeffe's, Horner's, or Newton's appear in most books on the theory of equations. With the advent of high-speed computing machines, Newton's method has become most important. Rather than assuming a straight line between two points on the curve, it makes use of one point and estimates where the approximating tangent to the curve at that point crosses the x-axis. Its simplicity is in the repetitive nature of the process, which can be used for any type of reasonably well-behaved function, whether polynomial or not.

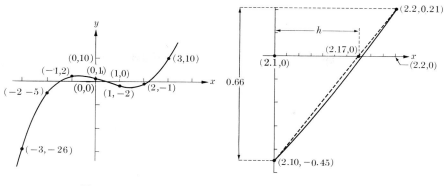

FIGURE 9–3   FIGURE 9–4

between the two points, by similar triangles

$$\frac{h}{0.45} = \frac{0.1}{0.66},$$

so that $h = 0.07$ approximately. Therefore, a good estimate for x is $2.1 + 0.07 = 2.17$. We now evaluate $f(2.17)$ and find it negative. From the way in which the curve is drawn, we realize that the root in question is greater than 2.17. By evaluating $f(2.18)$, we isolate this root without trying all the other eight possible values. This method of linear interpolation can be carried out for each new decimal, until the desired accuracy is obtained.

The beauty of this method is its simplicity. Moreover, it can be used to approximate any real root, provided the graph of the function actually crosses the x-axis, rather than merely being tangent to it.

The reader will recall that in Article 6–13 we found the circular functional values of θ, when θ was given in the table. If θ is some value between two given values in the table, we may use this same general method of linear interpolation. Specifically, if x and $x + (0.0001)r$ are consecutive values in Table I (the column marked radians), and r is any integer between 0 and 29,* we may approximate $\sin (x + r)$ by interpolating by proportion (assuming a straight line):

$$\sin (x + r) = \sin x + \frac{r}{29} [\sin (x + 0.0029) - \sin x]. \qquad (9\text{–}11)$$

---

* In almost every case the difference between two consecutive numbers in the appropriate column is 0.0029. Since we are dealing with approximations of irrational numbers (equal subdivisions of the arc length 2π of a unit circle), these numbers are not exact. It may happen that the difference is 0.0030, and if so, this should be taken into account. See, for example, the entries 0.3752 and 0.3782.

The other functional values are found by similar formulas.

EXAMPLE 2. Find sin 0.4236.

Solution. Since 0.4236 lies between 0.4218 and 0.4247, $r = 36 - 18 = 18$, so that

$$\sin 0.4235 = \sin 0.4218 + \tfrac{18}{29} (\sin 0.4247 - \sin 0.4218)$$
$$= 0.4094 + \tfrac{18}{29}(0.4120 - 0.4094)$$
$$= 0.4094 + 0.0016$$
$$= 0.4110.$$

EXAMPLE 3. Find cos 1.0071.

Solution. With 1.0071 between 1.0065 and 1.0094, we have $r = 6$, so that

$$\cos 1.0071 = \cos 1.0065 + \tfrac{6}{29} (\cos 1.0094 - \cos 1.0065)$$
$$= 0.5348 + \tfrac{6}{29}(0.5324 - 0.5348)$$
$$= 0.5348 - 0.0005$$
$$= 0.5343.$$

The table may also be interpolated to find the number, approximated to the nearest four decimal places, when the value of a function of this number lies between two entries in the table. If sin θ is given, we find two consecutive entries in the sine column between which the given value lies. Thus, letting $\theta = x + (0.0001)r$ where r is some integer between 0 and 29, and x and $x + 0.0029$ are the consecutive entries in the table, we find r by using the same approximating formula (Eq. 9–11) solved for $r/29$:

$$\frac{r}{29} = \frac{\sin (x + (0.0001r)) - \sin x}{\sin (x + 0.0029) - \sin x}. \tag{9-12}$$

Other functions follow the same pattern.

EXAMPLE 4. Find the number θ between 0 and $\pi/2$ if sin $\theta = 0.6231$.

Solution. We locate 0.6231 in the sine column between sin 0.6720 = 0.6225 and sin 0.6749 = 0.6248. Thus

$$\frac{r}{29} = \frac{0.6231 - 0.6225}{0.6248 - 0.6225}.$$

or

$$r = 29 \left(\frac{0.0006}{0.0023}\right) = 8,$$

so that $\theta = 0.6728$, approximated to the nearest four decimal places.

EXAMPLE 5. Find the number θ if $\cos \theta = 0.5741$.

Solution. We find $\cos 0.9570 = 0.5760$, and $\cos 0.9599 = 0.5736$.
Therefore,

$$\frac{r}{29} = \frac{0.5741 - 0.5760}{0.5736 - 0.5760},$$

so that

$$r = 29 \left(\frac{0.0019}{0.0024} \right) = 23,$$

and our result is $\theta = 0.9593$.

This same type of interpolation will be used in Chapters 13 and 15.

PROBLEMS

Plot the graphs of each of the functions associated with the following equations and find, accurately to two decimals, the value of the indicated real roots.

1. $x^3 - 3x^2 - x + 2 = 0$ (the least positive)
2. $x^3 + 3x^2 - 6x - 3 = 0$ (the greatest positive)
3. $x^3 - x^2 - 2x + 1 = 0$ (the least positive)
4. $x^3 - 3x + 1 = 0$ (the three real roots)
5. $x^3 - 7x + 7 = 0$ (the two roots between 1 and 2)
6. $x^4 - x^3 + 2x^2 - 3x - 3 = 0$ (all)
7. $x^4 - 2x^3 + x^2 - 1 = 0$ (all)
8. $x^4 - 4x^3 - 4x + 12 = 0$ (all)

Find accurately to three decimals the indicated principal roots.

9. $\sqrt[3]{6}$ 10. $\sqrt[3]{15}$ 11. $\sqrt[4]{2}$ 12. $\sqrt[5]{-9}$

13. Find the approximate value to four decimal places of each of the following by using Table I and interpolation.

(a) $\sin 1.2692$ (b) $\cos 0.5021$ (c) $\tan 0.8986$ (d) $\cos 1.1063$
(e) $\tan 0.6860$ (f) $\sin 2.2446$ (g) $\cos 2.6754$ (h) $\sin 0.1423$

14. Find the approximate value between 0 and $\pi/2$ of θ to four decimal places, by using Table I and interpolation, if

(a) $\tan \theta = 0.8172$,   (b) $\sin \theta = 0.5331$,
(c) $\cos \theta = 0.2717$,   (d) $\cos \theta = 0.9392$,
(e) $\sin \theta = 0.7531$,   (f) $\tan \theta = 0.8083$,
(g) $\cos \theta = 0.5386$,   (h) $\sin \theta = 0.9648$.

CHAPTER 10

INVERSE FUNCTIONS

In the last few chapters we have discussed rather specific types of functions. Under certain conditions the relation between functions becomes important. One of these relations will be especially useful for us in further discussions.

10–1 Inverse functions. If f is the function

$$f : x \rightarrow \frac{12 - 3x}{4} , \tag{10-1}$$

where both its domain and range is R, we have the defining equation $f(x) = (12 - 3x)/4$. If, in addition, the function g is defined

$$g : x \rightarrow \frac{12 - 4x}{3} , \tag{10-2}$$

where again this function has R for its domain and range, we can consider both $f[g(x)]$, and $g[f(x)]$. Specifically, since $g(x) = (12 - 4x)/3$ for all x, by $f[g(x)]$ we mean the functional value of f for $(12 - 4x)/3$, that is,

$$f\left(\frac{12 - 4x}{3}\right).$$

We have

$$f\left(\frac{12 - 4x}{3}\right) = \frac{12 - 3[(12 - 4x)/3]}{4} = \frac{12 - (12 - 4x)}{4} = x,$$

so that

$$f[g(x)] = x \tag{10-3}$$

for all x in the domain of g. In a similar way we can show that

$$g[f(x)] = x \tag{10-4}$$

for all x in the domain of f. Two functions of this type are *inverses* of each other.

Another rather simple example we might mention is the function f where $f : x \rightarrow 1/x$, for all $x \in R$, where $x \neq 0$. This function is its own inverse, since $f[f(x)] = 1/(1/x) = x$, for all $x \neq 0$.

The idea of inverse functions can be stated in general.

DEFINITION 10–1. *If f and g are two functions which are so related that f[g(x)] = x for every x in the domain of g and g[f(x)] = x for every x in the domain of f, then f and g are called* inverses *of each other.* Each function f and g has an inverse, and each function is the other's inverse.

Although each of the two functions in the examples we mentioned at the beginning of this section has an inverse, this is not always the case. Consider the function

$$f : x \rightarrow \frac{x^2 - 1}{x}, \qquad (10\text{–}5)$$

which is defined for all $x \in R$, $x \neq 0$. The function f does not have an inverse function. Let us prove this by assuming that f's inverse exists and is equal to g. If g is the inverse of f, we know that $g[f(x)] = x$ for all x in the domain of f. If $x = 1$, we have $g[f(1)] = g(0)$. Moreover, if $x = -1$, we have $g[f(-1)] = g(0)$. Therefore, $g[f(1)] = g[f(-1)]$. But since we have assumed g is the inverse of f, by definition $g[f(1)] = 1$, and $g[f(-1)] = -1$, so that $1 = -1$. Our assumption leads to a contradiction, so that no inverse function exists for this function f.

The reason for this difficulty should be clear if we examine the function f more closely. If we solve the defining equation $f(x) = (x^2 - 1)/x$ for x, we find, by clearing fractions, that $xf(x) = x^2 - 1$, or $x^2 - xf(x) - 1 = 0$. This equation is quadratic in x, so that

$$x = \frac{f(x) \pm \sqrt{[f(x)]^2 + 4}}{2}. \qquad (10\text{–}6)$$

Thus, for any particular value of $f(x)$, two different values of x correspond. For example, if $f(x) = 0$ (the case we considered above) $x = 1$ or -1. In other words, the function f maps both 1 and -1 into the same value in the range of f. No function which maps two distinct elements into the same element can have an inverse function. We state this as a theorem.

THEOREM 10–1. *If the function f has an inverse, then, for any two elements x_1 and x_2 in the domain of f, where $x_1 \neq x_2$, $f(x_1) \neq f(x_2)$.*

Proof. Let us assume the theorem is not true. Then we have $x_1 \neq x_2$, but $f(x_1) = f(x_2)$. Since the inverse exists, let us call it g and we have $g[f(x_1)] = g[f(x_2)]$. But since g is the inverse of f, $g[f(x_1)] = x_1$ and $g[f(x_2)] = x_2$, so that $x_1 = x_2$. Since this contradicts the fact that $x_1 \neq x_2$, our assumption was false, and the theorem is proved.

Recall from Article 1–1 the definition of a one-to-one correspondence for sets (Definition 1–1). We have shown that if f has an inverse the function is one-to-one, that is, each distinct element in the domain is mapped by the function into a distinct element in the range. The converse of this theorem is also true.

THEOREM 10–2. *If the function f is one-to-one, then f has an inverse.*

Proof. For any y in the range of f, there exists one and only one x in f's domain such that $y = f(x)$. If this element x is associated with the element y, a function g is defined which maps y into x, namely, $g: y \rightarrow x$, so that $x = g(y)$ where the domain of g is the range of f (and the range of g is the domain of f). Thus, $f[g(y)] = f(x) = y$ and $g[f(x)] = g(y) = x$. But this was precisely the definition of the fact that g is the inverse of f (and f the inverse of g).

Let us denote the inverse (if it exists) of any function f, by f^{-1} (read "f inverse" or "the inverse of f").

We have not only proved Theorem 10–2, but have shown that

$$f[f^{-1}(x)] = x \qquad \text{and} \qquad f^{-1}[f(x)] = x, \qquad (10\text{–}7)$$

whenever the inverse exists. Moreover, the inverse of f, f^{-1} will exist if and only if the function f is one-to-one.

If we think of f as defined by a set of ordered pairs and consider the inverse function f^{-1}, we are led to a most helpful consequence. Recall that f may be defined (Definition 5–2),

$$\{(x, y)|y = f(x)\}. \qquad (10\text{–}8)$$

Since this set of ordered pairs defines a function, no two of the ordered pairs have the same first element, and, moreover, if we assume f^{-1} exists (the function f is one-to-one), no two of the ordered pairs have the same second element. Therefore, if x is in the domain of f and $y = f(x)$, then, $x = f^{-1}(y)$, or the function f^{-1} may be defined as the set of ordered pairs where the numbers in the ordered pairs defining f are merely interchanged. That is, f^{-1} may be defined as the set

$$\{(y, x)|x = f^{-1}(y)\}. \qquad (10\text{–}9)$$

For example, if f is defined $f: x \rightarrow (12 - 3x)/4$, so that $f(x) = y = (12 - 3x)/4$, we may solve this equation $y = (12 - 3x)/4$ for x, obtain $x = (12 - 4y)/3$, and interchanging the x and y, have $y = (12 - 4x)/3$. Thus, $f^{-1}: x \rightarrow (12 - 4x)/3$. In general, if $y = f(x)$ is the defining equation for any function which has an inverse, its inverse may be obtained by interchanging the numbers x and y, so that $x = f(y)$, and then solving for y. The range of f will be the domain for f^{-1}, and the domain of f will be the range for f^{-1}. Certain difficulties may arise from this

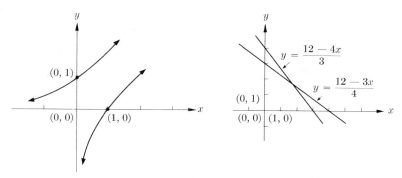

FIGURE 10–1

method,* and *care must be taken in choosing the domains and ranges of each function to guarantee that f is one-to-one.*

In the illustrations tabulated below, note that the domain and range of each function must be limited.

	$y = f(x)$		$y = f^{-1}(x)$	
(a)	$y = \dfrac{12 - 3x}{4}$	$(-\infty < x < \infty)$†	$y = \dfrac{12 - 4x}{3}$	$(-\infty < x < \infty)$
(b)	$y = \dfrac{1}{x}$	$(x \neq 0)$	$y = \dfrac{1}{x}$	$(x \neq 0)$
(c)	$y = \dfrac{x^2 - 1}{x}$	$(0 < x)$	$y = \dfrac{x + \sqrt{x^2 + 4}}{2}$	$(-\infty < x < \infty)$
		$(x < 0)$	$y = \dfrac{x - \sqrt{x^2 + 4}}{2}$	$(-\infty < x < \infty)$
(d)	$y = \sqrt{1 - x^2}$	$(0 \leq x \leq 1)$	$y = \sqrt{1 - x^2}$	$(0 \leq x \leq 1)$
		$(-1 \leq x \leq 0)$	$y = -\sqrt{1 - x^2}$	$(0 \leq x \leq 1)$
	$y = -\sqrt{1 - x^2}$	$(0 \leq x \leq 1)$	$y = \sqrt{1 - x^2}$	$(-1 \leq x \leq 0)$
		$(-1 \leq x \leq 0)$	$y = -\sqrt{1 - x^2}$	$(-1 \leq x \leq 0)$

The graphs of $f(x)$ and $f^{-1}(x)$ for illustrations (a) and the first function in (c) are shown in Fig. 10–1. Note that the curves for $y = f(x)$ and $y = f^{-1}(x)$ are symmetric with respect to the line $y = x$. Would you expect this always to be the case? Examine the graphs of the other functions in the illustrations.

---

* We may not be able to solve for y, as in the case $x = y - \sin y$.
† The notation $-\infty < x < \infty$ means all finite real values of x, both positive and negative.

PROBLEMS

Find the inverse of each of the functions defined by the following equations (Problems 1 through 11) if the inverse exists. If the inverse does not exist for the largest possible domain, limit the domain so that the inverse will exist. In each case, give the domain and range of both the function and its inverse.

1. $y = 5x - 6$ 2. $y = x^2$ 3. $y = x^2 - 4x$

4. $y = \dfrac{x}{x - 3}$ 5. $y = \dfrac{x^2 - 1}{x^2}$ 6. $y = \dfrac{x^2 - 1}{x}$

7. $y = x^n$ 8. $y = x^{2n} + 2x^n + 1$ 9. $y = \sqrt{x^2 - 4}$

10. $y = \dfrac{-3\sqrt{25 - x^2}}{5}$ 11. $y = \dfrac{x}{x^2 - 1}$

12. Explain why a line parallel to the x-axis or y-axis will intersect the graph of a function once at most if the function has an inverse.

13. We recall from the footnote in Article 6–3 that a function f is said to be increasing if $f(x_1) < f(x_2)$ whenever $x_1 < x_2$. Show that if f is increasing, f^{-1} exists.

14. We noticed that if (a, b) is any point on the graph of f, that (b, a) is a point on the graph of f^{-1}. Describe the relation between these two points relative to the graph of the straight line whose equation is $y = x$. This property is useful in sketching the graph of f^{-1} if the graph of f is known.

10–2 Graphing certain relations. If we consider the set of ordered pairs

$$\{(x, y) \mid xy - x^2 + 1 = 0\}, \qquad (10\text{–}10)$$

we may consider this set as a function $f: x \to y$, since for any value of x except zero, the equation sets up a unique corresponding value of y. We can see this is true, for if we solve $xy - x^2 + 1 = 0$ for y, we have $y = (x^2 - 1)/x$. However, if we solve the equation for x, we obtain $x = (y \pm \sqrt{y^2 + 4})/2$, so that we cannot consider the equation $xy - x^2 + 1 = 0$ as defining a function which maps $y \to x$, but merely a relation. Such relations, defined by similar equations, however, may be graphed. It is frequently helpful to use the expression for y, in terms of x, and for x, in terms of y, although they may not necessarily define a function.

EXAMPLE. Sketch the graph of the relation expressed by the equation $x^2 - 2xy + y^2 + 2x - 3y + 2 = 0$.

Solution. By using the quadratic formula to solve for x in terms of y, we find

$$x = y - 1 \pm \sqrt{y - 1}.$$

From this expression we may tabulate a few values, noticing that for each y, there are two corresponding values for x. For example, when

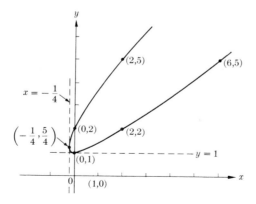

FIGURE 10–2

$y = 2$, $x = 2$ or 0. When $y = 1$, $x = 0$ is a double root and the curve is tangent to $y = 1$ at this point. Moreover, when $y < 1$, the values of x are imaginary, so that the curve lies only where $y \geq 1$.

Solving for y in terms of x, we find

$$y = \frac{2x + 3 \pm \sqrt{4x + 1}}{2}.$$

Again, we can easily find sets of values which satisfy the equation. In addition, the curve lies only where $x \geq -\frac{1}{4}$ and is tangent to the line $x = -\frac{1}{4}$ at $y = \frac{5}{4}$. The resulting curve, shown in Fig. 10–2, is a parabola, although its equation is not as simple as those considered in Article 7–3.

Systems of equations such as that considered in Example 2, Article 7–12, can now be solved graphically.

PROBLEMS

Sketch the graph of the relations expressed by each of the equations 1 through 10.

1. $16x^2 + 25y^2 - 400 = 0$ 2. $x^2 - y^2 - 1 = 0$

3. $xy = 1$ 4. $x - 2 = \dfrac{1}{y - 3}$

5. $4x^2 + 4y^2 - 12x - 10y + 5 = 0$ 6. $2xy + 4y - 6x = 0$

7. $x^2 + 2xy + y^2 - 2x - 2y = 1$ 8. $x^2 + xy + y^2 - 3y - 3 = 0$

9. $2x^2 + 3xy - 2y^2 - 5 = 0$ 10. $x^2 + 2xy + y^2 - 2x - 2y = 0$

11. Solve graphically Example 2, Article 7–12.
12. Solve graphically Problems 7, 9, Article 7–12.
13. Solve graphically Problems 8, 10, Article 7–12.

FIGURE 10–3   FIGURE 10–4

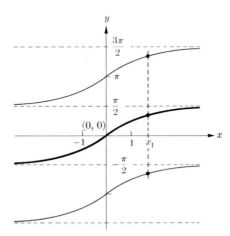

FIGURE 10–5

10–3 Inverse circular functions. The concept of an inverse relation or function is particularly important in studying the circular functions and their properties. In considering the function whose equation is $y = \sin \theta$, we may wish to talk about y, the sine of θ, but we might also wish to consider or emphasize the number θ, that is, θ whose sine is y. This emphasis is required so frequently that "θ a number whose sine is y," or the inverse relation of $y = \sin \theta$, is given a name and a notation. About 1730, Daniel Bernoulli and Leonhard Euler introduced the notation

$$\theta = \arcsin y \qquad (10\text{–}11)$$

to denote a value whose sine is y, and thus the name for this expression became *arcsine of y*. This was the first suitable notation for an inverse circular relation. Later, in 1813, John Herschel introduced another notation which has also remained in common use, $\theta = \sin^{-1} y$. When -1 is used in this manner, it must be understood that -1 is not an exponent, but is consistent with the currently used notation, f^{-1}, for the inverse of any function.

From the above definition, if $y = \arcsin \frac{1}{2}$, y is a number whose sine is $\frac{1}{2}$. Thus, y may be equal to $\pi/6$, $5\pi/6$, $13\pi/6$, $-7\pi/6$, and so forth, or, in general, $y = \pi/6 \pm 2n\pi$, or $5\pi/6 \pm 2n\pi$, where $n = 0, 1, 2, \ldots$ Moreover, these are the only values which y may have. This will be clear from the graph of the relation. From this one observation, we see that although $y = \sin x$ is a function equation, the inverse relation equation, $y = \arcsin x$, is infinitely many-valued.

The remaining inverse circular relations are defined in a corresponding way. The expression arccos x denotes a number whose cosine is x; arctan x denotes a number whose tangent is x; and so forth. The other three inverse circular relations, arccot x, arcsec x, and arccsc x, are of less importance. They can readily be expressed in terms of arctan x, arccos x, and arcsin x, respectively, by using Eqs. (6–11), (6–12), and (6–13). Thus the expression arccsc x may be considered equivalent to arcsin $1/x$. More specifically,

$$\operatorname{arccsc} 2 = \arcsin \tfrac{1}{2} = \pi/6,$$

and so on.

The graphs of the inverse circular relations show their behavior quite clearly. In considering the graph of $y = \arcsin x$, we merely think of the equivalent expression $x = \sin y$ and recall its graph. (This graph was shown in Fig. 6–7, with x and y for y and θ.) If we graph $x = \sin y$ on transparent paper with the x-axis vertical and the y-axis horizontal, turn the paper over, and rotate it clockwise through 90°, the result is the graph of $y = \arcsin x$, shown in Fig. 10–3. The graphs of $y = \arccos x$ and $y = \arctan x$, obtained in a similar way, are shown in Fig. 10–4 and Fig. 10–5. Note that arcsin x and arccos x are defined only for the domain where x is between -1 and 1, inclusive, although $\arctan x$ is defined for all finite values of x. Thus $\arcsin 2$ has no meaning,* since there is no real number whose sine is 2, but $\arctan 2$ does have meaning. From the graphs we observe once more that these inverse relations have infinitely many values for one value of x. Note this property in the case of each relation.

If the sine of a specific value of y, let us say y_1, is equal to x_1, what other values of y have the same sine? We recall that the addition or subtraction of integral multiples of 2π does not change the circular function of a number. Also, in the case of the sine function, we found that $\sin(\pi - y) = \sin y$. Therefore $\pi - y + 2n\pi$ will have the same sine as y. In other words, an even multiple of π must be added to y, or an even multiple of π must be added to $\pi - y$, for the number to have the same sine. Put into one equation, this results in

$$\arcsin x_1 = (-1)^n y_1 + n\pi \quad (-1 \leq x_1 \leq 1) \qquad \text{if} \quad \sin y_1 = x_1.$$

$$(10\text{--}12)$$

This is true for every integral value of n and gives a different value of $\arcsin x_1$ for each value of n. For example, when $n = 0$, $\arcsin x_1 = y_1$; when $n = 1$, $\arcsin x_1 = \pi - y_1$; when $n = -1$, $\arcsin x_1 = -(\pi + y_1)$; and so forth. That the formula gives all values of $\arcsin x_1$ should be clear from Fig. 10–3. These are indicated by the intersection of the dotted vertical line and the curve.

Since $\cos(2\pi + y) = \cos y$, and $\cos(-y) = \cos y$, it is easy to verify that the following expression gives all the values for $\arccos x_1$.

$$\arccos x_1 = \pm y_1 + 2n\pi \quad (-1 \leq x_1 \leq 1) \qquad \text{if} \quad \cos y_1 = x_1.$$

$$(10\text{--}13)$$

From the fact that both $\tan(\pi + y)$ and $\tan(2\pi + y) = \tan y$, we get the expression

$$\arctan x_1 = y_1 + n\pi \quad (-\infty < x_1 < \infty) \qquad \text{if} \quad \tan y_1 = x_1$$

$$(10\text{--}14)$$

for all the values of $\arctan x_1$.

---

* This is true in the present context of real values. In more advanced mathematics the circular functions may be treated in the context of complex values, and in such context $\arcsin 2$ is a complex number.

As examples of specific values of such inverse relations, we have

$$\arcsin \frac{1}{2} = (-1)^n \frac{\pi}{6} + n\pi,$$

$$\arccos \frac{1}{2} = \pm \frac{\pi}{3} + 2n\pi,$$

$$\arctan(-1) = -\frac{\pi}{4} + n\pi,$$

where n is any integer.

We have emphasized in this discussion that the circular inverse relations are many-valued. However, under suitable restrictions, these inverse relations may be made one-to-one, and in this way, we obtain the important *arc functions*. As is seen by the graph of $y = \arcsin x$ (Fig. 10–3), if the range of the relation is limited to $-\pi/2 \le \arcsin x \le \pi/2$, there is a unique value of y for each x of the domain. In a similar manner, the range for each of the other arc functions is restricted to distinguish between the inverse relations and functions. The capital letter A is used in writing the arc functions. Thus the range of each of the inverse circular functions is as follows:

$-\pi/2 \le \mathrm{Arcsin}\ x \le \pi/2,$	(10–15)
$0 \le \mathrm{Arccos}\ x \le \pi,$	(10–16)
$-\pi/2 < \mathrm{Arctan}\ x < \pi/2.$	(10–17)

The graphs of these functions are indicated in the figures by heavy lines. In the case of the functional values, the examples listed above become

$$\mathrm{Arcsin}\ \frac{1}{2} = \frac{\pi}{6}, \quad \mathrm{Arccos}\ \frac{1}{2} = \frac{\pi}{3}, \quad \mathrm{Arctan}\ (-1) = -\frac{\pi}{4}.$$

Other examples of functional values are

$$\mathrm{Arcsin}\ \left(-\frac{1}{2}\right) = -\frac{\pi}{6}, \quad \mathrm{Arccot}\ (-\sqrt{3}) = -\frac{\pi}{6},$$

$$\mathrm{Arccos}\ \left(-\frac{1}{2}\right) = \frac{2\pi}{3}, \quad \mathrm{Arcsec}\ \left(\frac{-2}{\sqrt{3}}\right) = \frac{5\pi}{6}.$$

PROBLEMS

Find the values of the following without using tables.

1. $\arcsin \sqrt{3}/2$ [*Hint:* We know $\sin \pi/3 = \sqrt{3}/2$. Therefore, $\arcsin \sqrt{3}/2 = (-1)^n\pi/3 + n\pi$.]

2. arctan 1   3. arccos $(-\frac{1}{2})$ 4. arcsin 0
5. arctan 0   6. arccos (-1) 7. arcsec $\sqrt{2}$
8. arccot $(-\sqrt{3})$ 9. Arccos 0   10. Arctan (-1)
11. Arcsin (-1) 12. Arccsc 2

Find the value of the following with the help of Table I.

13. arcsin 0.4067   14. arctan 1.5399
15. arccos 0.6293   16. Arccos 0.8450
17. Arcsin 0.9951   18. Arctan 0.3281

Solve each of the following for θ.

19. $y = \sin 4\theta$ [*Hint:* We know $4\theta = \arcsin y$. Therefore, $\theta = (\arcsin y)/4$.]
20. $y = \cos 3\theta$ 21. $y = 3 \tan 2\theta$
22. $y = \sin (\theta/2)$ 23. $2y = 4 \sec 2\theta$
24. $3y = 2 + \sin 3\theta$

25. Explain why the value of $y = \text{Arccos } x$ cannot be taken in the interval $-\pi/2 \le y \le \pi/2$.

Solve each of the following for x.

26. $y = \arcsin 2x$ 27. $y = \frac{1}{3} \arccos (4x - 4)$
28. $y = \arctan (x - 2)$ 29. $y = \arctan x - 2$
30. $y = \pi + 2 \arcsin x$ 31. $8y = (\pi/3) - 4 \arccos (2x + 1)$

10–4 Operations involving inverse circular functions. The most convenient way of considering various operations with the inverse relations and functions is to analyze several examples. Since the inverse circular functions are the same numbers θ for which we have established many formulas, it is sometimes clearer to substitute for an arc function or relation a number θ or ω. This type of substitution will be illustrated in the examples.

EXAMPLE 1. Find the value of $\sin (\arccos \frac{3}{5})$.

Solution. This example, similar to many problems in Chapter 6, asks for the sine of a number whose cosine is $\frac{3}{5}$. Let θ be this number. Then $\cos \theta = \frac{3}{5}$, and $\sin \theta = \pm\sqrt{1 - (\frac{3}{5})^2} = \pm\frac{4}{5}$.

EXAMPLE 2. Find the value of $\cos (\text{Arcsin } u + \text{Arccos } v)$.

Solution. If we let $\text{Arcsin } u = \theta_1$ and $\text{Arccos } v = \theta_2$, the example reduces to expressing $\cos (\theta_1 + \theta_2)$ in terms of u and v, where

$$\sin \theta_1 = u, \qquad \cos \theta_2 = v,$$

and therefore,

$$\cos \theta_1 = \sqrt{1 - u^2}, \qquad \sin \theta_2 = \sqrt{1 - v^2}.$$

(Explain why both radicals are positive.) Thus

$$\cos (\text{Arcsin } u + \text{Arccos } v) = \cos (\theta_1 + \theta_2)$$
$$= \cos \theta_1 \cos \theta_2 - \sin \theta_1 \sin \theta_2$$
$$= v\sqrt{1 - u^2} - u\sqrt{1 - v^2}.$$

EXAMPLE 3. Prove that Arctan $\frac{1}{2}$ + Arctan $\frac{1}{3}$ = $\pi/4$.

Solution. Since each of the two numbers on the left side is less than $\pi/4$, the left side represents a number between 0 and $\pi/2$, as does the number $\pi/4$ on the right side. If the tangents of two such numbers are equal, the numbers themselves are equal. Let us take the tangent of each member of the suspected equality, and if they are equal, we have proved the original relation. It should be emphasized that this will be true only because the tangent function between 0 and $\pi/2$ is one-to-one.

$$\tan \left(\text{Arctan } \frac{1}{2} + \text{Arctan } \frac{1}{3} \right) \overset{?}{=} \tan \frac{\pi}{4}$$

$$\frac{\tan (\text{Arctan } \frac{1}{2}) + \tan (\text{Arctan } \frac{1}{3})}{1 - \tan (\text{Arctan } \frac{1}{2}) \tan (\text{Arctan } \frac{1}{3})} \overset{?}{=} 1$$

$$\frac{\frac{1}{2} + \frac{1}{3}}{1 - \frac{1}{2} \cdot \frac{1}{3}} = 1.$$

PROBLEMS

Find the values of the following without the use of tables.

1. $\sin (\arctan \frac{3}{4})$
2. $\cos (\arcsin \frac{7}{25})$
3. $\tan (\arccos \frac{5}{13})$
4. $\sin [\arccos (-\frac{24}{25})]$
5. $\cos (\text{Arcsin } \frac{5}{6})$
6. $\tan [\text{Arcsin } (-\frac{3}{4})]$
7. $\sin (\arcsin u)$
8. $\cos (\text{Arccos } v)$
9. $\tan (\arccos u)$
10. $\sin (\arctan v)$
11. $\text{Arcsin } (\sin \pi/7)$
12. $\text{Arccos } [\cos (-\pi/5)]$
13. $\text{Arctan } (\cot 4\pi/9)$
14. $\text{Arcsin } (\cos \pi/7)$
15. $\text{Arccos } (\sin \pi/10)$
16. $\text{Arccot } [\tan (-\pi/5)]$
17. $\text{Arcsin } (\tan \pi)$
18. $\text{Arctan } (\sin 7\pi/2)$
19. $\sin (\arcsin u + \arccos v)$
20. $\cos (\arccos u + \arcsin v)$
21. $\sin (\arccos \frac{4}{5} + \pi)$
22. $\cos (\pi/2 - \arcsin \frac{5}{13})$
23. $\sin (\arcsin \frac{1}{4} + \arccos \frac{1}{4})$
24. $\cos (\arctan \frac{9}{40} - \arccos \frac{15}{17})$
25. $\tan (\text{Arcsin } \frac{5}{13} + \text{Arctan } (-\frac{3}{4})]$
26. $\cos [\text{Arccos } (-\frac{1}{2}) + \text{Arcsin } (-\frac{1}{3})]$
27. $\sin [2 \text{ Arcsin } \frac{4}{5} + \frac{1}{2} \text{ Arccos } \frac{1}{9}]$
28. $\cos (\text{Arcsin } \frac{3}{5} + \text{Arccos } \frac{5}{13} + \text{Arctan } \frac{8}{15})$

Verify the following equations without the use of tables.

29. $\text{Arctan } 3 + \text{Arctan } \frac{1}{3} = \pi/2$

30. Arcsin $\frac{3}{5}$ + Arccos $\frac{12}{13}$ = Arcsin $\frac{56}{65}$

31. Arctan $\frac{1}{3}$ + Arctan $\frac{1}{5}$ = Arctan $\frac{4}{7}$

32. Arctan $\frac{1}{7}$ + 2 Arctan $\frac{1}{3}$ = $\pi/4$

33. Arctan $\frac{1}{8}$ + Arctan $\frac{1}{5}$ + Arctan $\frac{1}{2}$ = $\pi/4$

34. Is the following equation true? Arctan 2 + Arctan 3 = $-\pi/4$. Explain your answer.

35. Note that in Problems 11 through 18 only functions were involved. Find all possible values of arcsin (cos θ). [*Hint:* Let y = arcsin (cos θ). Then sin y = cos θ = sin $(\frac{1}{2}\pi - \theta)$. Therefore, $y = \frac{1}{2}\pi - \theta + 2n\pi$ or $y = \pi - (\frac{1}{2}\pi - \theta) + 2n\pi = \frac{1}{2}\pi + \theta + 2n\pi$. Thus, combining these into a single expression, we have $y = \frac{1}{2}\pi \pm \theta + 2n\pi$.]

Find all possible values of the following.

36. arcsin (sin θ)　　　　　　　　　37. arccos (sin θ)

38. arccos (cos θ)　　　　　　　　　39. arctan (tan θ)

Solve the following equations for all possible values of x without using tables, and check carefully.

40. Arctan x + 2 Arctan 1 = $3\pi/4$

41. Arccos x + 2 Arcsin 1 = π

42. Arcsin x + Arccos $2x$ = $\pi/6$. [*Hint:* Let Arcsin x = α, Arccos $2x$ = β, and use sin $(\alpha + \beta)$ = sin α cos β + cos α sin β.]

43. Arcsin x + Arccos $(1 - x)$ = 0

44. Arcsin x + Arccos $(1 - x)$ = $\pi/2$

45. Arctan $(1 + x)$ + Arctan $(1 - x)$ = $\pi/2$

CHAPTER 11

PERMUTATIONS, COMBINATIONS, AND THE BINOMIAL THEOREM

Frequently we are asked to find the number of ways a set of objects may be arranged under certain conditions. How many ways can eight people be seated at a table? How many different license plates are possible if each consists of three numbers and two letters, and so on? Answers to these questions and many more important and complicated ones are possible by a process sometimes called *sophisticated counting*. Although an extensive treatment is impossible here, certain elementary aspects of the subject will be discussed, since it is so useful in mathematics and other natural and social sciences.

11–1 The fundamental principle. We shall begin by considering a simple example. Let us find how many numbers of two different digits can be formed from the four integers 1, 2, 3, and 4 if no digit is repeated. Any one of the four may be chosen for the tens digit of the number. With each particular choice of this type, there will remain three integers from which to choose the units digit. Thus, for each of the four choices, there are three more choices, making a total of $4 \cdot 3$ or 12 numbers in all. We have then,

$$
\begin{aligned}
&12, 13, 14, \text{ (1 for the tens digit)}, \\
&21, 23, 24, \text{ (2 for the tens digit)}, \\
&31, 32, 34, \text{ (3 for the tens digit)}, \\
&41, 42, 43, \text{ (4 for the tens digit)}
\end{aligned}
\tag{11–1}
$$

as the possible two-digit numbers.

This example can be illustrated (Fig. 11–1) by a simple tree diagram. If repetitions are permitted, the result is $4 \cdot 4 = 16$ possible two-digit numbers instead of 12.

A slightly more complicated problem would be to find how many numbers of three different digits could be formed with the same integers 1, 2, 3, and 4. Each of the 12 numbers listed in Eq. (11–1) can be regarded as representing the hundred and tens digits. Since two of the four integers have already been selected in each case, the possibility for the new units digit must be one of the two remaining integers. For example, with the first number 41, we may have 2 or 3, forming the numbers 412 or 413. We therefore have $(4 \cdot 3) \cdot 2$ or 24 numbers, each containing three digits, which can be formed from the given integers.

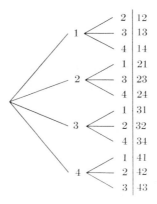

FIGURE 11–1

A tree diagram in this case would be similar to that in Fig. 11–1, but in addition, at the ends of each of the last branches there would be two additional branches. Similarly, if repetitions are permitted in this case the result would be $4 \cdot 4 \cdot 4 = 64$.

These examples have illustrated a fundamental principle.

FUNDAMENTAL PRINCIPLE. *If one thing can be done independently in n_1 different ways, and if a second thing can be done independently in n_2 different ways, and a third thing can be done independently in n_3 different ways, and so on (for any finite number of things), then the total number of ways in which all the things may be done in the stated order is $n_1 n_2 n_3 \cdots$.*

EXAMPLE 1. How many of the two-digit numbers in Eq. (11–1) are odd?

Solution. In order for any of these numbers to be odd, its last digit must be a 1 or 3. For each of these two possibilities there are three choices for the first digit, so that there are $2 \cdot 3$ or 6 of these two-digit numbers that are odd. Check the example and note that this is the case.

Although the order of choosing the number of possibilities for any particular position is arbitrary, it is frequently wise to perform any special operation first, as in the case of the choice of the units digit in Example 1.

EXAMPLE 2. How many different committees consisting of one Democrat and one Republican can be formed from seven Democrats and four Republicans?

Solution. The Democrat can be chosen in any one of seven ways, and independently, the Republican can be chosen in any one of four ways. Thus, by the fundamental principle, the total number of different possible committees is $7 \cdot 4 = 28$.

EXAMPLE 3. If two cubical dice are thrown, in how many ways can they fall?

Solution. Since each cube has six faces, each may fall independently any one of six different ways. Consequently, there are $6 \cdot 6 = 36$ possible ways for them to fall.

EXAMPLE 4. In a certain election, there are three candidates for president, four for vice-president, five for secretary, but only two for treasurer. In how many different ways may the election turn out?

Solution. With each of the three possibilities for president, there are four for vice-president. With each of these $(4 \cdot 3 = 12)$ possibilities, there are five possibilities for secretary, and so on. Thus the total number of different possible election results is

$$4(3)(5)(2) = 120.$$

PROBLEMS

1. A nickel and a dime are tossed on a table. In how many ways can they fall?

2. If all questions are answered in a true-false quiz of ten questions, how many ways are there of answering the entire quiz?

3. How many numbers of three different digits less than 500 can be formed from the integers 1, 2, 3, 4, 5, 6, 7?

4. If there are 12 milers entered in a race, in how many ways can first, second, and third place be awarded?

5. There are five main roads between the cities A and B, and four between B and C. In how many ways can a person drive from A to C and return, going through B on both trips, without driving on the same road twice?

6. How many numbers of at most three different digits can be formed from the integers 1, 2, 3, 4, 5, 6?

7. How many numbers of at least three different digits can be formed from the integers 1, 2, 3, 4, 5, 6?

8. A tennis club consists of 12 boys and 9 girls. How many mixed doubles teams (one boy and one girl) are possible? In how many ways can a mixed doubles match be arranged?

9. A freshman student must take a modern language, a natural science, a social science, and English. If there are four possible different modern languages, five natural sciences, three social sciences, but each student must take the same English course, in how many different ways can he select his course of study?

10. In selecting an ace, king, queen, and jack from an ordinary deck of 52 cards, how many ways may we choose if (a) they must be of different suits, (b) they may or may not be of different suits, (c) they must be of the same suit, (d) they must be in a particular suit?

11. If there are eight outside doors in a dormitory, in how many ways can a student enter one and (a) leave by a different door, (b) leave by any door?

12. A baseball stadium has four entrance gates and nine exits. In how many ways may two men enter together, but leave by different exits?

11–2 Permutations. We wish to define what is meant by a *permutation*.

DEFINITION 11–1. *Each different arrangement or ordered set of objects is called a* permutation of those objects.

For example, the numbers 423 and 234 consist of the same digits, but they are different numbers, since they are different order arrangements of the digits 2, 3, and 4. In general, if we have n objects and arrange r of them (where $r \leq n$) in a definite order, such an arrangement is called a permutation of n objects taken r at a time.

An expression for the total number of permutations of n objects taken r at a time is easily established by using the fundamental principle of Article 11–1. This expression, which is a functional value of the integers n and r will be denoted by $P(n, r)$.*

THEOREM 11–1. *The total number of permutations of n objects taken r at a time, $P(n, r)$, is given by the expression,*

$$P(n, r) = n(n-1)(n-2) \cdots (n-r+1). \qquad (11\text{–}2)$$

Proof. The possible number of arrangements of n things taken r at a time is equivalent to the number of ways of choosing from n different things to fill r positions. There are n choices for the first position, then $n-1$ choices for the second position, $n-2$ choices for the third, and so on. The rth position can be filled with any of the $n - (r-1) = n - r + 1$ remaining things, so that the r positions can be filled in $n(n-1)(n-2) \ldots (n-r+1)$ ways. Thus,

$$P(n, r) = n(n-1)(n-2) \ldots (n-r+1).$$

If we are interested in the permutation of n things taken n (or all) at a time, we note that $r = n$ in Eq. (11–2), and we have

$$P(n, n) = n(n-1)(n-2) \ldots 3 \cdot 2 \cdot 1 = n!. \qquad (11\text{–}3)$$

By multiplying the numerator and denominator of the right member of Eq. (11–2) by $(n-r)!$, we obtain an alternative formula for $P(n, r)$,

$$P(n, r) = \frac{n(n-1)(n-2) \ldots (n-r+1)(n-r)!}{(n-r)!}$$

---

* The symbol $_nP_r$ is also frequently used.

or

$$P(n, r) = \frac{n!}{(n - r)!}.$$ (11–4)*

EXAMPLE 1. Find the number of permutations of the four integers 1, 2, 3, and 4 taken two at a time.

Solution. Since we wish to find the number of permutations of four things taken two at a time,

$$P(4, 2) = 4 \cdot 3 = 12.$$

These twelve arrangements are listed in Article 11–1.

EXAMPLE 2. If four persons enter a bus in which there are ten vacant seats, how many ways are there for the four to be seated?

Solution. Since this represents the arrangement of ten seats taken four at a time,

$$P(10, 4) = 10 \cdot 9 \cdot 8 \cdot 7 = 5040.$$

EXAMPLE 3. In how many ways may five books be arranged on a shelf?

Solution. This represents the permutation of five things taken five at a time. Thus,

$$P(5, 5) = 5! = 120.$$

Although the number of permutations of the eight letters of the word "readings" is clearly 8!, the number of such permutations of the letters of "gargling" is somewhat less, since three of the letters are alike. An example will illustrate the next theorem.

EXAMPLE 4. Find the number of permutations of the eight letters of "gargling."

Solution. Considering all the letters different, we would have P, the required number of permutations, equal to 8!. This might be done by giving each of the g's a different subscript, such as g_1, g_2, and g_3. Actually, however, the three g's could be permuted among themselves in 3! ways. In fact, for each distinct arrangement of the other letters, this would be the case. Thus $3! \, P = 8!$, or

$$P = \frac{8!}{3!}.$$

The proof of the following general theorem parallels the reasoning in Example 4 and is left as an exercise.

---

* Factorial zero, 0!, is by definition equal to 1.

THEOREM 11–2. *If P represents the number of different permutations of n things taken all at a time, when p are of one kind, q are of another kind, r of a third kind, and so on, then*

$$P = \frac{n!}{p!\,q!\,r!\,\ldots}. \tag{11–5}$$

EXAMPLE 5. How many permutations are there of the 11 letters in "Mississippi" taken all together?

Solution. Since there are four s's, four i's, and two p's, we have

$$P = \frac{11!}{4!\,4!\,2!} = 34{,}650.$$

PROBLEMS

1. How many numbers of three different digits each can be formed from the digits 1, 2, 3, 4, 5, 6, 7, 8, 9?

2. How many numbers of three different digits each less than 700 can be formed from the digits in Problem 1?

3. How many numbers of at most three different digits each can be formed from the digits in Problem 1?

4. In how many ways can a class elect a president, vice-president, secretary, and treasurer from a class of 100 students?

5. In how many ways can four boys and three girls be seated in a row containing seven seats (a) if they may sit anywhere, (b) if the boys and girls must alternate?

6. In how many ways can four boys and four girls be seated in a row containing eight seats (a) if they may sit anywhere, (b) if the boys and girls must alternate?

7. A baseball manager insists on having his best hitter bat fourth and the pitcher bat last. In such circumstances, how many batting orders are possible?

8. In how many ways can eight people be seated in a row of eight seats if two people insist on sitting next to each other?

9. A language teacher wants to keep books of the same language together on his shelf. If he has 12 spaces for 5 French, 4 Italian, and 3 German books, in how many ways can they be placed on his shelf?

10. In how many ways can eight people be seated around a table?

11. In how many ways can eight people be seated around a table if two people insist on sitting next to each other?

12. How many license plates can be made using any two letters for the first two places and any of the numbers 0 through 9 for the last three?

13. Do Problem 12, with the condition that no letter or number be repeated.

14. How many permutations are there of the letters of the word (a) "algebra," (b) "college"?

15. How many permutations are there of the letters of the word "Tennessee"?

16. In how many ways can four red beads, five white beads, and three blue beads be arranged in a row?

17. In how many ways can seven different colored beads be made into a bracelet?

18. Show that $P(n + 1, r) \equiv (n + 1)P(n, r - 1)$.

19. Solve the equation $P(n, 5) = 20P(n, 3)$ for n.

20. Find the value of $P(5, 1) + P(5, 2) + P(5, 3) + P(5, 4) + P(5, 5)$.

11–3 Combinations. In contrast to a permutation, which is a certain ordered arrangement of different objects, a *combination* is a set or collection of objects in no particular order. Thus, by the combinations of n different objects taken r at a time ($r \leq n$), we mean all the possible selections of r different objects from the n objects, with no regard to order or arrangement. This total number of combinations is designated $C(n, r)$,* since it is again a functional value of n and r.

The difference between permutations and combinations, and an important one, is order or arrangement. The following theorem will clarify the distinction.

THEOREM 11–3. *The total number of combinations of n objects taken r at a time, $C(n, r)$, is given by the expression*

$$C(n, r) = \frac{n!}{(n - r)!r!}. \tag{11–6}$$

Proof. For any one of the $C(n, r)$ combinations, consisting of r different objects, these r objects may be rearranged by permuting them in $r!$ different ways. Thus, for each combination, there will be $r!$ permutations, so that for all the $C(n, r)$ possible combinations, there will be $C(n, r)r!$ different permutations. Since these are all the possible permutations of n objects taken r at a time, we have

$$C(n, r)r! = P(n, r),$$

or

$$C(n, r) = \frac{P(n, r)}{r!}. \tag{11–7}$$

If we now substitute the expression (Eq. 11–4) for $P(n, r)$, we get,

$$C(n, r) = \frac{n!}{(n - r)!r!}. \tag{11–6}$$

---

* The symbols $_nC_r$ and $\binom{n}{r}$ are also frequently used. We have chosen $C(n, r)$ since this notation is consistent with that for a functional value. It also may be typed more readily, an added advantage in computing machine language.

An immediate important result of this equation is that

$$C(n, r) = C(n, n - r).$$ (11–8)

This, of course, may be used to reduce the amount of computation involved, if n is relatively large, and $r \leq n$, but also large. (See Example 1.)

EXAMPLE 1. Compute $C(15, 12)$.

Solution. By using Eq. (11–7), the expression most frequently used in problems,

$$C(15, 12) = \frac{15 \cdot 14 \cdot 13 \cdot 12 \cdot 11 \cdot 10 \cdot 9 \cdot 8 \cdot 7 \cdot 6 \cdot 5 \cdot 4}{1 \cdot 2 \cdot 3 \cdot 4 \cdot 5 \cdot 6 \cdot 7 \cdot 8 \cdot 9 \cdot 10 \cdot 11 \cdot 12}$$

$$= \frac{15 \cdot 14 \cdot 13}{1 \cdot 2 \cdot 3} = C(15, 3),$$

so that $C(15, 12) = 455$.

EXAMPLE 2. In a class of 15 boys and 10 girls, in how many ways may a committee made up of 3 boys and 2 girls be selected?

Solution. Since order has nothing to do with membership on the committee, the boys may be selected in $C(15, 3)$ ways, while the girls may be selected in $C(10, 2)$ ways. By the fundamental principle, we have

$$C(15, 3) \cdot C(10, 2) = \frac{15 \cdot 14 \cdot 13}{1 \cdot 2 \cdot 3} \cdot \frac{10 \cdot 9}{1 \cdot 2}$$

$$= 20{,}475.$$

EXAMPLE 3. On a certain examination, the student must answer 8 out of the 12 questions, including exactly 5 of the first 6. In how many ways may he write the examination?

Solution. Since five of the first six must be answered, this may be done in $C(6, 5)$ ways. Having now answered five questions, he must answer three of the remaining six. This may be done in $C(6, 3)$ ways. Therefore the number of ways in which he can write the examination is given by

$$C(6, 5) \cdot C(6, 3) = 120.$$

Frequently we wish to find the total number of combinations of n things taken 1, 2, 3, . . . , or n at a time.

EXAMPLE 4. How many different sums of money can be made from a penny, a nickel, a dime, and a quarter?

Solution. Since there are four coins, the number of different amounts of money is

$$C(4, 1) + C(4, 2) + C(4, 3) + C(4, 4) = 15.$$

There will be a simpler method for this computation suggested in the next article. (See Problem 29, Article 11–4.)

PROBLEMS

1. Find the value of (a) $C(7, 4)$, (b) $C(10, 2)$, (c) $C(21, 19)$.

2. Find the value of

$$C(8, 3) + C(8, 4) + C(8, 5) + C(8, 6) + C(8, 7) + C(8, 8).$$

3. In how many ways may a committee of 4 be chosen from a group of 25?

4. From a group of 25 Democrats and 18 Republicans, how many committees consisting of 3 Democrats and 2 Republicans are possible?

5. From the group in Problem 4, if one of two specific Democrats is to be chairman, how many committees are possible with the same balance of Democrats and Republicans as previously stated?

6. How many football games are played if each of the nine football teams in a certain conference plays each of the other teams in that conference once?

7. On a college baseball squad, there are three catchers, five pitchers, seven infielders, and seven outfielders. How many different baseball nines can be formed?

8. In how many ways can a bridge hand of 13 cards be chosen from a deck of 52 cards?

9. In how many ways can a person get a bridge hand consisting of only aces or face cards?

10. In how many ways can a person get a bridge hand which consists of cards seven or lower?

11. In how many ways can a person get a bridge hand consisting of two aces, one king, one queen, three jacks, and the six other cards ten or less?

12. From four red balls, five white balls, and six blue balls, how many selections consisting of five balls can be made if two are to be red, one white, and two blue?

13. Without considering special cases, (a) how many straight lines are determined by nine points, (b) how many circles are determined by nine points?

14. How many triangles are determined by nine points no three of which lie on the same straight line?

15. How many tetrahedrons are determined by nine points no four of which lie in the same plane?

16. From a group of 15 people, how many committees can be formed consisting of two, three, or four people?

17. In how many ways may a college president's wife invite (a) two, (b) three, (c) two or more, of eight faculty wives to a tea?

18. How many different sums of money can be formed from a penny, nickel, dime, quarter, and half dollar if at least two coins are used?

n \ r	0	1	2	3	4	5	6
0	1						
1	1	1					
2	1	2	1				
3	1	3	3	1			
4	1	4	6	4	1		
5	1	5	10	10	5	1	
6	1	6	15	20	15	6	1

19. Solve for n the equation $C(n + 2, 4) = 6C(n, 2)$.

*20. Prove $C(n, r) + C(n, r - 1) \equiv C(n + 1, r)$.

*21. Examine the numbers listed in the table above. It represents $C(n, r)$ where the values for r are listed horizontally, and n vertically. For example, $C(4, 3) = 4$, since we go across the row corresponding to $n = 4$ and down the column corresponding to $r = 3$. In the space where this row and column intersect we have the number 4. Notice that the equation $C(n + 1, r) \equiv C(n, r) + C(n, r - 1)$ satisfies the entries.

22. The equation $C(n + 1, r) \equiv C(n, r) + C(n, r - 1)$ is called Pascal's Rule. Pascal (1623–1662) was one of the men in the seventeenth century to study this array of numbers in the table above in connection with his study of games of chance. The numbers in this array are called Pascal's Triangle. By using the equation, extend the table with n and r continuing to 10, and assuming $C(n, 0)$ and $C(n, n) = 1$.

23. Prove the relation

$$C(n, r + 1) = \frac{n - r}{r + 1} C(n, r), \qquad \text{for } 0 \le r < n.$$

By means of this formula, Pascal's Triangle can be constructed. Use it to find the numbers corresponding to $n = 7$, assuming $C(7, 0) = 1$.

24. Prove the relation $rC(n, r) = nC(n - 1, r - 1)$.

11–4 The binomial theorem. Relative to the ideas we have considered in this chapter is an important theorem in algebra. We learned in Chapter 3 the method of multiplying polynomials. By such multiplication we find,

$$(a + b)^1 = a + b,$$

$$(a + b)^2 = a^2 + 2ab + b^2,$$

$$(a + b)^3 = a^3 + 3a^2b + 3ab^2 + b^3,$$

and

$$(a + b)^4 = a^4 + 4a^3b + 6a^2b^2 + 4ab^3 + b^4.$$

If we examine these products, we immediately notice two things. (1) The coefficients are the same as those that appear in the table of Problem 21 in Article 11–3. (2) Each of the coefficients can be expressed in terms of the functional value $C(n, r)$. For example, $(a + b)^4 = C(4, 0)a^4 + C(4, 1)a^3b + C(4, 2)a^2b^2 + C(4, 3)ab^3 + C(4, 4)b^4$. From these two observations we would expect a similar expression for the expansion of $(a + b)^n$, where n is any positive integer. This, in fact, is the case, and is called the binomial theorem.

THEOREM 11–4. *The Binomial Theorem. For any positive integer n,*

$$(a + b)^n = C(n, 0)a^n + C(n, 1)a^{n-1}b + C(n, 2)a^{n-2}b^2 + \cdots$$
$$+ C(n, r)a^{n-r}b^r + \cdots + C(n, n)b^n. \tag{11–9}$$

Proof. For any positive integer n, $(a + b)^n$ is the product of n equal factors, that is,

$$(a + b)^n = \underbrace{(a + b)(a + b)(a + b) + \cdots + (a + b)}_{n \text{ factors}}. \tag{11–10}$$

In carrying out this multiplication, we choose either a or b from each of the n factors and multiply these n letters together. If we form all products by considering every possible choice of either a or b from each factor independently, and add these products together, we have $(a + b)^n$. Specifically, we get a^n by choosing the a from each of the n factors. We get $a^{n-1}b$ terms by choosing a from all but one factor and b from that one, and so on. In general, for any r where $0 \leq r \leq n$, we get $a^{n-r}b^r$ terms by choosing a from $n - r$ factors, and b from the other r factors. Let us focus our attention on choosing b from the r factors, and how many different possible choices of the r factors exist. Since, for such a term, we choose r factors from n choices, there are precisely $C(n, r)$ such terms, $a^{n-r}b^r$. Thus, $C(n, r)a^{n-r}b^r$ appears in the expansion. But, because of the range of r, we have the sum of all such terms with r from 0 to n, inclusive, which is precisely the statement of the theorem.

In Fig. 11–2, a tree diagram illustrates the set of possible products for $(a + b)^3$. If we start at point 0, any path through the tree to the right-hand edge represents one of the products in the identity. Notice that there is one a^3, three a^2b products, three ab^2 products, and one b^3, so that there are eight products in all, as there should be.

It is because of this theorem that $C(n, r)$, the combination of n objects taken r at a time, is often referred to as a binomial coefficient.

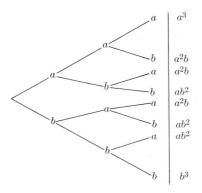

FIGURE 11–2

We immediately note the following properties of the expansion (Eq. 11–9) for any positive integer n.

1. The number of terms in any identity is $n + 1$.
2. The first term in the identity is a^n.
3. The exponent of a decreases by one and that of b increases by one from any term to the next term, so that the sum of the exponents of a and b in any term is n.
4. For the first and last, the second and next to last, the third and third from the last, and so forth, terms of the identity, the coefficients are the same. [Recall Eq. (11–8).]

These properties will be helpful in any use that is made of the theorem. In addition, it is important to note that the rth term in the expansion is

$$C(n, r - 1)a^{n-r+1}b^{r-1} = \frac{n(n - 1)(n - 2) \cdots (n - r + 2)}{(r - 1)!} \, a^{n-r+1}b^{r-1}.$$

$$(11–11)$$

EXAMPLE 1. Expand $(a + 2b)^6$ by the binomial theorem and simplify the result.

Solution. With a the first term and $2b$ the second in the binomial to be expanded, we have

$$(a + 2b)^6 \equiv a^6 + 6a^5(2b) + \frac{6 \cdot 5}{2!} \, a^4(2b)^2 + \frac{6 \cdot 5 \cdot 4}{3!} \, a^3(2b)^3$$

$$+ \frac{6 \cdot 5 \cdot 4 \cdot 3}{4!} \, a^2(2b)^4 + 6a(2b)^5 + (2b)^6$$

$$\equiv a^6 + 12a^5b + 60a^4b^2 + 160a^3b^3$$

$$+ 240a^2b^4 + 192ab^5 + 64b^6.$$

EXAMPLE 2. Find the first four terms of the expansion of $(x^3 - 3y^2)^{12}$.

Solution. Here $a = x^3$ and $b = -3y^2$. Thus,

$$(x^3 - 3y^2)^{12} \equiv (x^3)^{12} + 12(x^3)^{11}(-3y^2) + \frac{12 \cdot 11}{2!}(x^3)^{10}(-3y^2)^2$$

$$+ \frac{12 \cdot 11 \cdot 10}{3!}(x^3)^9(-3y^2)^3 + \cdots$$

$$\equiv x^{36} - 36x^{33}y^2 + 594x^{30}y^4 - 5940x^{27}y^6 + \cdots$$

Note from the method of this example that when the first term of the binomial is plus and the second minus, the signs in the expansion alternate.

The general term (Eq. 11–11) is of use in many problems involving a specific term.

EXAMPLE 3. Find the sixth term in the expansion of $[(1/2a) - 3]^{16}$.

Solution. In this example the first term is $1/2a$, and the second is -3, $n = 16$, and $r = 6$. If we substitute in Eq. (11–11), the sixth term is

$$\frac{16 \cdot 15 \cdot 14 \cdot 13 \cdot 12}{2 \cdot 3 \cdot 4 \cdot 5}\left(\frac{1}{2a}\right)^{11}(-3)^5 = -\frac{66339}{128a^{11}}.$$

PROBLEMS

Expand each of the following by the binomial theorem, and simplify if necessary.

1. $(a + b)^7$

2. $(xy - 2)^4$

3. $(2x + y^2)^5$

4. $\left(a^2 - \frac{x}{2}\right)^6$

5. $(5x - y^2)^4$

6. $(x^{-1} + 2y^{-2})^6$

7. $(x^{1/3} + y^{1/3})^6$

8. $(x^{2/3} - y^{2/3})^5$

9. $(x^{2/5} - 3y^{-2})^5$

10. $(ax^{1/2} - by^{1/3})^6$

Write and simplify the first four terms of the expansions for the following.

11. $\left(\frac{x^2}{2} + \frac{2}{y^2}\right)^{12}$

12. $(x^{1/3} - y^{1/3})^9$

13. $(x^{1/3} - y^{-1/3})^{11}$

14. $(x^{-2/3} + 2y^{2/3})^8$

15. $(1 + x)^k$

*16. $(1 + k)^{1/k}$

[*Hint:* Assume that the binomial theorem holds for $n = 1/k$.]

Write and simplify the indicated term in the expansions of the following.

17. Seventh term of $(2x - y)^{12}$

18. Ninth term of $\left(2 + \frac{x}{4}\right)^{15}$

19. Middle term of $(y^2 - \frac{1}{2})^8$ 　　20. Middle term of $\left(2 + \dfrac{3}{x}\right)^{10}$

21. Term involving x^7 of $(2x - 3)^{10}$

22. Term involving x^3 of $(5 - 2x)^6$

23. Term involving x^5 of $\left(x + \dfrac{1}{2x}\right)^7$

24. Term involving $\dfrac{x^2}{y^2}$ of $\left(\dfrac{x}{y} - \dfrac{y^2}{2x^2}\right)^8$

25. Prove that the $(r + 1)$st term of Eq. (11-9) is

$$\frac{n(n - 1)(n - 2) \cdots (n - r + 1)}{r!} \, a^{n-r}b^r.$$

26. Solve $C(n, 4) = 35$ for the positive integer n.

27. Prove that

$$2^n = (1 + 1)^n = 1 + C(n, 1) + C(n, 2) + C(n, 3) + \cdots + C(n, n).$$

28. Check the statement in Problem 27 for $n = 5$.

29. Solve Problem 18, Article 11–3 using Problem 27.

30. If n is even, prove $C(n, 0) + C(n, 2) + \cdots + C(n, n) = C(n, 1) + C(n_1 3) + \cdots + C(n, n - 1)$.

11–5 The expansion of $(1 + x)^n$. Applying the binomial theorem to $(1 + x)^n$, we have

$$(1 + x)^n \equiv 1 + nx + \frac{n(n - 1)}{2!} \, x^2$$

$$+ \frac{n(n - 1)(n - 2)}{3!} \, x^3 + \cdots$$

$$+ \frac{n(n - 1) \cdots (n - r + 2)}{(r - 1)!} \, x^{r-1} + \cdots, \qquad (11\text{–}12)$$

which contains $n + 1$ terms and is valid for all positive integers n. If n were any real number other than a positive integer, the expansion in Eq. (11–12) would not terminate. The question naturally arises: under what conditions would this relation still be valid?

Although the proof is beyond the scope of this book, it can be shown that a finite number of terms of the right member of Eq. (11–12) approximates $(1 + x)^n$, for any value of n which is not a positive integer if $|x| < 1$. It should be clear that the more terms that are considered, the closer the approximation will be, since the size of each term will normally be less in magnitude than the preceding one.

EXAMPLE 1.   Find the value of $(1.02)^{-4}$ correct to four significant figures.

Solution. We expand $(1.02)^{-4}$ by the relationship of Eq. (11–12).

$$(1.02)^{-4} = (1 + 0.02)^{-4}$$

$$= 1^{-4} + (-4) \cdot 1^{-5}(0.02) + \frac{(-4)(-5)}{2!} \cdot 1^{-6}(0.02)^2$$

$$+ \frac{(-4)(-5)(-6)}{3!} \cdot 1^{-7}(0.02)^3$$

$$+ \frac{(-4)(-5)(-6)(-7)}{4!} \cdot 1^{-8}(0.02)^4 + \cdots$$

$$= 1 - 0.08 + 0.004 - 0.00016 + 0.0000056 + \cdots$$

$$= 0.9238456.$$

We must consider a sufficient number of terms to guarantee the required accuracy. Since the last term above has a zero in the fifth decimal place, and each successive term is decreasing rapidly in size, no additional terms will affect our result, that is,

$$(1.02)^{-4} = 0.9238, \text{ correct to four significant figures.}$$

One of the more interesting results of the expansion of Eq. (11–12) occurs when $n = \frac{1}{2}$. We have

$$(1 + x)^{1/2} = 1 + \frac{1}{2}x + \frac{\frac{1}{2}(-\frac{1}{2})}{2!}x^2 + \frac{\frac{1}{2}(-\frac{1}{2})(-\frac{3}{2})}{3!}x^3 + \cdots$$

$$= 1 + \frac{x}{2} - \frac{x^2}{8} + \frac{x^3}{16} + \cdots \qquad (11\text{–}13)$$

In Fig. 11–3, we see the graph of $y = (1 + x)^{1/2}$, above it, the graph of $y = 1 + x/2$ (the approximation by two terms) and below it, the graph of $y = 1 + (x/2) - (x^2/8)$ (the approximation by three terms). Note how closely the two curves approximate the actual expansion. This is especially true for values of x near zero. For example, if $x = 0.21$, we have the exact value $y = (1 + 0.21)^{1/2} = \sqrt{1.21} = 1.1$. The approximations are

$$y \approx 1 + \frac{0.21}{2} = 1.105,^*$$

---

* The symbol $\approx$ is introduced to denote *approximately equal to.*

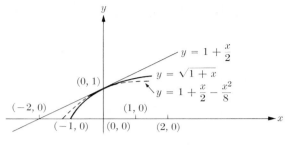

$$\text{Figure } 11\text{--}3$$

and

$$y \approx 1 + \frac{0.21}{2} - \frac{(0.21)^2}{8} = 1.09949.$$

This same formula may be used to find square roots for values not near zero if care is taken to reduce the problem to a similar form.

EXAMPLE 2. Find the value of $\sqrt{15}$ correct to four significant figures.

Solution. We use the relationship of Eq. (11–13).

$$\sqrt{15} = \sqrt{16 - 1} = (16 - 1)^{1/2} = [16(1 - \tfrac{1}{16})]^{1/2} = 4(1 - \tfrac{1}{16})^{1/2}$$

$$= 4\left[1 + \frac{1}{2} \cdot \left(-\frac{1}{16}\right) + \frac{\frac{1}{2}(-\frac{1}{2})}{2!}\left(-\frac{1}{16}\right)^2\right.$$

$$\left. + \frac{\frac{1}{2}(-\frac{1}{2})(-\frac{3}{2})}{3!}\left(-\frac{1}{16}\right)^3 + \cdots\right]$$

$$= 4[1 - \tfrac{1}{32} - \tfrac{1}{2048} - \tfrac{1}{65536} \cdots]$$

$$= 4[1 - 0.03125 - 0.000488 - 0.000015 \ldots]$$

$$= 3.8730, \text{ correct to four significant figures.}$$

By using the linear approximation, we obtain a good approximation with little work involved:

$$\sqrt{15} = \sqrt{16 - 1} = 4[1 - \tfrac{1}{16}]^{1/2} \approx 4[1 - \tfrac{1}{32}] = 3.875.$$

PROBLEMS

Write out the first four terms of each of the expansions for the following expressions.

1. $\dfrac{1}{1 + x} = (1 + x)^{-1}$

2. $\sqrt{1 + x}$

3. $\dfrac{1}{\sqrt{1 - x}}$

*4. $(1 + x)^{1/x}$

Compute each of the following to four significant figures.

5. $(1.01)^{-2}$ 6. $(1.03)^{-5}$ 7. $\sqrt[4]{1.02}$ 8. $\sqrt{1.05}$

9. $\sqrt{33}$ 10. $\sqrt[4]{17}$ 11. $\sqrt[3]{120}$ 12. $(1.01)^{10}$

13. Use the appropriate linear approximation for Problems 9, 10, and 11 to find the value.

CHAPTER 12

MATHEMATICAL INDUCTION

12–1 Mathematical induction. One of the most important methods of proof in mathematics is that of mathematical induction. The name is unfortunate, for we are likely to associate the word induction with inductive reasoning, by which a conclusion is drawn from a large number of special cases. No certain conclusion can be reached by the inductive logical process. Actually, mathematical induction is deductive in nature, for it leads to a firm conclusion. Since it will be a convenient method of proof for several important results that appear in our work, we shall consider the method in some detail. It is usually employed in proving the validity of a statement involving all positive integral values of n.

Let us illustrate this method of proof. Assume that we have an ordinary ladder with an indefinite number of steps and that we wish to prove that we can climb to any designated step. We can do this if we know two things: (a) we can climb to the first step; (b) if we are on any step, we can climb to the next higher step. Because of (a) we know that we can get on the first step. With this knowledge and the fact stated in (b), we know we can get on the second step. Again, with this knowledge and the general fact stated in (b), we know we can get on the third step, etc.

One of the methods of finding a square root on an ordinary computing or adding machine is based on the fact that the sum of n odd integers is equal to n^2. Specifically,

$$1 = \ 1 = 1^2,$$
$$1 + 3 = \ 4 = 2^2,$$
$$1 + 3 + 5 = \ 9 = 3^2,$$
$$1 + 3 + 5 + 7 = 16 = 4^2.$$

This property is true for all integers, and is not difficult to prove.

EXAMPLE 1. Prove by mathematical induction that for all positive integral values,

$$1 + 3 + 5 + \cdots + (2n - 1) \equiv n^2.$$

Solution. Part (a): *Verification for a specific value.* We have done this for $n = 1$, 2, 3, and 4, although such verification is necessary only for one value.

Part (b): *Induction property.* If the statement is true for $n = k$, where k denotes any value of n, then we wish to prove that it is true for

$n = k + 1$. Thus we assume we know this fact for $n = k$, namely,

$$1 + 3 + 5 + \cdots + (2k - 1) \equiv k^2.$$

Adding $2k + 1$ to both members, we have

$$1 + 3 + 5 + \cdots + (2k - 1) + (2k + 1) \equiv k^2 + (2k + 1)$$
$$\equiv (k + 1)^2.$$

This is precisely the equation $1 + 3 + 5 + \cdots + (2n - 1) \equiv n^2$ stated for $n = k + 1$. Thus the proof of Part (b) is complete.

Part (c): *Conclusion.* We know that the equation is true for $n = 1, 2, 3$, and 4. Since it is true for $n = 4$, and since we have proved the statement in Part (b), we know the original equation is true for $n = 4 + 1 = 5$; since it is true for $n = 5$, it is also true for $n = 6$. We may reason in this manner for all positive integral values of n.

We observe that a proof by mathematical induction consists of three parts.

Part (a). *Verification* of the validity of the statement or theorem for the smallest integral value of n for which the theorem is to hold. (This is analogous to being able to climb to the first step of the ladder.)

Part (b). *Proof of the inductive property.* If the statement or theorem is valid for $n = k$, where k denotes any value of n, then it is valid for $n = k + 1$. (This is analogous to being able to climb from any step of the ladder to the next higher step.)

Part (c). *Conclusion.* The statement or theorem is valid for all integral values of n equal to or greater than that for which it was verified in Part (a).

We know that $x - y$ is a factor of $x - y$, $x^2 - y^2$, and $x^3 - y^3$. Is it a factor of $x^n - y^n$ for any positive integer n?

EXAMPLE 2. Prove by mathematical induction that $x^n - y^n$ is divisible by $x - y$ for all positive integral values of n.

Solution. Part (a): When $n = 1$, $x^n - y^n$ becomes $x - y$, which is clearly divisible by $x - y$. When $n = 2$, $x^2 - y^2 \equiv (x + y)(x - y)$, which again is divisible by $x - y$.

Part (b): We assume that $x^k - y^k$ is divisible by $x - y$. With this assumption, we must show that $x^{k+1} - y^{k+1}$ is also divisible by $x - y$. If we add and subtract xy^k to $x^{k+1} - y^{k+1}$, we have

$$x^{k+1} - y^{k+1} \equiv x^{k+1} - xy^k + xy^k - y^{k+1}$$
$$\equiv x(x^k - y^k) + y^k(x - y).$$

Since each term of the right member of this identity is divisible by $x - y$, the right and therefore the left member is divisible by $x - y$. This completes Part (b).

Part (c): We know that the theorem is true for $n = 1$ and 2. Since it is true for $n = 2$, by Part (b) it is true for $n = 2 + 1 = 3$. Similar reasoning applies for all positive integral values of n.

The fact that both Parts (a) and (b) are necessary for complete proof must be stressed. Consider the following examples.

EXAMPLE 3. In Article 1–4 we considered prime numbers. Does the expression $n^2 - n + 11$ represent a prime number for all positive values of n? For $n = 1, 2, 3, 4$, and 5, we have the prime numbers 11, 13, 17, 23, and 31. Certainly Part (a) is satisfied for our statement. To show that the statement is not valid, however, let $n = 11$, and we have $11^2 - 11 + 11 = 11^2$, which is not a prime number.

EXAMPLE 4. For even integers, let us assume the nonvalid statement that

$$2 + 4 + 6 + \cdots + 2n = n^2 + n + 1$$

is true when $n = k$. We can then prove the statement's validity, given this basic assumption, for $n = k + 1$. We have

$$2 + 4 + 6 + \cdots + 2k = k^2 + k + 1.$$

Adding $2k + 2$ to both members of the equality, we obtain

$$2 + 4 + 6 + \cdots + 2k + 2k + 2 = k^2 + k + 1 + 2k + 2$$
$$= k^2 + 2k + 1 + k + 1 + 1 = (k + 1)^2 + (k + 1) + 1.$$

Thus, if the statement is valid for $n = k$, it is also valid for $n = k + 1$, and Part (b) has been proved. It is clear, however, that Part (a) and thus the statement itself is not valid, for consider the case where $n = 1, 2$, or 3. We would have $2 = 3$, $6 = 7$, or $12 = 13$, respectively.

We should emphasize that many proofs by mathematical induction are possible without adding the same quantity to both members of an equation known to be true. (This was the method in Example 1.)

PROBLEMS

By the method of mathematical induction, prove that the following are valid for all positive integral values of n.

1. $1 + 2 + 3 + \cdots + n = \dfrac{n(n + 1)}{2}$

2. $2 + 4 + 6 + \cdots + 2n = n(n + 1)$

3. $4 + 8 + 12 + \cdots + 4n = 2n(n + 1)$

4. $1 + 4 + 7 + \cdots + (3n - 2) = \dfrac{n(3n - 1)}{2}$

5. $1 + 3 + 6 + \cdots \dfrac{n(n + 1)}{2} = \dfrac{n(n + 1)(n + 2)}{6}$

6. $1^2 + 2^2 + 3^2 + \cdots + n^2 = \dfrac{n(n + 1)(2n + 1)}{6}$

7. $1^2 + 3^2 + 5^2 + \cdots + (2n - 1)^2 = \dfrac{n(2n - 1)(2n + 1)}{3}$

8. $\dfrac{1}{2} + \dfrac{1}{2^2} + \dfrac{1}{2^3} + \cdots + \dfrac{1}{2^n} = 1 - \dfrac{1}{2^n}$

9. $2 + 2^2 + 2^3 + \cdots + 2^n = 2^{n+1} - 2$

10. $1^3 + 2^3 + 3^3 + \cdots + n^3 = \dfrac{n^2(n + 1)^2}{4}$

11. $1^3 + 3^3 + 5^3 + \cdots + (2n - 1)^3 = n^2(2n^2 - 1)$

12. $\dfrac{1}{1 \cdot 2} + \dfrac{1}{2 \cdot 3} + \dfrac{1}{3 \cdot 4} + \cdots + \dfrac{1}{n(n + 1)} = \dfrac{n}{n + 1}$

13. $1 \cdot 2 + 2 \cdot 3 + 3 \cdot 4 + \cdots + n(n + 1) = \dfrac{n(n + 1)(n + 2)}{3}$

14. $1 \cdot 2 + 3 \cdot 4 + 5 \cdot 6 + \cdots + (2n - 1)(2n) = \dfrac{n(n + 1)(4n - 1)}{3}$

15. $1 \cdot 2 \cdot 3 + 2 \cdot 3 \cdot 4 + 3 \cdot 4 \cdot 5 + \cdots + n(n + 1)(n + 2)$

$$= \dfrac{n(n + 1)(n + 2)(n + 3)}{4}$$

*16. $t_1 + t_1 r + t_1 r^2 + \cdots + t_1 r^{n-1} = \dfrac{t_1 - t_1 r^n}{1 - r}$

*17. $t_1 + (t_1 + d) + (t_1 + 2d) + \cdots + t_1 + (n - 1)d = \dfrac{n[2t_1 + (n - 1)d]}{2}$

18. $x^{2n} - y^{2n}$ is divisible by $x - y$

19. $x^{2n-1} + y^{2n-1}$ is divisible by $x + y$

20. $n^3 + 2n$ is divisible by 3

21. If $a > -1$, $(a + 1)^n \geq 1 + na$

22. $\sin(\theta + n\pi) = (-1)^n \sin \theta$

23. $\cos(\theta + n\pi) = (-1)^n \cos \theta$

24. If n is a positive odd integer, $n(n^2 - 1)$ is divisible by 24.

25. $10^n + 3 \cdot 4^{n+2} + 5$ is divisible by 9

26. $2n \leq 2^n$

27. $2^{n-1} \leq n!$

*28. Prove by mathematical induction the generalization of Eq. (4–6), namely, that for an algebraic sum of any fixed number of terms

$$|a_1 + a_2 + \cdots + a_n| \leq |a_1| + |a_2| + \cdots + |a_n|.$$

Prove the following by the method of mathematical induction.

29. $\sin \theta + \sin 2\theta + \cdots + \sin n\theta \equiv \dfrac{\sin \frac{1}{2}(n+1)\theta \sin \frac{1}{2}n\theta}{\sin \theta/2}$

30. $\cos \theta + \cos 2\theta + \cdots + \cos n\theta \equiv \dfrac{\cos \frac{1}{2}(n+1)\theta \sin \frac{1}{2}n\theta}{\sin \theta/2}$

31. $\sin \theta + \sin 3\theta + \cdots + \sin (2n-1)\theta \equiv \dfrac{\sin^2 n\theta}{\sin \theta}$

32. $\cos \theta + \cos 3\theta + \cdots + \cos (2n-1)\theta \equiv \dfrac{\sin 2n\theta}{2 \sin \theta}$

33. Recursion formulas are helpful in many fields of mathematics. One such formula makes it possible to find the value of $\sin nt$ for any integer n if $\sin t$ and $\cos t$ are known. If $u_0 = 0$, $u_1 = 1$, and $u_n = (2 \cos t)u_{n-1} - u_{n-2}$ for $n = 2, 3, \ldots$, prove that $u_n = \sin nt/\sin t$ for $n = 0, 1, 2, \ldots$.

34. For the same values of u_n given in Problem 33, prove $(\cos t)u_n - u_{n-1} = \cos nt$ for $n = 0, 1, 2, \ldots$. This formula enables us to find $\cos nt$ if $\sin t$ and $\cos t$ are known. Such formulas are frequently used in work involving high-speed computing machines, because of the repetitive nature of the process.

35. In order to solve this problem, several completely different but important ideas must be used. The method of solution illustrates that many concepts are frequently needed to obtain one result. Let us consider the Fibonacci numbers defined by the recursion formula $u_0 = 0$, $u_1 = 1$, and $u_n = u_{n-1} + u_{n-2}$ for $n = 2, 3, 4, \ldots$. By direct computation, we find the sequence of u_n's to be: $0, 1, 1, 2, 3, 5, 8, 13, \ldots$.

(a) Form the quotients: u_1/u_2, u_3/u_4, u_5/u_6, u_7/u_8.

(b) Also form the quotients: u_2/u_3, u_4/u_5, u_6/u_7, u_8/u_9.

(c) Verify that the quotients in (a) decrease in size, that the quotients in (b) increase, and that both sets of quotients appear to "approach some value" between 0.625 and 0.615.

(d) Prove by induction: $u_1/u_2 > u_3/u_4 > \cdots > u_{2n-1}/u_{2n} > u_{2n+1}/u_{2n+2}\cdots$; we call $\{u_{2n-1}/u_{2n}\}$ a *decreasing* sequence.

(e) Prove by induction $u_2/u_3 < u_4/u_5 < \cdots < u_{2n}/u_{2n+1} < u_{2n+2}/u_{2n+3}\cdots$; we call $\{u_{2n}/u_{2n+1}\}$ an *increasing* sequence.

(f) Prove $u_{2n-1}/u_{2n} > u_{2m}/u_{2m+1}$ where m and n are any positive integers. Thus, the set $\{u_{2n-1}/u_{2n}\}$ is bounded below so that by the Completeness Property (Article 4–3) there exists a greatest lower bound G of this set. Similarly, the set $\{u_{2n}/u_{2n+1}\}$ is bounded above so that there exists a least upper bound L of this set.

(g) Show that for n sufficiently large, the expression

$$\left| \frac{u_{2n-1}}{u_{2n}} - \frac{u_{2n}}{u_{2n+1}} \right| = \left| \frac{u_{2n+1}u_{2n-1} - u_{2n}^2}{u_{2n+1}u_{2n}} \right|$$

can be made as small as we please. [*Hint:* Show (1) as n increases, the denominator increases, and (2) $u_{2n+1}u_{2n-1} - u_{2n}^2 = 1$ for all positive integers n.

(Use induction.) As a result of (f) and (g) we know that G, the greatest lower bound of $\{u_{2n-1}/u_{2n}\}$ is equal to L, the least upper bound of $\{u_{2n}/u_{2n+1}\}$. Let us denote this value by x, so that $G = L = x$. In addition, for n sufficiently large, there exist elements of both these sets arbitrarily close to x.]

(h) If we divide the original defining recursion formula

$$u_{2n+1} = u_{2n} + u_{2n-1} \qquad \text{by} \qquad u_{2n},$$

we have

$$\frac{u_{2n+1}}{u_{2n}} = 1 + \frac{u_{2n-1}}{u_{2n}} \qquad \text{or} \qquad \frac{1}{\dfrac{u_{2n}}{u_{2n+1}}} = 1 + \frac{u_{2n-1}}{u_{2n}}.$$

For n sufficiently large, we may approximate this equation by substituting x for u_{2n}/u_{2n+1} and u_{2n-1}/u_{2n}, so that $1/x = 1 + x$, or $x^2 + x - 1 = 0$. Solve this equation for the positive root x (why are we interested in the positive root?) and thus show that $x = G = L = (-1 + \sqrt{5})/2 = .618$ (approximately). [Recall Eq. (6–19) and Problem 24, Article 7–9.]

12–2 An alternative proof of the binomial theorem. It is quite possible to prove the binomial theorem by mathematical induction. The proof is given below and involves a certain facility with algebra. We give it to emphasize the importance of proofs by mathematical induction and to illustrate another important proof by induction, which does not involve the process of adding the same expression to both sides of an equation known to be true.

THEOREM 12–1. *For any positive integer n,*

$$(a + b)^n \equiv a^n + \frac{n}{1} a^{n-1}b + \frac{n(n-1)}{1 \cdot 2} a^{n-2}b^2$$
$$+ \frac{n(n-1)(n-2)}{1 \cdot 2 \cdot 3} a^{n-3}b^3 + \cdots + b^n. \tag{12-1}$$

Proof. We recall Eq. (11–11) the general expression for the rth term:

$$\frac{n(n-1)(n-2) \cdots (n-r+2)}{(r-1)!} a^{n-r+1}b^{r-1}. \tag{12-2}$$

We are now prepared to prove that Eq. (12–1) holds for all positive integral values of n. Since we have verified it for $n = 1, 2, 3,$ and 4 in Article 11–4, we need only to assume that it is valid for $n = k$, that is,

$$(a + b)^k \equiv a^k + ka^{k-1}b + \frac{k(k-1)}{2!} a^{k-2}b^2 + \cdots$$
$$+ \frac{k(k-1)(k-2) \cdots (k-r+2)}{(r-1)!} a^{k-r+1}b^{r-1} + \cdots + b^k, \tag{12-3}$$

and prove from this that it is valid for $n = k + 1$, or

$$(a + b)^{k+1} \equiv a^{k+1} + (k + 1)a^k b + \frac{(k + 1)k}{2!} a^{k-1} b^2 + \cdots$$

$$+ \frac{(k + 1)(k)(k - 1) \cdots (k - r + 3)}{(r - 1)!} a^{k-r+2} b^{r-1} + \cdots + b^{k+1}.$$

$$(12\text{--}4)$$

If we multiply each member of the identity (12–3) by $(a + b)$, we have

$$(a + b)^{k+1} \equiv a^{k+1} + ka^k b + \cdots \frac{k(k - 1) \cdots (k - r + 2)}{(r - 1)!} a^{k-r+2} b^{r-1}$$

$$+ \cdots + ab^k + a^k b + \cdots$$

$$+ \frac{k(k - 1) \cdots (k - r + 3)}{(r - 2)!} a^{k-r+2} b^{r-1} + \cdots + kab^k + b^{k+1}.$$

The terms through ab^k represent the right member of Eq. (12–3) multiplied by a, and the remaining terms represent the right member multiplied by b. To obtain the rth term in the result, we have written the rth term in the first half of the right member and the $(r - 1)$st term in the second, thus both contain $a^{k-r+2} b^{r-1}$. If we simplify the whole right member, the total coefficient of $a^{k-r+2} b^{r-1}$ will be

$$\frac{k(k - 1) \cdots (k - r + 2)}{(r - 1)!} + \frac{k(k - 1) \cdots (k - r + 3)}{(r - 2)!}$$

$$= \frac{k(k - 1) \cdots (k - r + 3)}{(r - 1)!} (k - r + 2)$$

$$+ \frac{k(k - 1) \cdots (k - r + 3)}{(r - 1)(r - 2)!} (r - 1)$$

$$= \frac{k(k - 1) \cdots (k - r + 3)}{(r - 1)!} [(k - r + 2) + (r - 1)]$$

$$= \frac{(k + 1)k(k - 1) \cdots (k - r + 3)}{(r - 1)!} .^*$$

Thus the total right side is exactly that of Eq. (12–4). The conclusion, Part (c), should be clear, and the proof is complete.

---

* It is interesting to note here that we are adding $C(k, r - 1)$ and $C(k, r - 2)$, and by Problem 20, Article 11–3 this is the expected result, $C(k + 1, r - 1)$.

CHAPTER 13

EXPONENTIAL AND LOGARITHMIC FUNCTIONS

We have considered in some detail the algebraic functions and one type of transcendental function, the circular functions. The inverse functions of the circular functions were also discussed. There are two other important transcendental functions, the exponential function and its inverse function, the logarithmic function. In this chapter we shall examine these two functions, their properties, and simple applications.

13–1 The exponential function a^x. Before we define an exponential function, we must define a^x, where a is any positive real number, and x is any real number. We are able to do this by using the Completeness Property (Article 4–3). We recall, for example, the set of rational approximations for $\sqrt{2}$. Since this set $A = \{1, 1.4, 1.41, 1.414 \ldots\}$ is bounded above, it has a least upper bound, which we call $\sqrt{2}$. If we wish to define $5^{\sqrt{2}}$, we consider the set $\{5^1, 5^{1.4}, 5^{1.41}, \ldots\}$ which is also bounded above. Its least upper bound is defined to be $5^{\sqrt{2}} = 9.738$ (approximately) and is well defined since 5^r is well defined where r is rational.

Our general definition is similar. If $a \in R$, $a > 1$, and $x \in R$, let $S = \{a^r | r \leq x, r \in F\}$. It should be clear that S is bounded above. For any $n \in I$ where $n > x$, $n > r$, so that $a^n > a^r$. (Problem 6, Article 4–1). Since for any x there always exists such an integer n, a^n is an upper bound of S. Thus, S has a least upper bound by the Completeness Property, and we may define a^x under these conditions.

DEFINITION 13–1. *Consider $a, x \in R$, and $a > 0$.*

(1) *If $a > 1$, a^x is the least upper bound of $\{a^r | r \leq x, r \in F\}$.*
(2) *If $a = 1$, $a^x = 1$.*
(3) *If $a < 1$, $1/a > 1$. Then $a^x = 1/(1/a)^x$.*

Since a^x has already been defined if $x \in F$ (Article 3–10), we now have a^x defined for all real x if $a > 0$. It is possible to show that these definitions of real exponents obey all the laws of exponents, although the proofs will not be given here.

With this understanding of the meaning of any real exponent, whether rational or irrational, let us consider the simplest exponential function f as follows:

$$\boxed{f : x \rightarrow a^x, \qquad a > 0} \qquad\qquad (13\text{–}1)$$

whose domain is R. Its defining equation is therefore, $y = f(x) = a^x$.

257

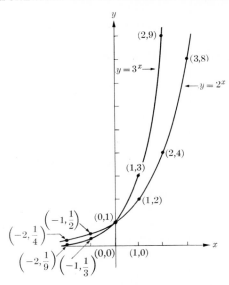

FIGURE 13–1

Now let us examine the graphs of the two special cases of this type of function, $y = 2^x$ and $y = 3^x$. These are sketched by plotting points whose coordinates satisfy the equations (Fig. 13–1).

x	-2	-1	0	1	2	3
y	$\frac{1}{4}$	$\frac{1}{2}$	1	2	4	8

$$y = 2^x$$

x	-2	-1	0	1	2
y	$\frac{1}{9}$	$\frac{1}{3}$	1	3	9

$$y = 3^x$$

The following properties of the function whose defining equation is $y = a^x$ should be apparent from the graphs.

1. The function is positive (its graph lies above the x-axis) for all values of x.

2. If $a > 1$, the function is an increasing function. As x takes on larger and larger values, so does the function, and as x decreases algebraically, the function approaches but never attains the value zero.

3. For all values of a, the function has the value 1 when $x = 0$.

4. There are no zeros of the function.

PROBLEMS

Sketch the graphs of the functions in 1 through 6.

1. 4^x 2. 10^x 3. 2^{-x} 4. $(\frac{1}{2})^x$ 5. 3^{-x} 6. $(\frac{1}{3})^x$

7. For the function whose defining equation is $y = a^x$ state a property corresponding to Property 2 if $0 < a < 1$.

13–2 Geometric progressions. We recall (Article 7–2) that a sequence is the range, or functional values of a function, the domain of which is either all or a part of the set of positive integers. We are now able to define a geometric progression by using the exponential function a^x.

DEFINITION 13–2. *A geometric progression is a sequence in which each term after the first is obtained by multiplying the same fixed number, called the* common ratio, *by the preceding term.*

ALTERNATIVE DEFINITION 13–2. *A geometric progression is any sequence for which the defining function has an equation of the form ka^u, where u is a linear equation in x.* (See Problem 28 of this article.)

ILLUSTRATION 1. The sequence $2, 4, 8, \ldots, 2^n$ is a geometric progression with the common ratio 2. The function defining this sequence is $f: x \rightarrow 2^x$.

ILLUSTRATION 2. The sequence $3, 1, \frac{1}{3}, \frac{1}{9}, \ldots$ is a geometric progression, with $\frac{1}{3}$ the common ratio. Its defining function is defined by $f(x) = 3^{2-x}$.

The general notation used for the geometric progression is similar to that of Article 7–2:

t_1, the first term,
r, the common ratio,
n, the number of terms,
t_n, the last or nth term.

Since each term is multiplied by the common ratio r to give its succeeding term, a geometric progression may be represented by

$$t_1, \quad t_1 r, \quad t_1 r^2, \quad t_1 r^3, \ldots, t_1 r^{n-1},$$

with the last value giving the expression for the nth term,

$$t_n = t_1 r^{n-1}. \tag{13–2}$$

EXAMPLE 1. Find the 10th term of the geometric progression $-8, 4, -2, \ldots$

Solution. With $t_1 = -8$, $r = -\frac{1}{2}$, and $n = 10$, we have

$$t_{10} = (-8)(-\tfrac{1}{2})^9$$

$$= (-8)(-\tfrac{1}{512}) = \tfrac{1}{64}.$$

EXAMPLE 2. If the 8th term of a geometric progression is 243 and the 5th term is 9, write the first three terms.

Solution. We have for $n = 8$,

$$t_8 = 243 = t_1 r^7,$$

and for $n = 5$,

$$t_5 = 9 = t_1 r^4.$$

If we divide the members of the first equation by those of the second, we get

$$r^3 = 27, \quad \text{or} \quad r = 3.$$

If we substitute this value in the second equation, we have

$$9 = t_1(3)^4, \quad \text{or} \quad 81 t_1 = 9,$$

$$t_1 = \tfrac{1}{9}.$$

Therefore the first three terms of the required series are $\tfrac{1}{9}$, $\tfrac{1}{3}$, and 1.

The expression for the value of the sum of n terms of any geometric progression is easily obtained. Writing out the sum and multiplying this expression by r, we have

$$S_n = t_1 + t_1 r + t_1 r^2 + \cdots + t_1 r^{n-2} + t_1 r^{n-1},$$

and

$$r S_n = t_1 r + t_1 r^2 + \cdots + t_1 r^{n-1} + t_1 r^n.$$

Subtracting the members of the second equation from those of the first, we have

$$S_n - r S_n = t_1 - t_1 r^n,$$

or

$$(1 - r)S_n = (1 - r^n)t_1,$$

and solving for S_n,

$$S_n = t_1 \frac{1 - r^n}{1 - r} \quad (r \neq 1),$$

which proves the following theorem.

THEOREM 13–1. *The sum of n terms of any geometric progression is given by the expression*

$$S_n = \frac{t_1(1 - r^n)}{1 - r} \quad (r \neq 1), \tag{13–3}$$

*where t_1 is the first term, r the common ratio, and n the number of terms.**

---

* This expression can also be proved by mathematical induction. (See Problem 16, Article 12–1.)

Since the last or nth term $t_n = t_1 r^{n-1}$ or $rt_n = t_1 r^n$, we also have

$$S_n = \frac{t_1 - rt_n}{1 - r} \qquad (r \neq 1).$$

(13–4)

We note that in Eqs. (13–3) and (13–4) $r \neq 1$. What can be said about any geometric progression when $r = 1$?

PROBLEMS

Write out the next three terms in each of the following geometric progressions, and find t_n and S_n.

1. 1, 4, 16, . . . to 8 terms
2. 27, 9, 3, . . . to 9 terms
3. $\frac{1}{125}$, $-\frac{1}{25}$, $\frac{1}{5}$, . . . to 7 terms
4. $P(1 + r)$, $P(1 + r)^2$, $P(1 + r)^3$, . . . to 10 terms

In Problems 5 through 11, three of the elements t_1, t_n, r, n, and S_n of the geometric progression are given. Find the missing elements in each case.

5. $t_1 = 2$, $r = 3$, $n = 6$ 6. $t_1 = 2$, $n = 4$, $t_n = 16$
7. $t_1 = 1$, $n = 3$, $S_n = 13$ 8. $r = -3$, $n = 5$, $t_n = 162$
9. $r = \frac{1}{3}$, $n = 5$, $S_n = \frac{4}{9}$ 10. $t_1 = 3$, $r = \frac{2}{5}$, $S_n = \frac{609}{125}$
11. $t_1 = -2$, $r = 2$, $t_n = -64$

12. Find the value of k so that $2k + 2$, $5k - 11$, and $7k - 13$ will form a geometric progression.

13. What are the first three terms of the geometric progression whose third term is $\frac{25}{4}$ and whose 7th term is $\frac{4}{25}$.

14. The second term of a geometric progression is $\frac{5}{4}$ and its 4th term is $\frac{1}{5}$. Find its third term.

15. In the geometric progression 18, -12, 8 . . . , which term is $\frac{512}{729}$?

*16. The terms between any two terms of a geometric progression are called the *geometric means* between these two terms. Insert four geometric means between $\frac{25}{4}$ and $\frac{8}{125}$.

17. Insert three geometric means between $\frac{27}{8}$ and $\frac{2}{3}$.

*18. Insert one geometric mean between $\frac{7}{8}$ and $\frac{175}{32}$. A single number of this kind is called the *geometric mean of two numbers*.

19. What is the geometric mean of the two numbers a and b?

20. Find the geometric mean of (a) 12 and $\frac{4}{3}$, (b) 28 and 112.

21. Prove that for the two unequal positive numbers a and b, the arithmetic mean is greater than the geometric mean.

22. The population of a certain town is 5000. If it increases 5% every year, what will the approximate population be at the end of 10 years?

23. A rubber ball is dropped from a height of 9 feet. If it rebounds one-third of the distance it has fallen after each fall, how far will it rebound the 6th time? Through what distance has it traveled when it strikes the ground the 7th time?

24. A man accepts a position at $3600 with the understanding that he will receive a 2% increase every year. What will his salary be after 10 years of service?

. 25. An automobile purchased for $3000 depreciates in value 12% every year. Find its value at the end of 5 years.

26. If a paper napkin 0.01 inch thick could be folded so that it was half as large but twice as thick, folded again in the same manner, and again until the process has been repeated 30 times, approximately how thick would the resulting piece of paper be?

27. If you had the choice of a salary of $1000 a day for a month of 31 days, or $1 for the first day's work, $2 for the second, $4 for the third, and each day thereafter for the rest of the month your salary would be doubled, which choice would result in the larger salary?

28. By using Eq. (13–2), prove that the two definitions of a geometric progression are equivalent.

13–3 Geometric progressions with infinitely many terms. In the discussion so far, we have considered only the sum of the terms of a finite sequence. If we consider the definition of the arithmetic progression, it should be clear that such a progression with an infinite number of terms has no finite sum. The same is true for a geometric progression with $|r|$ greater than 1. Each term being larger in size than the preceding one, no definite value representing such an infinite sum can exist. In fact, even if $r = 1$, each term is the same, so that no such infinite sum can exist.

If $|r| < 1$, we have a different situation. Consider the sum of the geometric progression

$$S_n = \frac{1}{2} + \frac{1}{4} + \frac{1}{8} + \cdots + \frac{1}{2^n}, \qquad (13\text{–}5)$$

where $r = \frac{1}{2}$.

One interpretation of S_n may be seen in Fig. 13–2, which represents a line segment one unit in length. The brackets denote the sum of the terms, and the numbers below denote the sum of the progression at any stage. Each term that is added represents a length of half the total length remaining between the point representing the finite sum and the point 1. The more terms considered in Eq. (13–5), the closer we get to the point 1. In fact, we may get as close as we please to 1 by considering a sufficient

FIGURE 13–2

number of terms, but no matter how many terms are considered, the sum will never exceed 1. Thus we say the limiting value of S_n is 1, and we write

$$S = \lim_{n \to \infty} S_n = 1. \tag{13–6}$$

This may be shown algebraically. Equation (13–3) may be written

$$S_n = \frac{t_1}{1 - r} - \frac{t_1 r^n}{1 - r}. \tag{13–7}$$

In the progression (13–5), $t_1 = r = \frac{1}{2}$, so that

$$S_n = \frac{\frac{1}{2}}{1 - \frac{1}{2}} - \frac{\frac{1}{2}(\frac{1}{2})^n}{1 - \frac{1}{2}}$$

$$= 1 - (\tfrac{1}{2})^n.$$

As n gets larger, $(\frac{1}{2})^n$ gets smaller, and in fact, $(\frac{1}{2})^n$ can be made as small in size as we please by choosing n sufficiently large. Thus, $\lim_{n \to \infty}(\frac{1}{2})^n = 0$, so that again we have

$$\lim_{n \to \infty} S_n = 1.$$

The same process holds for any geometric progression where $|r| < 1$. Using Eq. (13–7), we have

$$S_n = \frac{t_1}{1 - r} - \frac{t_1 r^n}{1 - r}.$$

If we let n increase without limit, since t_1 and r are fixed, and $|r| < 1$,

$$\lim_{n \to \infty} \frac{t_1 r^n}{1 - r} = 0.$$

THEOREM 13–2.* *The "sum" S of a geometric progression with infinitely many terms exists if $|r| < 1$, and*

$$\boxed{S = \lim_{n \to \infty} S_n = \frac{t_1}{1 - r}.} \tag{13–8}$$

EXAMPLE 1. Find the sum of the infinite geometric progression $\frac{3}{2}$, 1, $\frac{2}{3}$, $\frac{4}{9}$, ...

---

* Although we cannot add infinitely many terms, the limit $n \to \infty$ $S_n = S$ is called the "sum."

Solution. With $t_1 = \frac{3}{2}$ and $r = \frac{2}{3}$, we find

$$S = \frac{a}{1-r} = \frac{\frac{3}{2}}{1-\frac{2}{3}} = \frac{\frac{3}{2}}{\frac{1}{3}} = 4\frac{1}{2}.$$

EXAMPLE 2.   Convert the repeating decimal 3.242424 ... into an equivalent common fraction.

Solution. We can represent the number 3.242424 ... as the number 3 plus a geometric progression with $t_1 = 0.24$ and $r = 0.01$, since

$$3.242424 \ldots = 3 + (0.24 + 0.0024 + 0.000024 + \cdots).$$

The sum S, in the parentheses, may be given

$$S = \frac{t_1}{1-r} = \frac{0.24}{1-0.01} = \frac{0.24}{0.99} = \frac{8}{33}.$$

Thus

$$3.242424 \ldots = 3 + \tfrac{8}{33} = \tfrac{107}{33}.$$

This result may be checked by actually dividing 107 by 33.

We recall that any infinite repeating decimal can be converted into an equivalent common fraction. Moreover, any common fraction may be written as a periodic decimal. Recall Problems 4 and 5, Article 1–5.

PROBLEMS

Find the sum of each of the following infinite geometric progressions.

1. $1, \frac{1}{3}, \frac{1}{9}, \ldots$ 2. $128, 48, 18, \ldots$ 3. $16, -4, 1, \ldots$
4. $\frac{4}{3}, 1, \frac{3}{4}, \ldots$ 5. $2, \sqrt{2}, 1, \ldots$ 6. $\sqrt{2}+1, 1, \sqrt{2}-1, \ldots$

Convert each of the repeating decimals into equivalent common fractions.

7. $3.333 \ldots$ 8. $6.272727 \ldots$ 9. $0.555 \ldots$
10. $8.690909 \ldots$ 11. $5.818181 \ldots$ 12. $0.142857142857 \ldots$

13. The sum of an infinite geometric progression is $\frac{7}{2}$ and the first term is 3. What is the common ratio?

14. The length of the side of a square is 4 inches. A second square is inscribed by connecting the midpoints of the sides of the first square, a third by connecting the midpoints of the sides of the second, and so on. Find the sum of the areas of the infinitely many squares thus formed, including the first.

15. Find the sum of the perimeters of all the squares described in Problem 14.

16. If the original figure in Problem 14 were an equilateral triangle, with sides 4 inches long, and new equilateral triangles were formed in the same way, what would the sum of their areas be, including the area of the original figure?

17. A ball is dropped from a height of 48 feet and rebounds two-thirds of the distance it falls. If it continues to fall and rebound in this way, how far will it travel before coming to rest?

18. The middle third of a line 1 foot long is erased. From each of the two remaining thirds, the middle thirds are erased. From each of the four remaining ninths, the middle thirds are erased. If this process is continued indefinitely, what will be the sum of the lengths of the remaining line segments?

13–4 The logarithmic function. Since for any positive number x and any positive number $a \neq 1$, there is one and only one real value of y which satisfies the equation $a^y = x$,* we can solve this equation for y, and have y equal to the power to which a must be raised in order to obtain the number x. We thus obtain the following definition.

DEFINITION 13–3. *The exponent or power y to which the number a is raised to give the number x is called the* logarithm *of x to the base a, and is written*

$$y = \log_a x, \tag{13-9}$$

where $x > 0$, and $a > 0$, and $\neq 1$. This is the defining equation for the logarithmic function

$$\boxed{l: x \rightarrow \log_a x.} \tag{13-10}$$

It should be clear that if $f: x \rightarrow a^x$, the function $l: x \rightarrow \log_a x$ is actually f^{-1}. As a result, if we keep in mind that the two expressions

$$x = a^y \quad \text{and} \quad y = \log_a x \tag{13-11}$$

are equivalent, many of the logarithmic properties should be evident.

ILLUSTRATION 1.

$$\log_3 9 = 2 \quad \leftrightarrow 3^2 = 9.\dagger$$

$$\log_2 32 = 5 \quad \leftrightarrow 2^5 = 32.$$

$$\log_6 1 = 0 \quad \leftrightarrow 6^0 = 1.$$

$$\log_2 \tfrac{1}{16} = -4 \leftrightarrow 2^{-4} = \tfrac{1}{16}.$$

$$\log_8 4 = \tfrac{2}{3} \quad \leftrightarrow 8^{2/3} = 4.$$

Let us sketch the graphs of two logarithmic functions whose defining equations are $y = \log_2 x$ and $y = \log_3 x$ and, with the help of these

---

* The proof of this statement is beyond the scope of this book, but it should be evident from Fig. 13–2.

† The symbol $\leftrightarrow$ denotes "is the same as" or that the two expressions are equivalent.

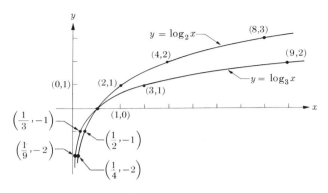

FIGURE 13–3

graphs (Fig. 13–3), consider some of the fundamental properties of the function $l: x \rightarrow \log_a x$.

x	$\frac{1}{4}$	$\frac{1}{2}$	1	2	4	8
y	-2	-1	0	1	2	3

$$y = \log_2 x \leftrightarrow 2^y = x$$

x	$\frac{1}{9}$	$\frac{1}{3}$	1	3	9
y	-2	-1	0	1	2

$$y = \log_3 x \leftrightarrow 3^y = x$$

1. The function is positive for all values of x greater than 1, but negative for all values of x less than 1. It is not defined for negative values of x.

2. The function is an increasing function.

3. The logarithm of any number with respect to itself as base is equal to 1. Graphically, all such curves pass through the point $(a, 1)$.

4. The function has $x = 1$ for its only zero.

There are several additional properties of logarithms which may be easily derived if we recall that a logarithm is an exponent. They will be stated and proved as theorems.

THEOREM 13–3. *The logarithm of the product of two quantities is equal to the logarithm of the first quantity plus the logarithm of the second,*

$$\log_a uv \equiv \log_a u + \log_a v. \tag{13–12}$$

Proof. Let u and v be any two positive quantities whose logarithms are x and y, respectively,

$$x = \log_a u \quad \text{and} \quad y = \log_a v,$$

or

$$a^x = u \quad \text{and} \quad a^y = v.$$

Multiplying the corresponding members of these equations, we have

$$uv = a^x a^y = a^{x+y},$$

which by the definition of a logarithm reduces to

$$\log_a uv = x + y = \log_a u + \log_a v.$$

THEOREM 13–4. *The logarithm of the quotient of two quantities is equal to the logarithm of the first quantity minus the logarithm of the second,*

$$\log_a \frac{u}{v} \equiv \log_a u - \log_a v. \qquad (13\text{–}13)$$

Proof. With the same assumptions as in Theorem 13–3, we have

$$\frac{u}{v} = \frac{a^x}{a^y} = a^{x-y}.$$

Written in terms of logarithms, this becomes

$$\log_a \frac{u}{v} = x - y = \log_a u - \log_a v.$$

THEOREM 13–5. *The logarithm of a power of a quantity is equal to the power multiplied by the logarithm of the quantity, that is,*

$$\log_a u^p \equiv p \log_a u. \qquad (13\text{–}14)$$

Proof. Let u be any positive quantity and its logarithm be x. Then $x = \log_a u$ or $a^x = u$. If we raise both members to the p power, we have

$$(a^x)^p = a^{xp} = u^p,$$

or, in terms of logarithms,

$$\log_a u^p = xp = p \log_a u.$$

ILLUSTRATION 2. Theorem 13–3 implies that

$$\log_{10} (47)(93) = \log_{10} 47 + \log_{10} 93$$

or

$$\log_{10} 4700 = \log_{10} 47 \cdot 100 = \log_{10} 47 + \log_{10} 100.$$

ILLUSTRATION 3. Theorem 13–4 implies that

$$\log_{10} \tfrac{82}{53} = \log_{10} 82 - \log_{10} 53.$$

Theorems 13–3 and 13–4 imply that

$$\log_{10} \frac{(48)(96)}{23} = \log_{10} 48 + \log_{10} 96 - \log_{10} 23.$$

ILLUSTRATION 4. Theorem 13–5 is used for both integral powers and roots,

$$\log_{10} 28^5 = 5 \log_{10} 28,$$

$$\log_{10} \sqrt[3]{472} = \log_{10} (472)^{1/3} = \tfrac{1}{3} \log_{10} 472.$$

PROBLEMS

Express the following in logarithmic notation, using Eq. (13–11).

1. $3^3 = 27$ 2. $5^4 = 625$ 3. $4^0 = 1$
4. $10^3 = 1000$ 5. $8^{4/3} = 16$ 6. $2^{-6} = \frac{1}{64}$
7. $10^{-3} = 0.001$ 8. $b^z = w$ 9. $4^1 = 4$

Express in exponent notation using Eq. (13–11).

10. $\log_2 \tfrac{1}{8} = -3$ 11. $\log_{36} 6 = \tfrac{1}{2}$ 12. $\log_{10} 1 = 0$

Find by inspection the value of x, a, or u in the following expressions.

13. $x = \log_4 16$ 14. $x = \log_7 1$ 15. $x = \log_9 \tfrac{1}{9}$
16. $x = \log_{\sqrt 6} 36$ 17. $\log_5 u = 2$ 18. $\log_a 16 = 4$
19. $x = \log_2 4^7$ 20. $\log_a 32 = -\tfrac{5}{7}$ 21. $\log_a \tfrac{2}{3} = -\tfrac{1}{3}$

Sketch the graphs of the following functions.

22. $y = \log_5 x$ 23. $y = \log_{1/2} x$
24. $y = \log_{10} x$ 25. $y = \log_{1/3} x$

Express as a single logarithm, using Theorems 13–3, 4, and 5.

26. $\log_a x + \log_a y - \log_a z$ 27. $\log_b (a + 2) - \log_b (a - 3)$
28. $4 \log_{10} x - 3 \log_{10} y$ 29. $\tfrac{1}{2} \log_a x - \tfrac{2}{3} \log_a y$
30. $\log_b 2x + 3 (\log_b x - \log_b y)$ 31. $-\log_a x + 6 \log_a (x - 1) + 3 \log_a x^2$

Write the logarithm of the given expression in terms of the logarithms of its factors.

32. $\log_{10} (895)(1.47)$ 33. $\log_{10} (60.3)^4$

34. $\log_{10} (68)^7 (\sqrt{147})$ 35. $\log_{10} \dfrac{(54.3)^3 (67)}{(93.9)(32.5)^2}$

13–5 Common logarithms. After the discussion in the previous article, it should be clear that any positive number other than 1 can be used as the base for a system of logarithms. For computational purposes, the most convenient system is that with 10 as its base. The first table of logarithms with 10 as the base was composed by Henry Briggs (1560–1631). The advantages of this system will become apparent as we proceed. In writing

$$10^3 = 1000$$
$$10^2 = 100$$
$$10^1 = 10$$
$$10^0 = 1$$
$$10^{-1} = 0.1$$
$$10^{-2} = 0.01$$
$$10^{-3} = 0.001$$

and considering this list as extending upward and downward indefinitely, we have a method for representing certain numbers as powers of ten. Although these special numbers are the only ones which can be written as 10 with an integral exponent, all positive numbers can be represented approximately as 10 with some exponent. This exponent, we realize from our definition of a logarithm (Eq. 13–9), is the logarithm of the number to the base 10, and will be called the *common logarithm of a number*. Through-out the rest of this book, the base 10 will be assumed when no base is indicated. Thus, log 1000 = 3, log 10 = 1, or log 0.001 = −3.

Not only do the powers of ten listed above have logarithms, but all positive numbers do. The values of the logarithms (to the base ten) of all positive numbers every hundredth of a unit between 1 and 10 have been approximated to four decimal places in Table II in the Appendix. For example, to find log 7.63, we look down the first column N of the table for 7.6 and then move to the right of 7.6 to the number which appears in the column headed by 3. Finding 0.8825, we have log 7.63 = 0.8825, which means, of course, $10^{0.8825} = 7.63$ (approximately).

Actually, by making use of the method of *linear interpolation*, similar to that used in Article 9–5, as well as Table II, we can find the logarithm of a number with four significant digits. If N lies between x and $x + 0.01$, then $N = x + 0.01r$, with r between 0 and 1, so that, assuming the graph of the logarithmic function is a straight line between x and $x + 0.01$,

$$\log N = \log x + r \left[\log (x + 0.01) - \log x\right]. \qquad (13\text{--}15)$$

EXAMPLE 1. Find log 3.476.

Solution. Since 3.47 < 3.476 < 3.48, we have

$$\log 3.476 = \log 3.47 + 0.6 \,(\log 3.48 - \log 3.47)$$
$$= 0.5403 + 0.6(0.5416 - 0.5403)$$
$$= 0.5403 + 0.0008$$
$$= 0.5411.$$

This number can have only four significant figures, since the logarithms in the table are only four-figure approximations.

If the logarithm of a number is given to four decimal places, it is also possible to find the number by using Table II. If $\log N$ appears in the middle of the table, the process used to find N is reversed. If $\log N$ lies between $\log x$ and $\log (x + 0.01)$, then $N = x + 0.01r$, with

$$ r = \frac{\log N - \log x}{\log (x + 0.01) - \log x}, \qquad (13\text{–}16) $$

rounded to the nearest tenth. (Why?)

EXAMPLE 2. Find N if $\log N = 0.7281$.

Solution. If we look in the middle of the table, we find

$$ 0.7275 < 0.7281 < 0.7284, $$

where
$$ \log 5.35 = 0.7284, $$
$$ \log 5.34 = 0.7275. $$

Therefore we have

$$ r = \frac{0.7281 - 0.7275}{0.7284 - 0.7275} = 0.7 \qquad \text{(rounded off),} $$

and $N = 5.347$.

PROBLEMS

Using Table II, find the logarithm of each of the following numbers.

1. 2.57	2. 3.89	3. 6.92	4. 7.65
5. 4.71	6. 9.80	7. 6.875	8. 8.924
9. 3.276	10. 1.892	11. 7.689	12. 5.873

Using Table II, find N in each of the following if $\log N$ is equal to:

13. 0.3856	14. 0.8756	15. 0.6149	16. 0.6405
17. 0.9415	18. 0.7657	19. 0.2675	20. 0.5217
21. 0.9229	22. 0.7578	23. 0.5069	24. 0.6745

In general, the logarithm of N has two parts: a whole number, called the *characteristic*, and a positive decimal (a number n such that $0 \leq n < 1$), called the *mantissa*. If the decimal point in a number is just to the right of the first nonzero digit, the logarithm of that number has 0 for its characteristic. All the numbers between 1 and 10 in Table II are of this type. Such a number is said to have its *decimal point in standard position.*

If any number is multiplied by 10, the decimal point is moved one place to the right, or if divided by 10, one place to the left. But each time a number is multiplied by 10, since

$$\log 10N = \log N + \log 10$$
$$= \log N + 1,$$

the logarithm of the number is increased by one. Likewise, if a number is divided by 10, its logarithm is decreased by one, for

$$\log \frac{N}{10} = \log N - \log 10$$

$$= \log N - 1.$$

Thus the general rule for obtaining the characteristic can be stated as a theorem.

THEOREM 13–6. *The characteristic of the logarithm of a number is equal to the number of places the decimal point has been moved from standard position. The characteristic is positive if the point has been moved to the right, negative if to the left.*

It is because of this property of our number system, and the corresponding ease of determining the characteristic, that logarithms to the base ten are used for computation.

The mantissa, that part of the logarithm which appears in the table, is not affected by the position of the decimal point in the number, but depends only on its succession of digits. Thus, because of the result of Example 1, $\log 347.6 = 2.5411$, since its characteristic is 2, while

$$\log 0.003476 = -3 + 0.5411.$$

The characteristic -3 is usually written $7 - 10$ (it is common practice for computational purposes to write any negative characteristic as a positive integer minus a multiple of 10), so that

$$-3 + 0.5411 = 7.5411 - 10.$$

PROBLEMS

Give the characteristic and mantissa of each of the following logarithms.

1. $\log N = 1.3782$
2. $\log N = 3.4729$
3. $\log N = 0.5728 - 3$
4. $\log N = 9.6847$
5. $\log N = 5.8723$
6. $\log N = 6.7253 - 10$
7. $\log N = -3.7285$
8. $\log N = -0.6892$

Find the logarithms of each of the following numbers, using Table II.

9. 329   10. 0.00874   11. 4728
12. 32.46   13. 0.07284   14. 0.6877

Find N in each of the following, using Table II.

15. $\log N = 3.8228$ 16. $\log N = 0.9643 - 2$
17. $\log N = 2.4268$ 18. $\log N = 9.8818 - 10$
19. $\log N = 7.5627 - 10$ 20. $\log N = -1.4892$

13–6 Computation by the use of logarithms. We are now prepared to show how any computation involving multiplication, division, raising to a power, or extracting roots is greatly simplified through the use of logarithms. The work should be outlined systematically before any actual computation is carried out. An orderly arrangement is most helpful, not only in simplifying the work but also in checking the result.

EXAMPLE 1. Use logarithms to compute $(1280 \cdot 0.849)/62.8$.

Solution. By letting $N = (1280 \cdot 0.849)/62.8$, we have, using Theorems 13–3 and 13–4, $\log N = \log 1280 + \log 0.849 - \log 62.8$. The work should then be arranged as follows:

$$
\begin{aligned}
\log 1280 &= \quad 3.1072 \\
(+) \log 0.849 &= \quad 9.9289 - 10 \\
\hline
\log \text{numerator} &= 13.0361 - 10 \\
(-) \log 62.8 &= \quad 1.7980 \\
\hline
\log N &= 11.2381 - 10 \\
N &= 17.3.
\end{aligned}
$$

N is given with three significant figures because the original numbers were of this type.

EXAMPLE 2. Compute by using logarithms: $\sqrt{0.01278}/(0.4825)^3$.

Solution. We know $\log N = \frac{1}{2} \log 0.01278 - 3 \log 0.4825$. Arranging our work, we have

$$
\begin{aligned}
\log 0.4825 &= \quad 9.6834 - 10 & \log 0.01278 &= 18.1065 - 20 \\
3 \log 0.4825 &= 29.0502 - 30 & \tfrac{1}{2} \log 0.01278 &= \quad 9.0532 - 10 \\
&= \quad 9.0502 - 10 & (-) \, 3 \log 0.4825 &= \quad 9.0502 - 10 \\
& & \hline
& & \log N &= \quad 0.0030 \\
& & N &= \quad 1.007.
\end{aligned}
$$

EXAMPLE 3. Find the value of $x = 52.8 \log 6.79$.

Solution. It is important to note that this example asks for the product of the two factors 52.8 and log 6.79, *not* 52.8 and 6.79. Thus,

$$\log x = \log 52.8 + \log [\log 6.79].$$

$$\log 52.8 = \quad 1.7226$$
$$(+) \log [\log 6.79] = \log 0.832 = \quad 9.9201 - 10$$
$$\log x = \quad 1.6427$$
$$x = \quad 43.9$$

PROBLEMS

Using logarithms, compute the value of the following to the correct number of significant figures.

1. $(367)(87.2)$

2. $(47.2)(0.897)$

3. $\dfrac{32.7}{(0.892)^{1/2}}$

4. $\dfrac{(245)(8.62)}{(7.84)^2}$

5. $(32.79)(497.2)(9.738)$

6. $\sqrt{756.9}\,(4.796)$

†7. $(-0.8472)^4$

8. $(-3.472)^{-3}$

9. $\dfrac{(6.892)(-0.9245)^{2/3}}{2.475}$

10. $\left(-\dfrac{47.2}{6.783}\right)^3$

11. $\dfrac{\sqrt{738.2}\,(38.74)}{(0.9576)^2(8743)}$

12. $\left[\dfrac{\sqrt{8453}\,(0.002477)}{347.9}\right]^{1/2}$

13. $4.72 \log 63.9$

14. $\log (\log 82.4)$

15. $\dfrac{\log 48.5}{\log 67.2}$

16. $\dfrac{\log 0.8924}{\log 5.237}$

13–7 Compound interest and its generalization. The study of compound interest makes use of logarithmic computation, and it also logically introduces another important system of logarithms.

If an amount of money P is invested at an interest rate of r (expressed in decimals) per year, the amount of interest at the end of one year is Pr, so that the total amount is $P + Pr = P(1 + r)$. If this amount then draws interest for a second year, at the end of two years the total amount is $P(1 + r) + P(1 + r)r = P(1 + r)[1 + r] = P(1 + r)^2$. This represents the compound amount of money at the end of two years due to its

---

† Although the logarithm of a negative number is not defined, the calculation may be carried out by considering all factors positive and prefixing the appropriate sign to the result.

investment at the interest rate r. If we continue this process, the amount P, invested for n years and compounded annually at the rate r, is given by

$$A = P(1 + r)^n. \qquad (13\text{--}17)$$

EXAMPLE 1. Find the compound amount at the end of eight years on an original principal of \$500 at 6% compounded annually.

Solution. Using Eq. (13–17), we have $P = 500$, $r = 0.06$, and $n = 8$. Thus,

$$A = 500(1 + 0.06)^8 = 500(1.06)^8.$$

$\log 1.06 = 0.0253$	$\log 500 = 2.6990$
$8 \log 1.06 = 0.2024$	$(+)\ 8 \log 1.06 = 0.2024$
	$\log A = 2.9014$
	$A = \$796.80.$

Since n represents the number of years and r the rate per year, we can consider the result due to amounts compounded anually, semiannually, quarterly, and so on, if we let s denote the number of conversion periods each year. Thus, in n years, with s conversion periods per year, the number of such periods is ns and the rate per period r/s, or

$$A = P \left(1 + \frac{r}{s}\right)^{ns}. \qquad (13\text{--}18)$$

EXAMPLE 2. If the \$500 in Example 1 were invested for eight years at 6% compounded quarterly, how large would the result be?

Solution. Since 6% compounded quarterly for eight years is $1\frac{1}{2}$% per period, with 32 periods, we have

$$A = 500(1.015)^{32},$$

which results in $A = \$804.20$.

Both this result and that in the first example are not very accurate, since four-place logarithm tables were used. For accurate results, since the exponent is large, either seven-place logarithmic or compound interest tables should be used.

One of the most important exponential functions is a direct result of a generalization of Eq. (13–18), which is sometimes called the *law of natural growth*. It has frequent applications in biology, chemistry, and economics, as well as in mathematics. Let us suppose that the number of conversion periods s increases indefinitely, so that the amount is compounded continuously. Letting $r/s = x$, and therefore $s/r = 1/x$, we have, from Eq. (13–18),

$$A = P\left[\left(1 + \frac{r}{s}\right)^{s/r}\right]^{rn} = P[(1 + x)^{1/x}]^{rn}. \qquad (13\text{–}19)$$

With s increasing indefinitely, for a fixed r, $r/s = x$ decreases indefinitely through positive values and approaches zero. If Eq. (13–19) is expanded by the binomial theorem (see Problem 4, Article 11–5),

$$A = P\left[1^{1/x} + \frac{1}{x} \cdot 1^{(1/x)-1} \cdot x + \frac{\frac{1}{x}\left(\frac{1}{x} - 1\right)}{2!} \cdot 1^{(1/x)-2} \cdot x^2 \right.$$
$$\left. + \frac{\frac{1}{x}\left(\frac{1}{x} - 1\right)\left(\frac{1}{x} - 2\right)}{3!} \cdot 1^{(1/x)-3} \cdot x^3 \cdots \right]^{rn}$$

$$= P\left[1^{1/x} + 1^{(1/x)-1} + \frac{1 - x}{2!} \cdot 1^{(1/x)-2} \right.$$
$$\left. + \frac{(1 - x)(1 - 2x)}{3!} \cdot 1^{(1/x)-3} + \cdots \right]^{rn},$$

and if we evaluate each term of this expression for x equals zero, we get

$$A = P\left(1 + 1 + \frac{1}{2} + \frac{1}{3!} + \cdots\right)^{rn}. \qquad (13\text{–}20)$$

Although we have by no means shown that this infinite sum has a definite value,* it would seem probable that the expression within the brackets of Eq. (13–19) does have a definite value if x is allowed to approach zero. Such is the case. This constant value, denoted by e, is a nonterminating, nonrepeating decimal, and therefore irrational (Article 1–5). To six significant figures,

$$e = \operatorname*{limit}_{x \to 0}\,(1 + x)^{1/x} = \left(1 + 1 + \frac{1}{2!} + \frac{1}{3!} + \cdots\right) = 2.71828. \qquad (13\text{–}21)$$

We thus have the function

$$\boxed{A = Pe^{rn},} \qquad (13\text{–}22)$$

---

* As in Article 11–5, any proof, in general, of the existence of a definite value for an infinite sum is beyond the scope of this book.

representing the amount of P compounded continuously for n years at a rate r.

EXAMPLE 3. The population of a certain locality is 20,000 and is increasing continuously at a rate $r = 0.037$, according to the law of natural growth, Eq. (13–21). Find the approximate population after 25 years.

Solution. With the formula $A = Pe^{rn}$, we have $P = 20,000$, $r = 0.037$, and $n = 25$. Therefore,

$$A = 20,000e^{(0.037)(25)}.$$

Solving by logarithms, we have

$$\log A = \log 20,000 + (0.037)(25) \log e.$$
$$\log 20,000 = 4.3010$$
$$(+)\ (0.037)(25) \log e = 0.4017$$
$$\overline{\log A = 4.7027}$$
$$A = 50,430 \text{ (approximate) population.}$$

PROBLEMS

1. Find the compound amount at the end of 10 years on an original principal of $200 at 4% (a) compounded annually, (b) compounded semiannually, (c) compounded quarterly, (d) compounded continuously.

2. Find the compound amount at the end of 20 years on an original principal of $3000 at 6% (a) compounded annually, (b) compounded monthly, (c) compounded continuously.

3. What time is required to double a certain amount (a) compounded annually at 6%, (b) compounded continuously at 6%? [*Hint:* Let $P = 1$ and $A = 2$.]

In Problems 4 through 8, we shall assume the law of natural growth (Eq. 13–22).

4. The population of a certain town is 80,000 and has been increasing continuously for the past 20 years at the rate $r = 0.025$. What was the population 20 years ago?

5. There are originally 1000 bacteria in a culture, and 4 hours later there are 4000. Find the rate of increase per hour of the bacteria.

6. If the growth of a certain bacteria in a culture increases at the rate $r = 0.24$ per hour, how long will it take 50 bacteria to become 1,000,000?

7. In a certain chemical reaction, the original concentration of 0.03 is reduced to 0.01 in 4 minutes. (a) What is the rate of decrease in the concentration per minute? (b) What will the concentration be in 10 minutes?

8. If radium decomposes according to the relation $y = y_0e^{-0.04t}$, where y_0 grams of radium reduce to y grams in t centuries, how long will it take one gram to reduce to one-half a gram?

13–8 Applications of the exponential functions. In the last article we saw one important application of the exponential function. Before examining other uses of this function, we shall discuss the method for finding the numerical value of a logarithm to any base and for changing from one base to another. Actually, the exponential function can be used to find the logarithm of a number to any base.

EXAMPLE 1. Find the value of $\log_4 15$.

Solution. If $y = \log_4 15$, we have the equivalent equation

$$4^y = 15.$$

Any such equation may be solved by taking the common logarithm of each member and finding the required value of y. Thus,

$$\log 4^y = \log 15,$$
$$y \log 4 = \log 15.$$

Solving for y, we have

$$y = \frac{\log 15}{\log 4} = \frac{1.1761}{0.6021} = 1.953.$$

If the logarithm of a number to one base is known, it is often desirable to find the logarithm of this number to a different base. Let

$$y = \log_a N.$$

Writing this in the equivalent form

$$a^y = N,$$

and taking the logarithm to the base b of each member, we have

$$\log_b a^y = \log_b N,$$

or

$$y \log_b a = \log_b N.$$

Recalling that $y = \log_a N$, we have

$$\boxed{\log_a N \cdot \log_b a = \log_b N.} \qquad (13\text{–}23)$$

Because of the importance of the case where one base is 10 and the other e, we note that in this case, with $a = e$ and $b = 10$, Eq. (13–22) reduces to

$$\log_{10} N = \log_e N \cdot \log_{10} e = 0.4343 \log_e N, \qquad (13\text{–}24)$$

and

$$\log_e N = \frac{1}{\log_{10} e} \cdot \log_{10} N = 2.303 \log_{10} N. \qquad (13\text{–}25)$$

These two expressions are used extensively in analytic work to change from the common logarithmic system to the logarithm system with base e, and vice versa.

EXAMPLE 2. Find $\log_e 3.24$.

Solution 1. By Eq. (13–25),

$$\begin{aligned}
\log_e 3.24 &= 2.303 \log 3.24 \\
&= (2.303)(0.5105) \\
&= 1.175.
\end{aligned}$$

Solution 2. This example may, of course, be solved as in Example 1. If we let

$$y = \log_e 3.24,$$
$$e^y = 3.24.$$

Taking the common logarithm of each member, we get

$$\log e^y = \log 3.24,$$

or

$$y \log e = \log 3.24.$$

Solving for y, we have

$$y = \frac{\log 3.24}{\log e} = \frac{0.5105}{0.4343} = 1.175.$$

The method used in solving Example 1 and in the second solution of Example 2 is similar to that used in solving many exponential as well as logarithmic equations.

EXAMPLE 3. Solve $4^{x+3} = 7^{x-1}$ for x.

Solution. If we take the common logarithms of both members,

$$\log 4^{x+3} = \log 7^{x-1}.$$

By using Theorem 13–5, we have

$$(x + 3) \log 4 = (x - 1) \log 7.$$

Solving this linear equation for x, we get

$$x \log 4 + 3 \log 4 = x \log 7 - \log 7,$$

$$x (\log 4 - \log 7) = -\log 7 - 3 \log 4,$$

$$x = \frac{\log 7 + 3 \log 4}{\log 7 - \log 4}$$

$$= \frac{2.6514}{0.2430} = 10.92 \text{ (approximately)}.$$

EXAMPLE 4. Solve $\log (x + 3) - \log x = 2$.

Solution. If we use Theorem 13–4,

$$\log (x + 3) - \log x = \log \frac{x + 3}{x} = 2,$$

so that

$$\frac{x + 3}{x} = 100, \qquad x + 3 = 100x,$$

$$99x = 3, \qquad \text{or} \qquad x = \tfrac{1}{33}.$$

PROBLEMS

Find the following logarithms.

1. $\log_2 14$ 2. $\log_5 27$ 3. $\log_7 128$ 4. $\log_{27} 15$
5. $\log_e 7$ 6. $\log_e 12$ 7. $\log_e 1.79$ 8. $\log_e 3.78$

Find the value of x in each of the following.

9. $\log_4 x = 23$ 10. $\log_{12} x = 17$
11. $\log_e x = 3.28$ 12. $\log_e x = 1.72$
13. $\log_e x = 0.8473$ 14. $\log_e x = 2.547$
*15. Prove the relation $\log_b a = 1/(\log_a b)$.

Solve the following exponential equations for x.

16. $3^x = 27$ 17. $2^x = 32$
18. $2^x = 27$ 19. $3^x = 32$
20. $3^{x+1} = 4^{x-7}$ 21. $5(6^x) = 21^{x-2}$
22. $17^{2x-3} = 25^{x-1}$ 23. $2.78^x = 7.38^{3x-1}$
24. $e^x + e^{-x} = 2$ [*Hint:* This is quadratic in e^x.]
25. $e^x - e^{-x} = 2$

Solve the following logarithmic equations for x.

26. $\log x - 2 \log 4 = \log 32$ 27. $\log (x + 2) - \log x = \log 12$
28. $\log (3x + 2) = \log (x - 4) + 1$ 29. $\log (x + 1) - \log x = 2.4742$

CHAPTER 14

APPLICATIONS OF THE CIRCULAR FUNCTIONS

The general type of application of circular functions stems from the fact that the solutions of a large number of the problems with which science deals today are periodic in nature. Problems with such solutions are found in astronomy and mechanics, and in dealing with the phenomena of light, sound, and electricity. The analysis of these problems requires, among other things, the frequent use of the circular functions, with special emphasis on certain of their properties and graphs. In this chapter we shall examine these properties and graphs in some detail. In addition, we shall consider certain applications which naturally arise.

14–1 Graphs of the curves $y = a \sin kx$. In drawing the graph of $y = \sin x$ (Fig. 6–7, Article 6–3), we might have plotted directly by assigning arbitrary values of x, computing the corresponding value of y for each x, and finding the points of the coordinates thus obtained. Although such a method can be used for sketching the graph of any circular function, it is seldom used for more general expressions, since it is more convenient to generalize from the simple curves already plotted. Occasionally, a few points are used for checking purposes.

The graphs of the function defined by $y = a \sin kx$ for different values of the constants a and k can be considered the graphs of the general "sine curves" of which $y = \sin x$ is a special case. Since the function $y = \sin x$ is periodic with a period of 2π [recall Eq. (6–5)], its graph has its greatest ordinate, one, when $x = \pi/2 \pm 2n\pi$. Thus the general function $y = a \sin kx$ (assuming $a > 0$ and $k > 0$) is also periodic, and repeats itself each time kx varies over a length of 2π, or x over the length $2\pi/k$. Thus its period is $2\pi/k$, and its graph will have its greatest ordinate when $x = \pi/2k \pm 2n\pi/k$. This greatest ordinate a, or *maximum* of the function, is called the *amplitude* of the function, and the length of one complete *cycle*, $2\pi/k$, is called its *period*.

To sketch the graph of any sine curve of the type $y = a \sin kx$, mark off from the origin on the positive x-axis a distance equal to one period. As in Fig. 6–7, the two end points and the midpoint of this interval are points on the curve. The graph takes on its greatest value (maximum) at the x-value midway between the first two points, and its numerically greatest negative value (minimum) midway between the last two points. These points will suffice to sketch the graph with fair accuracy. It will frequently be convenient to have the subdivisions on the two axes of

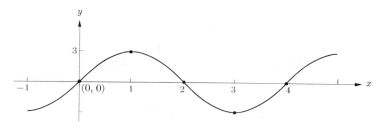

FIGURE 14–1

different length. It may also be clearer to express the horizontal units in terms of π.

EXAMPLE. Give the amplitude and period of the function defined by $y = 3 \sin (\frac{1}{2}\pi x)$ and sketch its graph.

Solution. The amplitude is 3 and its period is $2\pi/(\pi/2) = 4$. The distance marked off from the origin for one period of this graph is 4; the endpoints of this distance are $(0, 0)$ and $(4, 0)$ and the midpoint is $(2, 0)$. Since $a = 3$, the points of maximum value and of minimum value are $(1, 3)$ and $(3, -3)$, respectively. With this one period sketched, any number of additional periods can be added to the right or left. The graph of this function appears in Fig. 14–1.

This discussion has assumed that a and k are positive. If $k < 0$, the relationships between functions of positive and negative values* can be used to change kx to a positive value when x is positive. Thus, to complete the discussion, we need only consider $y = -a \sin kx$, where a and k are positive. This function has precisely the same graph as $y = a \sin kx$, except that for each value of x those values of y which were positive are now negative, and vice versa. In other words, the graph of $y = -a \sin kx$ might be described as a reflection about the x-axis of $y = a \sin kx$.

The same procedure which is used in plotting $y = a \sin kx$ may be used with slight modification in sketching $y = a \cos kx$. Its curve also has an amplitude of a and a period $2\pi/k$. The cosine curve differs from the corresponding sine curve, however, in that it is shifted to the left a distance equal to one-quarter of its period, since $\sin (x + \pi/2) = \cos x$. Compare Figs. 6–7 and 6–8.

PROBLEMS

Find the amplitude and period of each of the following and sketch their graphs.

1. $y = 5 \sin 2\pi x$ 2. $y = 2 \sin \frac{1}{2}x$
3. $y = 3 \sin \pi x/3$ 4. $y = 0.5 \cos 4x$

---

* $-\sin x = \sin (-x)$, $\cos x = \cos (-x)$, and so forth.

5. $y = 1.5 \cos \frac{3}{2}x$ 6. $y = \sin 6x$
7. $y = 2 \sin (-\frac{1}{4}x)$; how does this compare with $y = 2 \sin (\frac{1}{4}x)$?
8. $y = 2 \cos (-\frac{1}{4}x)$; how does this compare with $y = 2 \cos (\frac{1}{4}x)$?
9. $y = -0.5 \sin 3t$ 10. $y = 2 \sin 0.001\pi t$
11. $y = 100 \cos 0.0314t$ 12. $y = \sin 0.0025t$

14–2 Graphs of the curves $y = a \sin (kx + b)$.   In a discussion of the graphing of the circular functions, the more generalized sine function defined by $y = a \sin (kx + b)$ should be considered.   We have noticed that $\cos x = \sin (x + \pi/2)$ differs from $\sin x$ merely by a shift to the left a distance $\pi/2$. Similarly, the graph of $y = a \sin (kx + b) = a \sin k(x + b/k)$ differs from $y = a \sin kx$ only in its shift in the horizontal direction a distance b/k. Assuming $k > 0$, this shift, or displacement, is to the right or left according as $b/k < 0$ or $b/k > 0$. We call $|b/k|$ the *phase displacement*, and b the *phase constant* or *phase difference*. The functions have the same amplitude a and period $2\pi/k$.

The graph of $y = a \cos (kx + b)$ can be sketched either by considering it a generalization of $y = a \cos kx$ or a "shifted" sine curve.

EXAMPLE 1.   Give the amplitude, period, and phase displacement and sketch the graph of $y = 4 \sin (2x - \pi/3)$.

Solution. This function has an amplitude of 4 and a period of π. Since its phase displacement is $\pi/6$ (why?), its graph goes through the point $(\pi/6, 0)$ and continues to the right, completing one period as it passes through $(7\pi/6, 0)$. The graph is shown in Fig. 14–2.

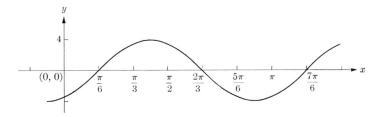

FIGURE 14–2

EXAMPLE 2.   Sketch the graph of $y = 3 \sin x + 4 \cos x$.

Solution. In Example 5, Article 6–9, we showed that

$$3 \sin x + 4 \cos x = 5 \sin (x + \theta_1),$$

where $\sin \theta_1 = \frac{4}{5}$ and $\cos \theta_1 = \frac{3}{5}$.   Thus, using Table I, $\theta_1 = 0.93$ (approximately), so that we may sketch the graph by considering the

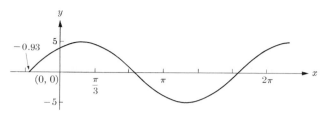

FIGURE 14–3

expression

$$y = 5 \sin (x + 0.93).$$

Be sure that the location of $(-0.93, 0)$ is consistent with the length of the period $2\pi = 6.28$. as in Fig. 14–3.

14–3 Graphing by addition of ordinates. Another very useful method of sketching is known as *composition of ordinates.* In Article 14–6 this method of graphing will be used in connection with certain applications.

EXAMPLE. Sketch the graph of $y = \sin x + \sin 2x$.

Solution. First, sketch on the same axes the graphs of the two separate functions defined by $y = \sin x$ and $y = \sin 2x$. Then the ordinate for any value of x is the sum of the ordinates for that value of x from each of the graphs, $y = \sin x$ and $y = \sin 2x$. This amounts to finding the height of the curve $y = \sin x + \sin 2x$ by adding the heights of the other two curves. Of course, the sign must be taken into account. The period of one of these functions is 2π and the other is π. Thus the period of the function defined by $y = \sin x + \sin 2x$ is 2π. The required graph appears in Fig. 14–4.

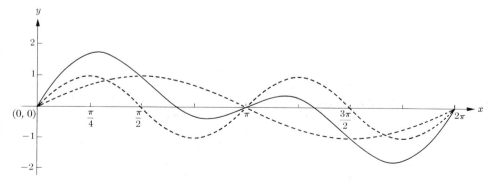

FIGURE 14–4

PROBLEMS

Sketch the graphs of the functions defined by the following equations, giving their amplitudes, periods, and phase displacements.

1. $y = 2 \sin (x - \pi/6)$
2. $y = 4 \sin (x - 1)$
3. $y = 0.5 \sin (2x + \pi/8)$
4. $y = 3 \cos (t/2 - 1)$
5. $y = \sin (t + 0.25)$
6. $y = 2 \sin [(t - 1)/3]$
7. $13y = 5 \sin x + 12 \cos x$
8. $y = \sin x + \cos x$
9. $y = 15 \sin x + 8 \cos x$
10. $y = 24 \sin x + 7 \cos x$
11. $y = 2 \sin x - 5 \cos x$
12. $y = 0.6 \sin 2x + 0.5 \cos 2x$

Sketch the graphs of the following functional equations by the method of addition of ordinates and give the period of each.

13. $y = \sin x + \cos x$ (Compare this curve with Problem 8.)
14. $y = 2 \sin x + 3 \cos 2x$
15. $y = 4 \cos x/2 - 3 \sin 2x$
16. $y = 0.26 \sin x + 0.47 \cos 3x$
17. $y = \sin x + \sin 2x + \sin 3x$

Sketch the graphs of the following functional equations.

18. $y = 2 (\sin x - \frac{1}{2} \sin 2x + \frac{1}{3} \sin 3x)$
19. $y = \sin x + \frac{1}{3} \sin 3x + \frac{1}{5} \sin 5x$
20. $y = \frac{4}{\pi} \left(\sin x - \frac{1}{3^2} \sin 3x \right)$

Sketch the graphs of the functional equations in Problems 21 through 23, choosing the same units on both axes.

21. $y = x + \sin x$
22. $y = x - \sin x$
23. $y = x - 2 \sin x$

24. What can be said about the number of zeros for the functions defined in Problems 21 through 23? [Recall Eq. (6–64).]

14–4 Simple harmonic motion.

The notion of simple harmonic motion is fundamental to any discussion of periodic phenomena. Examples of bodies which move approximately according to the laws of harmonic motion are the bob of a simple pendulum, a floating cork in turbulent water, a particle in a vibrating violin string, a point on the prong of a tuning fork, a particle of air during the passage of a simple sound wave, and a particle of earth during a small earthquake. Actually, any body whose position d on a straight line is given at any instant t by the equation $d = a \sin \omega t$ is said to describe *simple harmonic motion.* Hence we need only recall the properties of this circular function to recognize some of the features of simple harmonic motion.

Simple harmonic motion is oscillatory in character, repeating itself in definite intervals of time. Thus it is periodic. The *amplitude* of the motion is the magnitude of the maximum value of $a \sin \omega t$, or a, that is, the magnitude of the displacement from the central point of the motion. The time required for one complete vibration or one cycle is called the *period* $(2\pi/\omega)$. The number of complete periods per unit time, namely $1/(2\pi/\omega)$ or $\omega/2\pi$, is called the *frequency* of the simple harmonic motion. The *phase* at any

FIGURE 14–5

instant is the fractional part of the period which has elapsed since the body passed through its central position in the positive direction. Actually, the position of the body need not be given from the time when $t = 0$, but may be given from any time t_0. Thus the more general equation may be written $d = a \sin \omega(t - t_0)$. We have learned that this more general equation represents the same curve, except for a shift along the t-axis. This equation also describes simple harmonic motion, for it can be written $d = a \sin \omega t'$, where $t' = t - t_0$. Since $y = a \sin kt$ and $y = a \cos kt$ differ only in phase, $d = a \cos \omega t$ also is used to describe simple harmonic motion.

It is interesting to observe that a graph of a simple harmonic motion can be obtained directly from a demonstration of such motion. Let us consider, for example, the swinging of a simple pendulum from a fixed point and the marking of its trace on a sheet of paper moving at a constant velocity. From Fig. 14–5 it is clear that the displacement of the bob from its central position is a sine function of the time.

One of the most elementary examples of simple harmonic motion is illustrated by a point moving at uniform speed around the circumference of a unit circle. Consider the circle with center at O and a radius one in Fig. 14–6. If the point P is thought of as moving with constant or uniform velocity on the circle, the question arises as to the type of motion of the

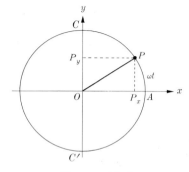

FIGURE 14–6

point P_x or P_y, that is, the projection of P on the x-axis or the projection of P on the y-axis. Suppose the uniform velocity of P along the circle is ω units per second, and the point P starts at A. Then the distance along the circle traveled by P in any time t, expressed in seconds, is ωt; thus P_y moves so that its y-coordinate is given by $y = \sin \omega t$, and the projection of P on the y-axis describes simple harmonic motion. It is interesting to note that P_y is at the origin when $t = 0$ and, as P_y moves up, its speed decreases until it is 0 at C. The point P_y then moves down, increasing in speed until it attains its maximum as it passes through O, diminishing again in speed until it becomes 0 at C'; it then moves up with increasing speed to its starting point O. Then the whole motion is repeated. Actually, the speed of any body describing simple harmonic motion increases and decreases in the manner described.

Problems

1. What can be said about the motion of the point P_x in Fig. 14–6? Obtain an expression of its position at any time t.

2. The following equations represent simple harmonic motions. Give their amplitudes, their periods, their frequencies, and sketch their graphs.

(a) $y = 8 \sin 2x$ (b) $y = 10 \sin (t/3)$

(c) $y = \frac{1}{4} \sin 3t$ (d) $y = 7 \cos 5x$

(e) $y = 4 \sin 2\pi x$ (f) $y = a \sin \omega t$

3. A particle moves along a line in such a way that its displacement from a fixed point of the line is given by $d = 2 \sin^2 t$. Can this motion be expressed as simple harmonic motion? What is its period? [*Hint:* Can $\sin^2 \theta$ be expressed in terms of $\cos 2\theta$?]

4. Quantity of electric current is measured in amperes, a unit proportional to the number of electrons which pass a fixed point in a wire during one second. For a simple generator this quantity of current is expressed by

$$I = a_1 \sin \omega t.$$

Give the expression for I if the amplitude is 10 and the current is 60-cycle. Sketch the graph of this expression. The 60-cycle current (i.e., current with a frequency of 60 cycles per second) is the one in most common use at the present time in this country.

5. The flow of electricity is dependent upon the *electromotive force*, measured in volts. The expression for the electromotive force for a simplified generator is given by

$$E = a_2 \sin \omega t.$$

How can E be expressed in terms of t if the amplitude is 8 and the current is 60-cycle?

6. The amount of power of an electric current to light lamps, generate heat, or operate machinery is dependent on its energy at any time t. This electrical

power is usually expressed in kilowatts and is given by the expression $P = EI$. For the 60-cycle current mentioned in Problems 4 and 5, show that P can be written in the form

$$P = a_1 a_2 \sin^2 \omega t.$$

Find the period of this periodic function. Note that P, E, and I, in Problems 4, 5, and 6, are all examples of *simple harmonic behavior*.

7. If a flute is played softly in the middle register, the sound that is produced closely approximates a *simple sound*. A simple sound is defined as one which produces on the oscillograph a wave that may be represented by a simple harmonic curve, that is, by $y = a \sin \omega t$. Give the expression for such a sound and draw the graph of its equation if the given frequency is 400 cycles per second and the amplitude is 0.001 inch.

8. The pressure in a traveling sound wave is given by

$$p = 10 \sin 200\pi \left(t - \frac{x}{1000} \right) \text{ dynes/cm}^2,$$

where t is in seconds and x in centimeters. Sketch p as a function of x at the following definite times: $t = 0$, 1/400, 2/400, 3/400, and 4/400 sec.

9. The equation of a traveling transverse wave in a certain chord is given by the expression

$$y = 25 \sin \pi(0.20t - 0.01x),$$

where x is in centimeters and t is in seconds. Graph this equation when $x = 10$, 25, and 100 cm.

14–5 Addition of two general sine functions. In order to observe certain applications of graphing, let us consider the combining of two sine functions.

(1) Any two general sine functions of the same period are represented by

$$y_1 = a \sin (\omega t + \alpha)$$

and   (14–1)

$$y_2 = b \sin (\omega t + \beta).$$

Their amplitudes are a and b, their phase difference is $\beta - \alpha$, and their common period is $2\pi/\omega$. We shall show that the sum of these two functions of the same period is itself a sine function of that period.

$$
\begin{aligned}
y = y_1 + y_2 &= a \sin (\omega t + \alpha) + b \sin (\omega t + \beta) \\
&= a (\sin \omega t \cos \alpha + \cos \omega t \sin \alpha) + b (\sin \omega t \cos \beta + \cos \omega t \sin \beta) \\
&= A \sin \omega t + B \cos \omega t,
\end{aligned}
$$
                                                                                              (14–2)

where

$$A = a \cos \alpha + b \cos \beta$$

and

$$B = a \sin \alpha + b \sin \beta.$$

We recall that $A \sin \omega t + B \cos \omega t = r \sin (\omega t + \delta)$, where

$$r = \sqrt{A^2 + B^2}$$

$$= \sqrt{(a^2 \cos^2 \alpha + 2ab \cos \alpha \cos \beta + b^2 \cos^2 \beta)}$$
$$+ (a^2 \sin^2 \alpha + 2ab \sin \alpha \sin \beta + b^2 \sin^2 \beta)$$

$$= \sqrt{a^2 + b^2 + 2ab (\cos \alpha \cos \beta + \sin \alpha \sin \beta)}$$

$$= \sqrt{a^2 + b^2 + 2ab \cos (\beta - \alpha)},$$

and where

$$\sin \delta = \frac{B}{r} \qquad \text{and} \qquad \cos \delta = \frac{A}{r}.$$

Hence, $y = a \sin (\omega t + \alpha) + b \sin (\omega t + \beta) = r \sin (\omega t + \delta)$, where r and δ have the values just found.

We have proved an important theorem.

THEOREM 14–1. *The sum of any two general sine curves of the same period, regardless of their phase and amplitude, is a general sine curve with that same period.*

This result may be generalized to include the sum of any finite number of general sine curves of the same period. It is especially useful in the fields of electricity and sound, as the problems of this article will indicate.

(2) The equations of two general sine functions of *different frequencies*, when they are in phase at $t = 0$, can be given by

$$y_1 = a \sin 2\pi n_1 t \qquad \text{and} \qquad y_2 = a \sin 2\pi n_2 t. \qquad (14\text{–}3)$$

The resulting sine function is then obtained by combining these functions, $y = y_1 + y_2$. Thus,

$$y = y_1 + y_2 = a (\sin 2\pi n_1 t + \sin 2\pi n_2 t),$$

and by Eq. (6–54), Article 6–12, with $\alpha + \beta = 2\pi n_1 t$ and $\alpha - \beta = 2\pi n_2 t$,

$$y = 2a \sin 2\pi \frac{n_1 + n_2}{2} t \cos 2\pi \frac{n_1 - n_2}{2} t. \qquad (14\text{–}4)$$

This result does not represent an exact sine function, but it does under certain conditions approximate the sine function. If $n_1 - n_2$ is small compared with n_1 and n_2, the resulting equation may be regarded as a "sine function with a slowly varying amplitude." Let

$$n = \frac{n_1 + n_2}{2}, \qquad \gamma = \frac{n_1 - n_2}{2}.$$

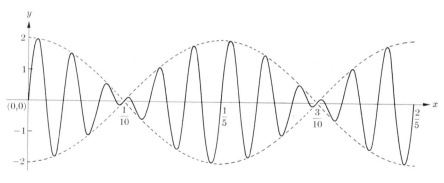

FIGURE 14–7

Thus γ is small compared with n and, as a result of this substitution, we have

$$y = 2a \cos 2\pi\gamma t \sin 2\pi nt. \qquad (14\text{–}5)$$

Since γ is small in comparison with n, $\cos 2\pi\gamma t$ varies very slowly compared with $\sin 2\pi nt$; that is, the number of oscillations of the frequency n is large during the time it takes the cosine to go through one period. Thus the resultant curve becomes a sine curve of slowly varying amplitude. In the case of sound waves, this periodic variation of amplitude is heard as "beats." The number of beats per second is equal to the number of times per second the wave, $y = \sin 2\pi nt$, has a value of 1 and -1. The principle of beating is used in connection with radio, television, wireless waves, telephone, and high-frequency electric current.

EXAMPLE. Sketch the graph of the curve $y = \sin 50\pi t + \sin 60\pi t$.

Solution. By using Eq. (14–5), we have

$$y = \sin 50\pi t + \sin 60\pi t$$
$$= 2 \cos 5\pi t \sin 55\pi t.$$

Since $\sin 55\pi t$ always lies between 1 and -1, the curve lies between the two curves $y = \pm 2 \cos 5\pi t$, touching them at the points where $\sin 55\pi t = \pm 1$. Thus it touches when $t = 1/110$, $3/110$, $5/110$, and so forth. The graph is shown in Fig. 14–7.

It is important to understand that this discussion has been based on two sine functions with the *same* amplitudes. In the case when the amplitudes are not the same, not only is the amplitude of the resultant a varying amplitude, but also the frequency varies. Thus, there is no similarity of this behavior to that of a simple sine function.

PROBLEMS

1. Two atmospheric waves give rise to pressure variations at a given point in space according to the equations

$$p_1 = a \sin 2\pi nt \quad \text{and} \quad p_2 = a \sin\left(2\pi nt - \frac{2\pi}{3}\right).$$

Calculate the amplitude of the resultant wave at this point in space.

2. Express $y = 4 \sin (\theta + \pi/6) + 5 \sin (\theta - \pi/3)$ in the form

$$y = r \sin (\theta + \delta).$$

3. The electromotive force E (recall Problem 5, Article 14–4) in a circuit is given by $E = 80 + 8.2 \sin \omega t + 4.8 \cos \omega t - 0.8 \sin 3\omega t + 1.2 \cos 3\omega t$. Express E in the form $A_0 + A_1 \sin (\omega t + \alpha_1) + A_2 \sin (3\omega t + \alpha_2)$, finding the values of A_0, A_1, A_2, α_1, and α_2.

4. Sketch the graphs of Problems 2 and 3. The graphs may be completed by the method of Article 14–3 called *composition of ordinates* or the *principle of superposition*.

5. Moving or traveling waves are sometimes reflected from the boundaries of the bodies in which they move and thus introduce waves that travel in the opposite direction. These add to the original waves to produce the resulting wave according to the principle of superposition. Consider a column of air in which the equation of the original wave is given by

$$y_1 = a \sin 2\pi n \left(t - \frac{x}{V}\right)$$

and the equation of the reflected wave is

$$y_2 = a \sin 2\pi n \left(t + \frac{x}{V}\right).$$

The resulting wave is $y = y_1 + y_2$. Prove by using Eq. (6–54), Article 6–12, with $\alpha + \beta = 2\pi n(t - x/V)$ and $\alpha - \beta = 2\pi n(t + x/V)$, that

$$y = 2a \sin 2\pi nt \cos \frac{2\pi nx}{V}.$$

This is the equation for the so-called *standing wave*. It is thus named because at certain positions in the body in which the waves are moving y is always 0; these values for x are the values for which $\cos 2\pi nx/V = 0$, that is,

$$\frac{2\pi nx}{V} = \frac{\pi}{2}, \quad \frac{3\pi}{2}, \quad \frac{5\pi}{2}, \quad \text{etc.}$$

For what values of x is $y = 0$? It is interesting to note that this resulting wave at any given time t is a simple harmonic expression in x; at any position x, it represents a simple harmonic expression of t. In all musical instruments sound is produced by standing waves.

By making use of the method described in (2) of this article, sketch the graphs of:

6. $y = \sin 200t + \sin 210t$ 7. $y = \sin 80t + \sin 100t$

14–6 Harmonic analysis and synthesis. It can be demonstrated mathematically that any periodic piecewise continuous* curve may be approximated by a finite sum of sine and cosine curves, where the lowest frequency in the sum produces the period of the curve itself, while the remaining terms have frequencies which are integral multiples of the lowest. This extremely useful method of analyzing a curve or function, known as *harmonic analysis*, was first announced by J. B. J. Fourier in 1807 and first published in Paris in 1822. It might be expected that the method was discovered through the study of sound and wave motion, but, although the result is extremely useful in such studies, the principle was actually found in the course of Fourier's study of the conduction of heat.

Fourier's Theorem may be stated in mathematical form for the periodic curve y by the approximate equality

$$y \approx a_0 + a_1 \sin \theta + a_2 \sin 2\theta + a_3 \sin 3\theta + \cdots + a_n \sin n\theta$$
$$+ b_1 \cos \theta + b_2 \cos 2\theta + b_3 \cos 3\theta + \cdots + b_n \cos n\theta.$$

In this expression y is the ordinate of the original curve for any particular value x, and θ, expressed in terms of x, is $2\pi x/L$. Thus, the use of values of x ranging from 0 to L, where L is the period of the curve, is equivalent to letting θ range from 0 to 2π. With the exception of a_0, which simply denotes the displacement of the entire curve from the original reference axis, each individual sine or cosine curve enters into the composite. In passing, we might mention that there are machines, called *harmonic analyzers*, which can obtain the expressions for all Fourier coefficients of any given curve. That is, from the curve as a drawing, it is possible with such a machine to obtain the equation of the curve.

The converse of the analytic process which we have discussed is also useful. This process, called *harmonic synthesis*, might be described as the combining of several simple curves in order to obtain their resultant or composite curve. In some cases this may be accomplished by calculations. It may always be accomplished, although only approximately, by the graphical method of adding the measured ordinates of the individual curves and plotting the results, as suggested in Article 14–3.

Great advances in various fields have been made through the use of harmonic analysis. In the study of musical sound waves the tones of different musical instruments have been recorded, their waves produced on the oscillograph, and the result discussed mathematically by means of harmonic analysis. One of the results of this study was the development

---

* Such a curve, defined on an interval of the x-axis, consists of "pieces of curves" in the intuitive sense. Any technical definition is impossible at this mathematical level.

of the electric organ. The science of *seismology*, which deals with the phenomena and origins of earthquakes, employs harmonic analysis because of the nature of the earthquake's vibratory motion and resulting wave form. When the vibrations are not large, the motion is essentially a simple harmonic motion; in the more general case, the wave is a composite wave. The waves are recorded by an instrument called the *seismograph*, and from this record the amplitude, direction of motion, and amount of periodicity of each vibration may be computed. Harmonic analysis and synthesis are used in predicting the tides. One of the important functions of the United States Coast and Geodetic Survey is the annual preparation and publication of a tidal calendar. This "Tide Table," issued one to two years in advance, predicts every high and low water at most of the principal seaports of the world. The time of the predicted occurrences is correct to the nearest minute, and the height to the nearest tenth of a foot. These predictions are made mechanically by using the circular functions in connection with the periodic movements of the sun and moon.

CHAPTER 15

APPLICATIONS OF THE CIRCULAR FUNCTIONS TO ANGLES

There are two types of applications of the circular functions which are of importance. In the last chapter, we discussed the general type of application. A more specific type is that of the functions where the real number θ is the measure of an angle. In this chapter we shall consider this application and, with it, the solution of triangles and the establishing of relationships between the sides and angles of a triangle. We begin with the notion of an angle.

15–1 Angles. In plane geometry an angle is usually defined as the configuration consisting of two half-lines (rays) radiating from a point. However, in trigonometry we add to this definition by stating that an angle thus defined by two half-lines has a measure which corresponds to the amount of rotation required to move a ray from the position of one of these lines to the other. Consider Fig. 15–1, with the two lines m and n intersecting at O and lying in a plane perpendicular to our line of vision. If we regard m as the *initial side* and n as the *terminal side* of the angle with O as its vertex, there are two possible directions of rotation of the initial side m. The angle is said to be positive if the rotation is counterclockwise, but negative if clockwise. A curved arrow will indicate the direction of rotation.

Let us now consider a ray m which issues from the origin of a rectangular coordinate system and coincides with the positive x-axis (Fig. 15–2). As this ray rotates, any point P on m will trace out part or all of the circumference of a circle of radius OP. In fact, the circumference may be traced several times. After the rotation, OP will be in some position OP', where the circular arc $\overset{\frown}{PP'}$, denoted by s, may be used to measure the angle POP'. An angle such as POP' is said to be in *standard position*, and to be in the quadrant in which its terminal side OP' is located.

FIGURE 15–1

293

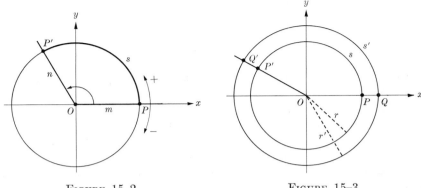

FIGURE 15–2   FIGURE 15–3

The most logical units for measuring the magnitude of an angle would seem to be the number of revolutions resulting from the rotation from the initial to the terminal side of the angle. Since the number of revolutions of any angle is determined by the ratio of the intercepted circular arc length s to the circumference of the circle, we make the following definition.

DEFINITION 15–1. *The magnitude of an angle in revolutions is given by the relation:*

$$Angle^* \ in \ revolutions \ = \ \frac{s}{2\pi r}. \tag{15–1}$$

For example, if P traces out an arc one-half the circumference, the corresponding angle is measured as one-half a revolution. Likewise, if the arc is twice the circumference, the angle measure is two revolutions.

Consider the two concentric circles at O, in Fig. 15–3, with $\overset{\frown}{PP'}$ an arc of length s on the circle of radius r, and $\overset{\frown}{QQ'}$ an arc of length s' on the circle of radius r'. It should be intuitively clear that each arc length is the same portion of the corresponding circumference, so that

$$\frac{s'}{2\pi r'} = \frac{s}{2\pi r}.$$

This may be proved by using the theorem that similar triangles have proportional sides. If we recall the definition of arc length from Article 4–6, $s'/r' = s/r$, and our result follows. The magnitude of any angle is thus independent of the length of its initial or terminal side.

---

* Since we so frequently consider the magnitude of an angle rather than the angle itself, we shall ordinarily use the word "angle" in place of "measure of the angle."

Although the use of revolutions is the most natural method for measuring angles, there are other more convenient systems. The system most commonly used in practical work such as surveying and navigation is the *sexagesimal system,* in which the degree* is the fundamental unit. In this system one revolution = 360° (degrees), 1° = 60′ (minutes), and 1′ = 60″ (seconds).

DEFINITION 15–2. *The magnitude of an angle in degrees is given by the relation:*

$$\text{Angle in degrees } = \text{ (number of revolutions)}(360°). \qquad (15\text{–}2)$$

For example, one-half a revolution is 180°, or an angle of two revolutions is 720°.

The system used in calculus and other more advanced mathematics is the *radian system.* If we recall that the circumference of the unit circle is 2π, we see the reason for the following definition.

DEFINITION 15–3. *An angle of one revolution is equal to an angle whose measure is 2π radians.*

We immediately see that

$$\text{Angle in radians } = \text{ (number of revolutions)}(2\pi). \qquad (15\text{–}3)$$

For example, one-half a revolution is π radians, or an angle of two revolutions is 4π radians. The reason for the definition of radian measure should be apparent. The measure of an angle in radians is precisely the real number θ for which all the circular functions have been defined. It is for this reason that we were able to use the column designated "radians" in Table I in the Appendix, when we were interested in a circular function of any real number θ. We shall, therefore, agree that when no unit of measure is designated, radian measure is understood.

We have two immediate results from these definitions. Solving Eqs. (15–2) and (15–3) for number of revolutions and equating, we find the relationship between an angle expressed in degrees and radians to be

$$\frac{\text{Angle in degrees}}{360°} = \frac{\text{Angle in radians}}{2\pi}. \qquad (15\text{–}4)$$

---

* The origin of the use of the degree for measurement is discussed by O. Neugebauer in *Studies of the History of Science.* Philadelphia: University of Pennsylvania Press, 1941. Bicentennial Conference. Chapter on "Ancient Astronomy," p. 16.

EXAMPLE 1. An angle of 45° is equal to

$$\frac{45°}{360°}\,2\pi = \frac{\pi}{4}\text{ radians.}$$

EXAMPLE 2. An angle of $5\pi/6$ radians is equal to

$$\frac{5\pi/6}{2\pi}\,360° = 150°.$$

EXAMPLE 3. To express an angle of one radian in degrees, the same method is used:

$$1\text{ radian} = \frac{1}{2\pi}\,360° = \frac{360°}{2\pi} = 57°18'\text{ (approximately).}\quad(15\text{--}5)$$

Similarly, for an angle of one degree,

$$1° = 2\pi\left(\frac{1°}{360°}\right) = 0.01745\text{ radian (approximately).}\quad(15\text{--}6)$$

EXAMPLE 4. Transform an angle of 194°23′ to radian measure.

Solution. In Table I in the Appendix, the angles are given in both degrees and radians. We may use this table to change from one system to the other. Since

$$194°23' = 180° + 14°23',$$

we work with 14°23′,

$$14°20' = 0.2502\text{ radian,}$$

and

$$14°30' = 0.2531\text{ radian.}$$

Since 23′ is 0.3 of the difference between 30′ and 20′, the radian measure of the required angle is greater than 0.2502 by 0.3 of the difference between 0.2531 and 0.2502, or by linear interpolation,

$$14°23' = 0.2511\text{ radian.}$$

Therefore,

$$194°23' = (\pi + 0.2511)\text{ radians}$$

$$= 3.3927\text{ radians (approximately).}$$

The second result shows one advantage of the radian system in measuring angles.

We are able to express the length of a circular arc in terms of its radius and the subtending central angle measured in radians. Writing Eq. (15–3) with the substitution from Eq. (15–1), we have

$$\text{Angle in radians} = \frac{s}{2\pi r}\,(2\pi) = \frac{s}{r}.$$

Therefore the length of the circular arc s cut by a central angle θ (measured in radians) in a circle of radius r is given by

$$s = r\theta. \qquad\qquad (15\text{–}7)$$

Note that $s = \theta$, as it should be if we consider the length on the unit circle with $r = 1$.

EXAMPLE 5. A circle has a radius of 40 inches. (a) How long is the arc subtended by a central angle of 36°? (b) How large is the central angle that subtends an arc of 15 inches?

Solution. (a) Since the number of radians corresponding to 36° is $\pi/5$,

$$s = 40\left(\frac{\pi}{5}\right) = 8\pi \text{ inches.}$$

If we use an approximation for π, this answer can be written to any desired degree of accuracy. (b) Again using $s = r\theta$, we have $15 = 40\theta$ or $\theta = \frac{3}{8}$ radian. If the result is desired in degrees, we merely change $\frac{3}{8}$ radian into degrees, obtaining $21°30'$.

PROBLEMS

1. In a rectangular coordinate system, locate the following angles in standard position, showing the initial and terminal sides. Use a curved arrow to indicate the direction in which the angle is measured.

(a) $\frac{1}{4}$ rev   (b) $-\frac{3}{4}$ rev   (c) 3 rev   (d) $\frac{3}{8}$ rev
(e) $-\frac{1}{6}$ rev   (f) $-\frac{5}{4}$ rev   (g) $\frac{5}{6}$ rev   (h) $-\frac{5}{3}$ rev

2. Repeat Problem 1 for the following angles expressed in degrees.

(a) 45°   (b) 135°   (c) −225°   (d) −300°
(e) 240°   (f) 450°   (g) 720°   (h) −120°

3. Repeat Problem 1 for the following angles expressed in radians.

(a) $\pi/6$ (b) $2\pi/3$ (c) $\pi/4$ (d) $4\pi/9$
(e) $-3\pi/2$ (f) $-5\pi/6$ (g) $5\pi/12$ (h) -5π

4. Express the angles given in Problems 1 and 2 in radian measure, leaving the answer in terms of π.

5. Express the angles given in Problems 2 and 3 in revolutions.

6. Express the angles given in Problems 1 and 3 in degrees.

7. Transform the following angles to radians, using Table I if needed, and giving the answer to four decimal places.

(a) 27°   (b) 156°20′   (c) 47°
(d) 189°32′   (e) 253°10′   (f) −378°49′

8. Transform the following angles to degrees and minutes, using Table I if needed, and giving the answer to the nearest minute.

(a) $\pi/8$ (b) $-2\pi/13$ (c) 0.2443   (d) −1.3730
(e) 1.8600   (f) $\frac{9}{4}$ (g) −1.2900   (h) 5.7200

9. Express each of the following as a single angle in degrees and minutes from 0′ to 59′.

(a) 15°27′ + 32°14′   (b) 18°41′ + 15°12′
(c) 13°32′ + 37°28′   (d) 142°5′ + 8°55′
(e) 29°43′ + 51°38′   (f) 61°19′ + 23°58′
(g) 180° − 15°13′   (h) 90° − 47°38′
(i) 360° − 147°23′   (j) 270° − 63°48′
(k) $\frac{1}{2}$(18°47′ + 56°29′)   (l) $\frac{1}{2}$(56°28′ − 47°36′)

10. If an arc 20 feet long subtends an angle of 2 radians at the center of a circle, find its radius.

11. If a wheel of radius 2 feet rolls 3 feet, how many radians has it turned? How many degrees has it turned?

12. In a circle of radius 14 inches, how long an arc does a central angle of 82° intersect?

13. How many degrees are there between the minute and hour hands of a clock at 4:00? At 1:00? At 9:15? At 5:47?

14. Assuming that the earth's radius is 3960 miles, find the distance on the surface of the earth from Columbus Ohio, to the equator. The latitude of Columbus is 40°.

15. If a point on the circumference of a wheel whose diameter is 20 inches travels 3000 feet per minute, through how many radians does the wheel turn in one second?

16. For small angles, the intercepted arc and chord are approximately the same length. Assuming that the earth moves around the sun in a circle of radius 93,000,000 miles, find the sun's diameter if it subtends an angle of 32′ at the earth.

15–2 Circular functions of angles. We note that the radian measure of an angle is the same real number as θ for which the circular functions were originally defined. With this association or correspondence, we are able to define any circular function of θ, where θ is the radian measure of an angle, as the circular function of the real number θ.

DEFINITION 15–4. *If $\theta \in R$, then any circular function of the angle whose radian measure is θ is equal to that circular function of θ.*

ILLUSTRATIONS.

(a) If A is an angle whose measure is $45°$ or $\pi/4$ radians, then

$$\sin A = \sin 45°$$
$$= \sin (\pi/4 \text{ radians})$$
$$= \sin \pi/4 = 1/\sqrt{2}.$$

(b) If B is an angle whose radian measure is 1, then

$$\tan B = \tan (1 \text{ radian})$$
$$= \tan 57°18' \quad \text{(See Example 3, Article 15–1)}$$
$$= \tan 1.$$

When $\sin \pi/4$ or $\tan 1$ are written, it should be clear from the context whether a function of a real number or of an angle, in radian measure, is intended. We shall, therefore, not complicate our notation as some books do, by using $\sin \pi/4^{(r)}$, but merely write $\sin \pi/4$ to indicate also the sine of an angle whose radian measure is $\pi/4$, and so on.

Because of Definition 15–4, we can find the circular functions of any angle, whether it is expressed in radians or degrees. In some case special angles may lead to exact values of the functions as in Article 6–4, but in general, the use of Table I will be necessary, as discussed in Article 6–13. Linear interpolation, of course, may also be necessary.

EXAMPLE 1. Find the exact value of $\sin 330°$.

Solution. Since an angle of $330° =$ an angle whose radian measure is $11\pi/6$, we, therefore, can say $\sin 330° = \sin 11\pi/6 = -\frac{1}{2}$.

EXAMPLE 2. Find the value of $\cos 23°10'$.

Solution. If we look in Table I, column one, marked "degrees," we find $23°10'$. As we did in Article 6–13, we look in the row of $23°10'$ under the cosine column, and find 0.9194, so that $\cos 23°10' = 0.9194$.

PROBLEMS

Give the exact numerical value of each of the following.

1. $\sin 120° \cos 150° + \cos 120° \sin 150°$
2. $\csc 150° - \cos 240° + \tan 120°$
3. $\sin 330° \cos 120° \tan 135°$
4. $\sin 150° \cos 120° \tan 225°$

Find all the angles, expressed in degrees, between $0°$ and $360°$ that satisfy each of the following equations.

5. $\sin \theta = \frac{1}{2}$ 6. $\cos \theta = -\frac{1}{2}$ 7. $\tan \theta = 1/\sqrt{3}$
8. $\sin \theta = -\sqrt{3}/2$ 9. $\tan \theta = -1$ 10. $\cos \theta = -\sqrt{2}/2$

11. $\sin \theta = \sqrt{2}/2$ 12. $\sec \theta = 2$ 13. $\cot \theta = -\sqrt{3}$
14. $\csc \theta = 2/\sqrt{3}$

15. Find the approximate value of each, and thus determine which is larger.

(a) $\sin 2$ and $\sin 2°$
(b) $\cos 4$ and $\cos 4°$ (See Illustration b.)
(c) $\tan 1$ and $\tan 1°$

16. Express $\sin 624°$ as a function of a positive acute angle less than $45°$. [*Hint:* Since $624° = 6.90° + 84°$, by using Eq. (6–34) we have $\sin 624° = -\sin 84°$. From Eq. (6–22), $-\sin 84° = -\cos 6°$. It might be wise to review Article 6–10, with the relations between degree and radian measure in mind.]

17. Express each of the following as a function of a positive acute angle less than $45°$.

(a) $\sin 196°$ (b) $\cos 147°$
(c) $\sin 319°$ (d) $\cos 254°$
(e) $\tan 294°$ (f) $\cos 728°$
(g) $\sin (-625°)$ (h) $\cos (-435°)$

18. Express each of the following as a function of a positive acute angle less than $45°$.

(a) $\tan 1004°$ (b) $\sin 248°25'$
(c) $\cos 106°18'$ (d) $\tan 163°17'$
(e) $\cos 204°46'$ (f) $\tan 136°34'$
(g) $\sin 156°39'$ (h) $\cos 229°$

19. Find the value of each of the following by using Table I.

(a) $\sin 14°20'$ (b) $\tan 52°40'$
(c) $\cos 28°50'$ (d) $\sin 63°30'$
(e) $\tan 21°10'$ (g) $\cos 72°20'$
(g) $\sin 115°30'$ (h) $\cos 161°10'$

20. In solving triangles, we frequently wish to interpolate between two values in Table I when the angle is given in degrees. Explain why $\sin (x + r)$ may be approximated from the table by the formula

$$\sin (x + r) = \sin x + \frac{r}{10} [\sin (x + 10) - \sin x]$$

if x and $x + 10$ are consecutive angles in the table, measured in minutes, and if r is an integer between 0 and 10. [Compare Eq. (9–11).] Other functions are found by similar formulas.

21. Find $\sin 24°16'$. [*Hint:* Since the angle $24°16'$ lies between $24°10'$ and $24°20'$

$$\sin 24°16' = \sin 24°10' + \tfrac{6}{10} (\sin 24°20' - \sin 24°10')$$
$$= 0.4094 + \tfrac{6}{10} (0.4120 - 0.4094)$$
$$= 0.4094 + 0.0016$$
$$= 0.4110.]$$

22. Find the approximate value of each of the following by using Table I and interpolation.

(a) sin 72°43'   (b) cos 28°46'
(c) tan 51°29'   (d) cos 63°23'
(e) tan 39°18'   (f) sin 128°36'
(g) cos 153°17'   (h) sin 8°9'

23. Find the angle θ between 0° and 90° using Table I if:

(a) sin θ = 0.4253,   (b) tan θ = 1.1237,
(c) cos θ = 0.8857   (d) sin θ = 0.8450,
(e) tan θ = 0.2156,   (f) cos θ = 0.2447,
(g) sin θ = 0.3475,   (h) cos θ = 0.7844.

24. The table may also be interpolated to find an angle, approximated to the nearest minute, when the value of a function of this angle lies between two entries in the table. If sin θ is given, we find two consecutive entries in the sine column between which the given value lies. Thus, letting $\theta = x + r$, where r is some integer between 0 and 10, and x and $x + 10$ are the consecutive entries in the table, we find r by using the approximation

$$\frac{r}{10} = \frac{\sin(x + r) - \sin x}{\sin(x + 10) - \sin x}.$$

Explain how this formula is obtained.

25. Find the angle θ between 0° and 90° if sin θ = 0.6231.

[*Hint:* We locate 0.6231 in the sine column between sin 38°30' = 0.6225 and sin 38°40' = 0.6248. Thus,

$$\frac{r}{10} = \frac{0.6231 - 0.6225}{0.6248 - 0.6225},$$

or

$$r = 10\left(\frac{0.0006}{0.0023}\right) = 3,$$

so that $\theta = 38°33'$, approximated to the nearest minute.]

26. Find the approximate value between 0° and 90° of θ to the nearest minute, by using Table I and interpolation, if:

(a) tan θ = 0.8172,   (b) sin θ = 0.5331,
(c) cos θ = 0.2717,   (d) cos θ = 0.9392,
(e) sin θ = 0.7531,   (f) tan θ = 0.8083,
(g) cos θ = 0.5386,   (h) sin θ = 0.9648.

27. In trigonometry there are frequently computations involving a large amount of multiplication and division. To shorten such work, the logarithms of the circular functions have been tabulated in Table III. Although the entries are logarithms (with the characteristics included), the form of the table is the

same as that of Table I, and it is used in exactly the same manner.   Find log sin 36°17′.

[*Hint:* Since the angle 36°17′ lies between 36°10′ and 36°20′,

$$\log \sin 36°17′ = \log \sin 36°10′ + \tfrac{7}{10} (\log \sin 37°20′ - \log \sin 37°10′)$$
$$= (9.7710 - 10) + \tfrac{7}{10}[(9.7727 - 10) - (9.7710 - 10)]$$
$$= (9.7710 - 10) + \tfrac{7}{10}(0.0017)$$
$$= (9.7710 - 10) + 0.0012$$
$$= 9.7722 - 10.]$$

28. By using Table III, and interpolation if necessary, find the value of each of the following.

(a) log sin 13°20′   (b) log cos 45°30′
(c) log sin 67°32′   (d) log cos 38°21′
(e) log tan 72°47′   (f) log sin 115°18′
(g) log cos 68°56′   (h) log sin 51°49′

29. Find the angle θ between 0° and 90° if log tan θ = 0.1947.

[*Hint:* We locate 0.1947 in the log tangent column between

$$\log \tan 57°20′ = 0.1930 \qquad \text{and} \qquad \log \tan 57°30′ = 0.1958.$$

Thus,

$$\frac{r}{10} = \frac{0.1947 - 0.1930}{0.1958 - 0.1930},$$

or

$$r = 10(\tfrac{17}{28}) = 6,$$

so that θ = 57°26′, approximated to the nearest minute.]

30. Find the value of θ between 0° and 90° to the nearest minute by using Table III, and interpolation if necessary, for the following.

(a) log sin θ = 9.2870 − 10   (b) log cos θ = 9.8365 − 10
(c) log tan θ = 9.7353 − 10   (d) log cos θ = 9.7316 − 10
(e) log sin θ = 9.2278 − 10   (f) log tan θ = 0.4937
(g) log cos θ = 9.9797 − 10   (h) log sin θ = 9.8761 − 10

Using logarithms, compute the value of the following to the correct number of significant figures.

31. $\dfrac{32.86 \sin 27°42′}{\sin 54°17′}$.   [*Hint:* Let x = the required value. Then

$$x = \frac{32.86 \sin 27°42′}{\sin 54°17′}.$$

We have

$$\log x = \log 32.86 + \log \sin 27°42′ - \log \sin 54°17′.$$

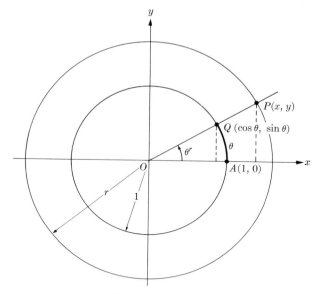

FIGURE 15–4

Arranging our work, we get

$$\log 32.86 \;=\; 1.5167$$
$$(+) \log \sin 27°42' \;=\; 9.6673 - 10$$
$$\log \text{numerator} \;=\; 11.1840 - 10$$
$$(-) \log \sin 54°17' \;=\; 9.9095 - 10$$
$$\log x \;=\; 1.2745$$
$$x \;=\; 18.81.]$$

32. 48.7 tan 58°30′

33. $\dfrac{68.2 \sin 37°20'}{\sin 49°50'}$

34. 897.2 cos 63°48′

35. (189)(256) cos 27°11′

The question naturally arises: What do the circular functions of angles indicate geometrically, and how can they be used?

Consider an *angle* θ, in standard position, which has been generated by the portion of the rotating ray of length r (Fig. 15–4). Let (x, y) be the coordinates of P, the point on the terminal side of the angle, a distance r from the origin. If Q denotes the point of intersection of OP and the unit circle, the length of OQ is one and the length of arc $\widehat{AQ}$ is $|\theta|$, so that the coordinates of Q are $(\cos \theta, \sin \theta)$. If perpendiculars are drawn from Q

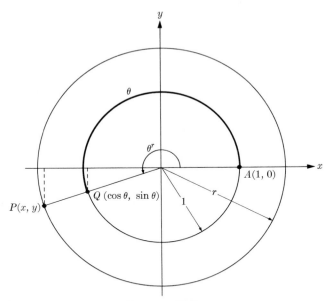

FIGURE 15–5

and from P to the x-axis, similar right triangles are found, so that

$$\frac{x}{\cos \theta} = \frac{r}{1} \qquad \text{and} \qquad \frac{y}{\sin \theta} = \frac{r}{1} \qquad (15\text{--}8)$$

so that $x = r \cos \theta$ and $y = r \sin \theta$.

If P, and thus Q, is in some quadrant other than the first, as in Fig. 15–5, either or both of the coordinates of P may be negative, in which case the corresponding coordinates of Q will agree in sign, so that relation (Eq. 15–8) will still be true. We have thus proved the following important theorem.

THEOREM 15–1. *If $P(x, y)$ is a point a distance r from the origin, on the terminal side of an angle θ, in standard position, the coordinates of P are given in terms of r and θ, by the expressions*

$$\boxed{x = r \cos \theta \qquad \text{and} \qquad y = r \sin \theta.} \qquad (15\text{--}9)^*$$

It is interesting to note that if $r = 1$, $P(x, y)$ lies on the unit circle and coincides with Q so that $x = \cos \theta$ and $y = \sin \theta$ as we would expect.

---

*These equations, with certain conditions on θ, are frequently referred to as the polar coordinate expressions for x and y.

As a result of Theorem 15–1, we prove the following theorem, the results of which are frequently taken as the definitions of the circular functions, when defined in terms of an angle.

THEOREM 15–2. *If $P(x, y)$ is a point, a distance r from the origin, on the terminal side of an angle θ, in standard position, the circular functions of the angle θ are given by the expressions*

$$
\begin{array}{llll}
\sin \theta = \dfrac{y}{r}, & & \cos \theta = \dfrac{x}{r}, & \\[2mm]
\tan \theta = \dfrac{y}{x} & (x \neq 0), & \cot \theta = \dfrac{x}{y} & (y \neq 0), \\[2mm]
\sec \theta = \dfrac{r}{x} & (x \neq 0), & \csc \theta = \dfrac{r}{y} & (y \neq 0).
\end{array}
\qquad (15\text{--}10)
$$

Proof. Since $r \neq 0$, we obtain the first two equations directly from Eq. (15–9). Since, by Eq. (6–4) $\tan \theta \equiv \sin \theta / \cos \theta$, we have $\tan \theta = (y/r)(x/r) = y/x$. The other equations can be established in a similar way by using the reciprocal identities, Eqs. (6–11) to (6–13).

EXAMPLE 3. Let θ be an angle in standard position with its terminal side passing through $(-3, 4)$. Find $\sin \theta$, $\cos \theta$ and $\tan \theta$.

Solution. Since $x = -3$ and $y = 4$, $r = \sqrt{(-3)^2 + 4^2} = 5$. Thus, $\sin \theta = \frac{4}{5}$, $\cos \theta = -\frac{3}{5}$, and $\tan \theta = -\frac{4}{3}$. (Compare Example 1, Article 6–2.)

PROBLEMS

In each of the following, the terminal side of the angle, in standard position, passes through the indicated point. Sketch and find the circular functions of each angle.

1. $(3, 4)$	2. $(-5, 12)$	3. $(-4, 3)$
4. $(24, -7)$	5. $(-8, -15)$	6. $(10, -8)$
7. $(0, -2)$	8. $(-1, 7)$	9. $(6, 0)$

10. For any angle θ in standard position with its terminal side intersecting the circle of radius r at P, show that P has coordinates $(r \cos \theta, r \sin \theta)$. This is a most important concept.

15–3 General discussion of triangle solutions.

The entire point of view with regard to solving triangles has changed during the last few years. Many numerical methods, numerous formulas, and detailed study with many exercises had been considered an important part of trigonometry. More recently, however, the analytic part of trigonometry, with its applications in advanced mathematics and science, has become more important. New developments have produced extremely accurate graphical methods and have also made possible the use of high-speed numerical calculators. We shall concentrate our attention on the fundamental theorems and not emphasize long and detailed processes.

If a certain number of the sides and angles of a triangle are known, the triangle can be solved by finding the remaining sides and angles. We shall derive two of the many formulas used in solving triangles and consider certain special cases of these formulas. Other formulas and relations between the sides and angles of a triangle appear in the examples and problems.

While deriving these relations, it is important to recall that a triangle is determined when (1) two angles and one side are given, (2) two sides and the included angle are given, (3) three sides are given if the longest side is less than the sum of the other two. Also, there are at most two triangles when (4) two sides and an angle opposite one of them is given. These are the four types of problems we wish to solve. We shall denote the three angles at the vertices of any triangle ABC by α, β, and γ, respectively, and the corresponding opposite sides by a, b, and c.

15–4 The Law of Sines. Let us derive the first of two general laws, the *Law of Sines*. This law involves the sides of the triangle and the sines of its angles, and it will be proved by analytic methods. If we choose a rectangular coordinate system so that the angle α of the triangle ABC is in standard position (see Fig. 15–6), the coordinates of B are ($c \cos \alpha$, $c \sin \alpha$). (Recall Problem 10, Article 15–2, or Theorem 15–1.) If, however, the origin of the coordinate system is at C, with $(180° − \gamma)$ in standard position, the coordinates of B are

$$[a \cos (180° − \gamma), a \sin (180° − \gamma)].$$

Since, in either case, the y-coordinates of B are equal (the same distance above the x-axis), we have

$$c \sin \alpha = a \sin (180° − \gamma)$$
$$= a \sin \gamma.$$

Dividing each member of this equation by $\sin \alpha \sin \gamma$, we obtain

$$\frac{c}{\sin \gamma} = \frac{a}{\sin \alpha}.$$

With a different choice of the x-axis, $b/\sin \beta = a/\sin \alpha$, and hence we have proved the following theorem.

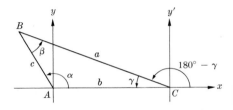

FIGURE 15–6

THEOREM 15–3. *In any triangle with angles α, β, and γ and corresponding opposite sides a, b, and c the following relationship is true:*

$$\frac{a}{\sin \alpha} = \frac{b}{\sin \beta} = \frac{c}{\sin \gamma}.$$ (15–11)

This relationship enables us to solve the problems mentioned in (1) and (4) of Article 15–3. However, before we consider general problems solved by Eq. (15–11), let us consider an extremely important special case. The more general problems will be discussed in Article 15–7.

15–5 Solution of right triangles. If γ is a right angle equal to 90°, in Eq. (15–11) the equations reduce to $\sin \alpha = a/c$ and $\sin \beta = b/c$. But with $\gamma = 90°$ and $\alpha + \beta + \gamma = 180°$, $\beta = 90° - \alpha$, so that $\cos \alpha = b/c$. Since $\tan \alpha = \sin \alpha/\cos \alpha$, we also have $\tan \alpha = a/b$. From these special conditions, an important corollary should be clear. It may also be considered a direct consequence of the original definitions of these circular functions.

COROLLARY 15–3. *In any right triangle with $\gamma = 90°$,*

$$\sin \alpha = \frac{a}{c} = \frac{side\ opposite\ \alpha}{hypotenuse},$$ (15–12)

$$\cos \alpha = \frac{b}{c} = \frac{side\ adjacent\ \alpha}{hypotenuse},$$ (15–13)

$$\tan \alpha = \frac{a}{b} = \frac{side\ opposite\ \alpha}{side\ adjacent\ \alpha}.$$ (15–14)

The following remarks on significant figures will also be helpful in the solving of triangles.

1. Results can be no more accurate than the given sides and angles. We agree to set up the following table for accuracy.

Significant figures for sides:	Angles to the nearest:
2	degree
3	ten minutes
4	minute
5	tenth of a minute

2. If the results are required to only two or three significant digits, the slide rule should be used for the computation. The slide rule can also be employed as a check on the work, unless the answers are to be more accurate than the slide rule will allow.

3. If the results are to be correct to several significant digits, tables should be used. When calculating machines are available, the natural functions and arithmetical methods are usually employed. But since the majority of students do not have access to machines, the logarithmic solution is the logical one. This is the method used in most of the examples.

4. In solving problems, it is advisable to draw the triangle, label the known parts, and make a complete systematic outline of the work before any computation is done.

EXAMPLE 1. In the right triangle ABC, $b = 47.25$, $\alpha = 41°19'$. Find the remaining parts and the area.

Solution. We first draw the triangle and label numerically the parts that are given, as in Fig. 15–7. Then $\beta = 90° - \alpha = 48°41'$. To find a, we use the relation $\tan \alpha = a/b$, and to find c, we use $\cos \alpha = b/c$:

$$a = 47.25 \tan 41°19' \qquad\qquad c = \frac{47.25}{\cos 41°19'}$$

$\log 47.25 = \quad 1.6744$	$\log 47.25 = 11.6744 - 10$
$(+) \log \tan 41°19' = \quad 9.9440 - 10$	$(-) \log \cos 41°19' = \quad 9.8757 - 10$
$\log a = 11.6184 - 10$	$\log c = \quad 1.7987$
$a = 41.54$	$c = 62.90$

The area of the triangle is $K = \frac{1}{2}ab$.

$$\log 41.54 = 1.6184$$
$$(+) \log 47.25 = 1.6744$$
$$\overline{\log ab = 3.2928}$$
$$(-) \log\ 2 = 0.3010$$
$$\overline{\log K = 2.9918}$$
$$K = 981.2$$

Here the results are correct to four significant figures, as in Table III.

EXAMPLE 2. Solve the right triangle in which $a = 284.1$ and $c = 326.7$.

Solution. Draw the triangle and label numerically the parts that are known, as in Fig. 15–8. Since a and c are given, we use the relation

FIGURE 15–7

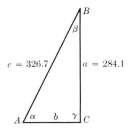

FIGURE 15–8

$\sin \alpha = a/c$ to find α and then $\cos \alpha = b/c$ to find b:

$$\sin \alpha = \frac{284.1}{326.7}$$

$$b = 326.7 \cos 60°24'$$

$\log 284.1 = \quad 12.4534 - 10$

$(-) \log 326.7 = \quad 2.5141$

$\log \sin \alpha = \quad 9.9393 - 10$

$\alpha = 60°24'$

$\beta = 29°36'$

$\log 326.7 = \quad 2.5141$

$(+) \log \cos 60°24' = \quad 9.6937 - 10$

$\log b = \quad 12.2078 - 10$

$b = 161.4$

Log $\cos \alpha$ can be found in the table when $\log \sin \alpha$ is located. This is one of the advantages in first arranging the work systematically.

Vectors. In science and engineering, physical entities such as velocity, acceleration, or force require not only magnitude but also direction for their complete determination. They are represented by line segments with an arrowhead on one end to show direction. The length of the segment, by reference to some scale, denotes magnitude. Such line segments are called *vectors*. For example, with a scale of 40 pounds to the unit, the vector in Fig. 15–9 might represent a force of 200 pounds acting in the direction 30° with the positive x-axis. A bold-face letter **v** will denote the vector, while the ordinary v will designate its length.

FIGURE 15–9

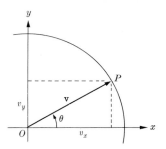

FIGURE 15–10

Since **v**, with its initial point at 0, as in Fig. 15–10, has v for its length and makes an angle θ with the positive x-axis, its terminal point P has coordinates $(v \cos \theta, v \sin \theta)$. These coordinates, denoted by v_x and v_y, are called the x- and y-components of **v** and satisfy the relations

$$
\begin{aligned}
v_x &= v \cos \theta, & v^2 &= v_x^2 + v_y^2, \\
v_y &= v \sin \theta, & \tan \theta &= \frac{v_y}{v_x}.
\end{aligned}
\tag{15–15}
$$

EXAMPLE 3. Find v_x and v_y for the vector with $v = 247$ and $\theta = 37°40'$.

Solution.

$$v_x = 247 \cos 37°40' = (247)(0.7916) = 196,$$
$$v_y = 247 \sin 37°40' = (247)(0.6111) = 151.$$

By considering $\mathbf{v}_x$ and $\mathbf{v}_y$ vectors, we can think of **v** as the single vector equivalent to these two. More generally, a vector **v** is the resultant or sum of two vectors $\mathbf{v}_1$ and $\mathbf{v}_2$ if as a single force it will produce the same result as the two forces acting together. If $\mathbf{v}_1$ and $\mathbf{v}_2$ are two nonparallel vectors emanating from the same point, their resultant **v** is the vector from that point having the length and direction of the diagonal of the parallelogram determined by $\mathbf{v}_1$ and $\mathbf{v}_2$. This notion is first used in Problem 22.

PROBLEMS

In solving the problems, a calculating machine should be used for some of the computations if possible. Logarithms should be used for others. All solutions should be checked.

1. Find the unknown sides and angles of each of the following triangles. In each, $\gamma = 90°$.

(a) $\alpha = 37°20'$, $a = 243$ (b) $\alpha = 62°40'$, $b = 796$

(c) $a = 3.28,\ b = 5.74$ (d) $b = 68.4,\ c = 96.2$
(e) $\beta = 51°10',\ c = 0.832$ (f) $\alpha = 37°40',\ a = 54.8$
(g) $a = 37.9,\ b = 57.3$ (h) $\beta = 41°25',\ c = 3265$
(i) $a = 5429,\ c = 6294$ (j) $a = 3.273,\ b = 7.647$
(k) $\beta = 62°57',\ a = 0.8263$ (l) $\beta = 47°23',\ b = 72.55$
(m) $b = 3572,\ c = 4846$ (n) $\alpha = 24°47',\ b = 318.4$

2. In a circle of radius 96.4 inches, what is the central angle that subtends a chord of 40.3 inches?

3. A rectangular lot is 102 by 296 feet. Find the length of the diagonal and the angles it makes with the longest side.

4. A telegraph pole is braced by wires from the ground which are attached at a point 18.6 feet up the pole. Find the length of a wire that makes an angle of 26°20′ with the vertical.

5. Find the area of a parallelogram whose sides are 33.7 and 15.2 inches if the angle between them is 67°40′.

6. One of the equal sides of an isosceles triangle is 6.73 inches and one of the base angles is 27°10′. Find the base and altitude.

7. A 36-foot ladder is used to reach the top of a 28-foot wall. If the ladder extends 2 feet past the top of the wall, find its inclination to the horizontal.

8. A hemispherical bowl of inside radius 8.00 inches is level and is filled with water to a depth of 2.00 inches. Through what angle may it be tilted before the water spills?

9. A piece of wire 24.78 inches long is bent so as to form an isosceles triangle with one angle 97°26′. Find the length of each side of the triangle formed.

*10. From a point on the ground 152.3 feet away from the foot of a flagpole, the *angle of elevation* of the top of the pole is 31°46′. How high is the flagpole? [*Hint:* When the object observed is above the horizontal plane, the angle between the line of sight from the eye to the object and the horizontal is called the *angle of elevation*. When the object observed is below the horizontal plane, the angle is called the *angle of depression*.]

11. From a lighthouse 75.3 feet above the level of the water, the angle of depression of a boat is 23°40′. How far is the boat from a point at water level directly under the point of observation?

12. Find the height of a balloon directly above a town A if the angle of depression of town B, 6.23 miles from A, is 15°20′.

13. From a lookout tower 80.0 feet high, a man observes from a position 6.5 feet below the top of the tower that the angle of elevation of the top of a certain tree is 12°40′ and that the angle of depression of its base is 72°20′. If the base of the tower and tree are at the same level, what is the height of the tree?

14. From a point 20.75 feet above the surface of the water, the angle of elevation of a building at the edge of the water is 38°16′, while the angle of depression of its image in the water is 56°28′. Find the height of the building and the horizontal distance from the point of observation.

15. From a mountain 1780 feet high, the angle of depression of a point on the nearer shore of a river is 48°40′ and of a point directly across on the opposite side is 22°20′. What is the width of the river between the two points?

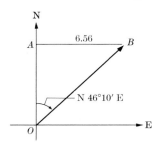

FIGURE 15–11

16. At a certain point the angle of elevation of a mountain peak is 40°20'. At a point 9560 feet farther away in the same horizontal plane, its angle of elevation is 29°50'. Find the distance of the peak above the horizontal plane.

*17. Lighthouse B is 6.56 miles directly east of lighthouse A. A ship at O observes that A is due north and that the bearing of OB is N 46°10' E. How far is the ship from A? From B? [*Hint:* The *bearing* of a line in a horizontal plane is the acute angle made by this line with a north-south line. In giving the bearing of a line, the letter N or S is written before the value and E or W follows the value. Thus, in Fig. 15–11, the bearing of OB is read "north 46°10' east."]

18. An airplane is 115 miles due east of radio station A; a second radio station is 136 miles due north of A. What are the distance and bearing of the second radio station from the airplane?

19. Because of a certain wind, a boat sails 4728 feet in the direction S 47°29' W. How far south has it gone? How far west has it gone?

20. Find v_x and v_y for each of the vectors with v and θ given as follows:

(a) $v = 75$, $\theta = 60°$;   (b) $v = 48$, $\theta = 136°$;
(c) $v = 4.72$, $\theta = 217°10'$;   (d) $v = 58.47$, $\theta = 47°18'$.

21. Find the length and direction for each of the vectors if

(a) $v_x = 3$, $v_y = 4$;   (b) $v_x = 23$, $v_y = 45$;
(c) $v_x = -16.2$, $v_y = 28.7$;   (d) $v_x = 382.4$, $v_y = -768.3$.

22. If a force of 658.4 pounds is acting east and another of 316.2 pounds is acting north, what are the magnitude and direction of their resultant?

23. A balloon is rising at the rate of 12 ft/sec and at the same time is being blown horizontally by a wind at 18 ft/sec. Find the angle its path makes with the vertical and determine its actual velocity.

24. A river runs directly east at 1.28 mi/hr. If a swimmer can swim at the rate of 1.75 mi/hr in still water and he starts swimming north directly across the river, in what direction is he actually moving? Where does he hit the opposite bank if the river is one mile wide?

25. In which direction should the swimmer in Problem 24 head in order to reach a point directly across the river?

26. An airplane travels with a speed of 145 mi/hr in calm air. The wind is blowing with a velocity of 23 mi/hr from N 27° E. (a) If the plane is headed in a direction N 63° W, find the magnitude of the speed and the direction of the

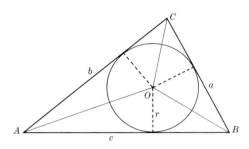

FIGURE 15–12   FIGURE 15–13

airplane with reference to the ground. (b) In what direction must the airplane be headed in order to fly in the direction N 63° W, and what would be its actual speed in the air?

27. Find the resultant of the following sets of forces, where f is the magnitude and θ the angle each force makes with the positive x-axis.

(a) $f_1 = 15$, $\theta_1 = 65°$, $f_2 = 37$, $\theta_2 = 142°$
(b) $f_1 = 6280$, $\theta_1 = 37°10'$, $f_2 = 2840$, $\theta_2 = -16°40'$
(c) $f_1 = 6800$, $\theta_1 = 210°$, $f_2 = 7200$, $\theta_2 = 315°$, $f_3 = 5600$, $\theta_3 = 90°$

[*Hint:* Although we could find the resultant as the diagonal of the parallelogram, it is simpler in such problems to work with components. Obtain the sum of the x-components as one force, the sum of the y-components as another, and then find the resultant of these two.]

28. The circle with center at O in Fig. 15–12 is circumscribed about the triangle and OD is drawn perpendicular to BC. What is the relation of $\angle BOD$ to α? Using the right triangle BDO, prove $\sin \alpha = a/2R$. With the necessary additional construction, prove the Law of Sines.

29. In the right triangle ABC, with $\alpha = 30°$, $AB = 2$. D is chosen on AC so that $DC = BC$, and from D a line is drawn perpendicular to AB, meeting AB at K. Show $\angle DBK = 15°$ and, by finding the lengths of the various lines, prove

$$\sin 15° = \frac{\sqrt{6} - \sqrt{2}}{4}.$$

*30. Using Fig. 15–13, where the inscribed circle in triangle ABC has r for its radius, prove the area $K = rs$, where $s = (a + b + c)/2$.

15–6 The Law of Cosines. We shall now prove another important relationship, *the Law of Cosines*.

THEOREM 15–4. *In any triangle, with angles α, β, and γ and corresponding opposite sides a, b, and c,*

$$\boxed{a^2 = b^2 + c^2 - 2bc \cos \alpha.} \tag{15–16}$$

Proof. Refer to Fig. 15–6, where the angle α of the triangle ABC is in standard position, with the vertex C at $(b, 0)$. If we recall that the coordinates of B are $(c \cos \alpha, c \sin \alpha)$, we have by Eq. (4–9) the distance between $B(c \cos \alpha, c \sin \alpha)$ and $C(b, 0)$:

$$\sqrt{(c \cos \alpha - b)^2 + (c \sin \alpha - 0)^2}.$$

But this length is the length of a, so that

$$a = \sqrt{c^2 \cos^2 \alpha - 2bc \cos \alpha + b^2 + c^2 \sin^2 \alpha},$$

or

$$a^2 = b^2 + c^2 - 2bc \cos \alpha.$$

Similarly, we obtain

$$b^2 = a^2 + c^2 - 2ac \cos \beta, \tag{15–17}$$
$$c^2 = a^2 + b^2 - 2ab \cos \gamma. \tag{15–18}$$

These three relations make up the Law of Cosines. They hold for all triangles and are used to solve problems of types (2) and (3) in Article 15–3. If $\gamma = 90°$ in Eq. (15–18), $c^2 = a^2 + b^2$. For this reason, the Law of Cosines is sometimes called *the generalization of the Pythagorean Theorem.*

15–7 Applications involving oblique triangles. To clarify the use of the Laws of Sines and Cosines, let us consider the following examples.

EXAMPLE 1. Solve the triangle ABC of Fig. 15–14 if $a = 524.7$, $\beta = 46°24'$, and $\gamma = 98°41'$.

Solution. First, $\alpha = 180° - (46°24' + 98°41') = 34°55'$. With the value of α known, we can use the Law of Sines to find b and c.

$$b = \frac{a}{\sin \alpha} \sin \beta \qquad\qquad c = \frac{a}{\sin \alpha} \sin \gamma$$

$\log 524.7 =$	$12.7199 - 10$	$\log \dfrac{a}{\sin \alpha} =$	2.9622
$(-) \log \sin 34°55' =$	$9.7577 - 10$	$(+) \log \sin 98°41' =$	$9.9950 - 10$
$\log \dfrac{a}{\sin \alpha} =$	2.9622	$\log c =$	$12.9572 - 10$
$(+) \log \sin 46°24' =$	$9.8599 - 10$	$c =$	906.2
$\log b =$	$12.8221 - 10$		
$b =$	663.9		

This example illustrates type (1) in Article 15–3.

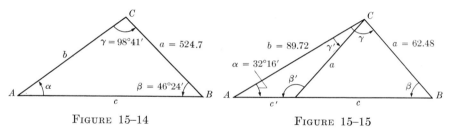

FIGURE 15–14   FIGURE 15–15

EXAMPLE 2.   Find all triangles for $a = 62.48$, $b = 89.72$, and $\alpha = 32°16'$.

Solution. The *ambiguous type* of problem (4) is illustrated here. We have the possibility of two solutions, since $\sin (180° - \beta) = \sin \beta$. If we use the Law of Sines and solve for β, we find two values, for each of which there is a corresponding γ and c. Thus we have two distinct solutions, as is suggested in Fig. 15–15.

$$\sin \beta = b \, \frac{\sin \alpha}{a}$$

$$\log \sin 32°16' = 9.7274 - 10$$

$$(-) \log 62.48 = 1.7958$$

$$\log \frac{\sin \alpha}{a} = 7.9316 - 10$$

$$(+) \log 89.72 = 1.9529$$

$$\log \sin \beta = 9.8845 - 10$$

$$\beta_1 = 50°2' \quad \text{or} \quad \beta_2 = 129°58'$$

Thus,

$$\gamma_1 = 180° - (\alpha + \beta_1) = 97°42',$$
$$\gamma_2 = 180° - (\alpha + \beta_2) = 17°46'.$$

Then

$$c_1 = \frac{a}{\sin \alpha} \sin \gamma_1 \qquad\qquad c_2 = \frac{a}{\sin \alpha} \sin \gamma_2$$

$$\log \frac{a}{\sin \alpha} = \quad 2.0684 \qquad\qquad \log \frac{a}{\sin \alpha} = \quad 2.0684$$

$$(+) \log \sin 97°42' = \quad 9.9961 - 10 \qquad (+) \log \sin 17°46' = \quad 9.4845 - 10$$

$$\log c_1 = \quad 12.0645 - 10 \qquad\qquad \log c_2 = \quad 11.5529 - 10$$

$$c_1 = 116.0, \qquad\qquad\qquad c_2 = 35.72.$$

EXAMPLE 3.   Find the third side of the triangle with $b = 47$, $c = 58$, and $\alpha = 63°$.

Solution. For this problem, type (2) of Article 15–3, we use the Law of Cosines. It should be emphasized that with four-place tables this law produces no more than two significant figures for the third side, since a square root is involved.

$$a^2 = (47)^2 + (58)^2 - 2 \cdot 47 \cdot 58 \cos 63°$$
$$= 2209 + 3364 - 2475.2$$
$$= 3097.8$$

Thus,

$$a = 56 \text{ (approximately).}$$

The other angles can be found by using the Law of Sines.

It is clear from Example 3 that the Law of Cosines does not lend itself to problems of this type when more than two significant figures are desired. Another law, called the *First Law of Tangents*, can be used in such cases. From the relationship $a/\sin \alpha = b/\sin \beta$, it is not difficult to show that

$$\frac{\sin \alpha - \sin \beta}{\sin \alpha + \sin \beta} = \frac{a - b}{a + b}.$$

If we use this and Problem 25, Article 6–9, we have

$$\boxed{\frac{\tan \frac{1}{2}(\alpha - \beta)}{\tan \frac{1}{2}(\alpha + \beta)} = \frac{a - b}{a + b}.} \qquad (15\text{–}19)$$

This equation and the five similar formulas obtained by interchanging and rotating letters constitute the *First Law of Tangents*. (See Problem 7.)

EXAMPLE 4. Solve the triangle with $a = 16.47$, $b = 25.49$, and $c = 33.77$.

Solution. This example of type (3) again requires the use of the Law of Cosines. We find

$$a^2 = \ 271.26, \qquad 2ab = \ 839.64,$$
$$b^2 = \ 649.74, \qquad 2ac = 1112.4,$$
$$c^2 = 1140.4, \qquad 2bc = 1721.6,$$

so that

$$\cos \alpha = \frac{b^2 + c^2 - a^2}{2bc} = \ 0.8823, \qquad \text{or} \qquad \alpha = 28°5',$$

$$\cos \beta = \frac{a^2 + c^2 - b^2}{2ac} = \ 0.6850, \qquad \text{or} \qquad \beta = 46°46',$$

$$\cos \gamma = \frac{a^2 + b^2 - c^2}{2ab} = -0.2613, \qquad \text{or} \qquad \beta = 105°9'.$$

The solution is easily checked, since $\alpha + \beta + \gamma = 180°$.

Example 4 could be solved using five-place tables of logarithms, but the process is long because of the form of the Law of Cosines. However, the *Second Law of Tangents* lends itself to large numbers as well as logarithmic computation. By adding 1 to both members of the expression for $\cos \alpha$ in Example 4, dividing each side by 2, and factoring the right side, we get

$$\frac{1 + \cos \alpha}{2} = \frac{(b + c + a)(b + c - a)}{4bc}.$$

Also,

$$\frac{1 - \cos \alpha}{2} = \frac{(a + b - c)(a - b + c)}{4bc}.$$

Now, letting $(a + b + c)/2 = s$ in these expressions, and recalling Eqs. (6–49) and (6–51), we have

$$\sin \frac{\alpha}{2} = \sqrt{\frac{(s - b)(s - c)}{bc}}$$

and

$$\cos \frac{\alpha}{2} = \sqrt{\frac{s(s - a)}{bc}}.$$

If we divide we get

$$\boxed{\tan \frac{\alpha}{2} = \frac{r}{s - a},} \qquad (15\text{–}20)$$

where

$$\boxed{r^* = \sqrt{\frac{(s - a)(s - b)(s - c)}{s}}.}$$

Equation (15–20) and the analogous formulas

$$\tan \frac{\beta}{2} = \frac{r}{s - b}$$

and

$$\tan \frac{\gamma}{2} = \frac{r}{s - c}$$

are called the *Second Law of Tangents* and give the angles of any triangle in terms of its three sides. (See Problem 10.)

---

* With the results of Problem 30, Article 15–5 and Problem 12 of this article, r is found to be the expression for the radius of the inscribed circle of any triangle.

PROBLEMS

1. Solve the following triangles ABC, given

(a) $\alpha = 62°40'$, $\beta = 79°20'$, $a = 147$;
(b) $\beta = 81°43'$, $\gamma = 57°51'$, $c = 47.35$;
(c) $\alpha = 47°57'$, $\gamma = 118°11'$, $b = 87270$;
(d) $\beta = 14°36'$, $\gamma = 53°8'$, $b = 8.367$.

2. Find and draw all triangles with $a = 62.48$, $b = 43.17$, and $\alpha = 32°16'$, Compare Example 2. [*Hint:* It is impossible to have two solutions, since $\beta_2 + \alpha > 180°$.]

3. Is there a triangle with $a = 62.48$, $b = 143.4$, and $\alpha = 32°16'$? Compare Example 2, and draw the figure. [*Hint:* Can $\sin \beta$ be greater than one?]

4. In the type of problem where two sides and an angle less than 90° and opposite one of these sides are given, we note various possibilities by comparing Example 2 with Problems 2 and 3. Assuming a, b, and α are given, explain the following with the aid of Fig. 15–16.

$\alpha < 90°$	$\alpha > 90°$
$a < b \sin \alpha$ gives no solution.	$a \leq b$ gives no solution.
$a = b \sin \alpha$ gives a special right triangle.	$b < a$ gives one solution.
$b \sin \alpha < a < b$ gives two solutions.	
$a \geq b$ gives one solution.	

5. In each of the following either show that there is no solution or find all solutions.

(a) $b = 59.4$, $c = 72.3$, $\beta = 38°40'$
(b) $a = 49.3$, $c = 8.72$, $\alpha = 45°10'$

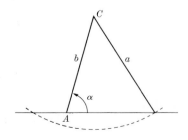

FIGURE 15–16

(c) $a = 14.72$, $b = 25.64$, $\beta = 147°47'$
(d) $b = 4.927$, $c = 5.764$, $\gamma = 57°18'$

6. Solve each of the following triangles for the side opposite the given angle.

(a) $a = 4$, $b = 7$, $\gamma = 30°$
(b) $a = 7.6$, $c = 9.2$, $\beta = 47°$
(c) $b = 8.3$, $c = 4.4$, $\alpha = 138°$

*7. Solve the following triangles with

(a) $b = 18.62$, $c = 35.61$, $\alpha = 52°18'$.

[*Hint:* Use the First Law of Tangents with $c - b = 16.99$, $c + b = 54.23$, $\frac{1}{2}(\gamma + \beta) = 63°51'$, and find $\frac{1}{2}(\gamma - \beta)$.   Then $\frac{1}{2}(\gamma + \beta) + \frac{1}{2}(\gamma - \beta) = \gamma$, and so on.]

(b) $a = 463$, $b = 628$, $\gamma = 57°40'$.

8. Solve the following triangles with

(a) $a = 356.8$, $c = 551.4$, $\beta = 87°48'$;
(b) $b = 321.0$, $c = 672$, $\alpha = 124°16'$.

9. Solve the following triangles by the Law of Cosines.

(a) $a = 4$, $b = 5$, $c = 6$;
(b) $a = 32$, $b = 56$, $c = 63$.

*10. Solve the following triangles by the most convenient method.

(a) $a = 18.76$, $b = 25.31$, $c = 29.65$.

Hint: If using logarithms and the Second Law of Tangents, arrange your work systematically:

$$2s = 73.72$$
$$s = 36.86$$
$$s - a = 18.10$$
$$s - b =$$
$$s - c =$$

$$\log (s - a) =$$
$$\log (s - b) =$$
$$(+) \log (s - c) =$$
$$\log \text{ numerator} = 3.1782$$
$$(-) \log s =$$
$$\log r^2 =$$
$$\log r = 0.8058$$

$$\log r =$$
$$(-) \log (s - a) = \underline{\qquad}$$
$$\log \tan \frac{\alpha}{2} =$$
$$\frac{\alpha}{2} =$$

$$\log r =$$
$$(-) \log (s - b) = \underline{\qquad}$$
$$\log \tan \frac{\beta}{2} =$$
$$\frac{\beta}{2} =$$

$$\log r =$$
$$(-) \log (s - c) = \underline{\qquad}$$
$$\log \tan \frac{\gamma}{2} =$$
$$\frac{\gamma}{2} =$$

(b) $a = 523$, $b = 576$, $c = 615$;
(c) $a = 0.8147$, $b = 0.6834$, $c = 0.3449$;
(d) $a = 4.32$, $b = 5.78$, $c = 13.44$.

*11. Prove that the area of the triangle in Fig. 15–6 is given by the formula

$$K = \tfrac{1}{2}bc \sin \alpha.$$

Rotation of letters yields

$$K = \tfrac{1}{2}ac \sin \beta = \tfrac{1}{2}ab \sin \gamma.$$

*12. Using the values for $\sin \theta/2$ and $\cos \theta/2$ given in the discussion which follows Example 4 and also the formula $\tfrac{1}{2} \sin \alpha = \sin \alpha/2 \cos \alpha/2$ (Eq. 6–43), prove

$$K = \sqrt{s(s - a)(s - b)(s - c)}.$$

It is from this expression and the result $K = rs$, Problem 30, Article 15–5, that we establish the value

$$r = \sqrt{\frac{(s - a)(s - b)(s - c)}{s}},$$

where r is the radius of the inscribed circle.

13. Use the results of Problem 11 and the Law of Sines to show that

$$K = \frac{a^2 \sin \beta \sin \gamma}{2 \sin \alpha} = \frac{b^2 \sin \gamma \sin \alpha}{2 \sin \beta} = \frac{c^2 \sin \alpha \sin \beta}{2 \sin \gamma}.$$

14. Find the areas of the triangles in previous problems designated by the instructor.

15. Find the lengths of the sides of a parallelogram if its diagonal, which is 72.83 inches long, makes angles with the sides of 27°52′ and 16°41′, respectively.

16. What angle does the slope of a hill make with the horizontal if a tree 74.3 feet tall, growing on the slope of the hill, is found to subtend an angle of 19°30′ from a point 147 feet from the foot of the tree? (The distance is measured along the slope straight down the hill.)

17. Two airways cross each other at an angle of 49°. At a certain instant, airplane A is 32 miles from the crossing, while B is 76 miles from the crossing. What is the distance between them at this instant? (Two solutions.)

18. Two sides of a parallelogram are 68 and 83 inches and one of the diagonals is 42 inches. Find the angles of the parallelogram.

19. From a point in the same horizontal plane with the base of a building, the angles of elevation of the top and the bottom of a flagpole on top of the building are 64°40′ and 59°50′ respectively. If the building is 112 feet high, how tall is the flagpole?

20. As a train is traveling due north on a certain track, the engineer observes a column of smoke in a direction N 20°20′ E. After traveling 475 feet, he observes the same smoke in a direction S 71°40′ E. How far was the smoke from the first point of observation? From the second? How far was it from the track?

21. A battleship is moving along the shoreline in a direction N 18°40′ E at a constant rate of 36.5 mi/hr. If a squadron of airplanes traveling 186 mi/hr is due east of the battleship, in what direction should they fly in order to reach the battleship as quickly as possible?

*22. If **R** is the resultant of two forces f_1 and f_2, and R, f_1, and f_2 represent their respective magnitudes, explain the formula $R^2 = f_1^2 + f_2^2 + 2f_1f_2 \cos \theta$, where θ is the angle between the two forces. (Recall Problem 22, Article 15–5.) Find the magnitude and direction of the resultant of two forces: 75 pounds acting due north and 93 pounds acting N 63° W.

23. An airplane travels with a speed of 153 mi/hr in calm air. If the wind is blowing with a velocity of 27 mi/hr from S 21° W and the plane is headed in a direction S 53° E, find the magnitude of the speed of the airplane and its direction with reference to the ground.

24. The resultant of two forces of 61.3 pounds and 34.9 pounds is a force of 73.7 pounds. What angle does the resultant make with each of the two forces?

CHAPTER 16

COMPLEX NUMBERS

The possibility of extensions or generalizations of the real number system was mentioned in Article 1–5. One of these extensions is the algebra of all ordered pairs of real numbers. We shall briefly discuss this very useful generalization, and then we shall consider one of its most common interpretations in some detail.

16–1 Algebra of ordered pairs. With the set of all ordered pairs of real numbers (x, y) as elements, we can construct a generalized algebra. We shall show that the set $P = \{(x, y)|x, y \in R\}$ is a *field* where the two operations of addition and multiplication are defined by Eqs. (16–1) and (16–4).* Before we do, however, we must define what is meant by the equality of two elements. (Recall Problem 12, Article 1–3.)

DEFINITION 16–1. *Two ordered pairs (x_1, y_1) and (x_2, y_2) are said to be equal if and only if $x_1 = x_2$ and $y_1 = y_2$.*

Thus, $(x + 2y, 2x - y) = (4, 3)$ if and only if $x + 2y = 4$ and $2x - y = 3$ or, specifically, $x = 2$ and $y = 1$.

We are now ready to define the operations of addition and multiplication for ordered pairs, and with these definitions demonstrate that P is a field.†

DEFINITION 16–2. *The sum of two ordered pairs (x_1, y_1) and (x_2, y_2) is the ordered pair $(x_1 + x_2, y_1 + y_2)$ and is written*

$$(x_1, y_1) + (x_2, y_2) = (x_1 + x_2, y_1 + y_2). \qquad (16\text{–}1)$$

For example, $(2, 1) + (3, 2) = (2 + 3, 1 + 2) = (5, 3)$.

It is clear because of the method of statement of this definition, that P is closed under the operation of addition. Further, the operation is commutative and associative, since real numbers themselves enjoy these properties. (See Problems 1 and 2.)

---

* Recall the field Axioms, Chapter 2.

† These definitions of equality, addition, and multiplication are by no means the only possible ones for ordered pairs, but have been chosen specifically for the introduction of the complex number system.

Since, by Eq. (16–1), $(x, y) + (0, 0) = (x, y)$ for all (x, y), and $(0, 0)$ is an ordered pair, the identical element for addition exists and is equal to $(0, 0)$. Further, $(x, y) + (-x, -y) = (0, 0)$ for all (x, y), so that an inverse element exists for the operation of addition. As in the case of real numbers, where the solution for x of the equation $a + x = b$, written $b - a$, is called the *difference* (recall Definition 2–1 and Problem 7, Article 2–4), the solution for (x, y) in the equation

$$(x_1, y_1) + (x, y) = (x_2, y_2) \qquad (16\text{–}2)*$$

is called the *difference of the two ordered pairs* (x_2, y_2) and (x_1, y_1). Since Eq. (16–2) implies

$$x_1 + x = x_2, \qquad y_1 + y = y_2,$$

or

$$x = x_2 - x_1, \qquad y = y_2 - y_1,$$

the difference (x, y) is written as the ordered pair $(x_2 - x_1, y_2 - y_1)$, or

$$(x_2, y_2) - (x_1, y_1) = (x_2 - x_1, y_2 - y_1). \qquad (16\text{–}3)$$

The definition of multiplication is not so obvious as that of addition.

DEFINITION 16–3. *The product of two ordered pairs* (x_1, y_1) *and* (x_2, y_2) *is the ordered pair* $(x_1 x_2 - y_1 y_2, x_1 y_2 + x_2 y_1)$, *and is written*

$$(x_1, y_1) \cdot (x_2, y_2) = (x_1 x_2 - y_1 y_2, x_1 y_2 + x_2 y_1). \qquad (16\text{–}4)$$

For example, $(2, 1) \cdot (3, 2) = (2 \cdot 3 - 1 \cdot 2, 2 \cdot 2 + 3 \cdot 1) = (4, 7)$.

Again, it is clear by definition, that P is closed under the operation of multiplication. Moreover, the operation of multiplication is commutative and associative. (See Problems 5 and 6.)

Since, by Eq. (16–4), $(x, y) \cdot (1, 0) = (x, y)$ for all (x, y), and $(1, 0)$ is an ordered pair, the identical element for multiplication exists, and is equal to $(1, 0)$. Also, since

$$\left(\frac{x}{x^2 + y^2}, \frac{-y}{x^2 + y^2} \right)$$

exists when $(x, y) \neq (0, 0)$ and

$$(x, y) \cdot \left(\frac{x}{x^2 + y^2}, \frac{-y}{x^2 + y^2} \right) = (1, 0)$$

---

* Equations (16–2) and (16–5) have unique solutions for (x, y).

for all $(x, y) \neq (0, 0)$, the inverse element for the operation of multiplication exists. It can also be demonstrated that the distributive law holds for the elements of P. (See Problem 9.)

In the case of real numbers, division is defined in terms of multiplication, and the definition for the quotient of two ordered pairs follows the same pattern. (Recall Definition 2–2 and Problem 11, Article 2–4.) Since the real number $x = a/b$ is defined by the equation $bx = a$, we define the quotient of two ordered pairs (x_1, y_1) and (x_2, y_2) as the ordered pair (x, y) ,which is the solution of the equation

$$(x_2, y_2) \cdot (x, y) = (x_1, y_1), \qquad (x_2, y_2) \neq (0, 0). \qquad (16\text{--}5)$$

Using Eq. (16–4), we get

$$(xx_2 - yy_2, xy_2 + x_2y) = (x_1, y_1),$$

and therefore

$$x_2x - y_2y = x_1, \qquad y_2x + x_2y = y_1.$$

Solving for x and y, we find the solution

$$x = \frac{x_1x_2 + y_1y_2}{x_2^2 + y_2^2}, \qquad y = \frac{x_2y_1 - x_1y_2}{x_2^2 + y_2^2}.$$

Thus the quotient of two ordered pairs may be written

$$\frac{(x_1, y_1)}{(x_2, y_2)} = \left(\frac{x_1x_2 + y_1y_2}{x_2^2 + y_2^2}, \frac{x_2y_1 - x_1y_2}{x_2^2 + y_2^2} \right). \qquad (16\text{--}6)$$

For example,

$$\frac{(4, 8)}{(3, 1)} = (2, 2).$$

PROBLEMS

1. Show that the addition defined for ordered pairs by Eq. 16–1 is commutative, that is,

$$(x_1, y_1) + (x_2, y_2) = (x_2, y_2) + (x_1, y_1).$$

2. Show that this addition is associative, that is,

$$[(x_1, y_1) + (x_2, y_2)] + (x_3, y_3) = (x_1, y_1) + [(x_2, y_2) + (x_3, y_3)].$$

3. Show that $(x, y) + (0, 0) = (x, y)$ for all $(x, y) \in P$. What axiom of a field does this represent?

4. Show that $(x, y) + (-x, -y) = (0, 0)$ for all $(x, y) \in P$. What axiom of a field does this represent?

5. Show that the multiplication defined for ordered pairs by Eq. (16–4) is commutative, that is,

$$(x_1, y_1) \cdot (x_2, y_2) = (x_2, y_2) \cdot (x_1, y_1).$$

6. Show that this multiplication is associative, that is,

$$[(x_1, y_1) \cdot (x_2, y_2)] \cdot (x_3, y_3) = (x_1, y_1) \cdot [(x_2, y_2) \cdot (x_3, y_3)].$$

7. Show that $(x, y) \cdot (1, 0) = (x, y)$ for all $(x, y) \in P$. What axiom of a field does this represent?

8. Show that

$$(x, y) \cdot \left(\frac{x}{x^2 + y^2}, \frac{-y}{x^2 + y^2} \right) = (1, 0)$$

for all $(x, y) \in P$. What axiom of a field does this represent?

9. Show that the distributive axiom for the elements of P is satisfied.

10. As a result of Problems 1 through 9 and the closure of P under addition and multiplication, what can be said about P?

11. Show that $(x, y) \cdot (0, 0) = (0, 0)$.

12. Show that $(x, y) = (y, x)$ if and only if $x = y$.

13. Show that $(0, 1)^2 = (0, 1) \cdot (0, 1) = (-1, 0)$.

Express each of the following as a single ordered pair.

14. $(0, 1)^4$ 15. $(0, 1)^3$ 16. $(0, 1)^8$

Find the value of (x, y) in Problems 17 through 25.

17. $(x, y) = (2, 3) + (4, 5)$ 18. $(x, y) = (-2, 1) + (3, -7)$

19. $(x, y) = (3, -1) - (4, -2)$ 20. $(3, 1) = (x, y) + (5, -1)$

21. $(x, y) = (3, 1) \cdot (2, 3)$ 22. $(x, y) = (-1, 2) \cdot (3, -5)$

23. $(x, y) = (2, -1)/(-1, 3)$ 24. $(x, y) = (23, 11)/(5, -1)$

25. $(x, y) = (-\frac{1}{2}, \sqrt{3}/2)^3$

16–2 Complex numbers. One of the most common interpretations of the algebra of ordered pairs discussed in Article 16–1 is the algebra of complex numbers. The expression $x + yi$, where x and y are real numbers and i has the property that $i^2 = -1$, is called a *complex number*. If $y = 0$, of course the complex number is real; but if $y \neq 0$, the complex number is said to be *imaginary*. With $y \neq 0$ and $x = 0$, $x + yi$ is a *pure imaginary*.

With the numbers x and y obeying the ordinary laws for real numbers, and the new element i obeying the law

$$i^2 = -1,$$

the complex numbers $x + yi$ may be thought of as an abbreviation for the ordered pair (x, y). To show that this is the case, the reader should verify that the complex numbers $x + yi$ satisfy the same laws as the ordered pairs (x, y). Specifically, in considering the sum of two complex numbers, we have

$$(x_1 + y_1 i) + (x_2 + y_2 i) = (x_1 + x_2) + (y_1 + y_2)i. \qquad (16\text{-}7)$$

The product of two complex numbers is given by

$$(x_1 + y_1 i) \cdot (x_2 + y_2 i) = x_1 x_2 + x_1 y_2 i + x_2 y_1 i + y_1 y_2 i^2$$
$$= (x_1 x_2 - y_1 y_2) + (x_1 y_2 + x_2 y_1)i. \qquad (16\text{-}8)$$

We see in this equation the reason for defining the product of two ordered pairs as in Eq. (16-4). The quotient of two complex numbers is given by

$$\frac{x_1 + y_1 i}{x_2 + y_2 i} = \frac{(x_1 + y_1 i)(x_2 - y_2 i)}{(x_2 + y_2 i)(x_2 - y_2 i)}$$

$$= \frac{x_1 x_2 - x_1 y_2 i + x_2 y_1 i - y_1 y_2 i^2}{x_2^2 - x_2 y_2 i + x_2 y_2 i - y_2^2 i^2}$$

$$= \frac{x_1 x_2 + y_1 y_2}{x_2^2 + y_2^2} + \frac{x_2 y_1 - x_1 y_2}{x_2^2 + y_2^2} i. \qquad (16\text{-}9)$$

Thus the ordered pair (x, y) may be regarded as representing the complex number $x + yi$, and the set of ordered pairs P may be regarded as the set of all complex numbers. This set of all complex numbers is usually denoted by C.

Two complex numbers which differ only in the sign of their imaginary parts are called *conjugates* of each other. Thus, $3 + 2i$ and $3 - 2i$ or $5i$ and $-5i$ are conjugate complex numbers or, more generally, $x + yi$ and $x - yi$ are numbers of this type. (Note Problems 9 and 10.)

It is unfortunate that the word "imaginary" has been applied to the numbers $x + yi$ where $y \neq 0$. Although these numbers were originally introduced to solve quadratic equations, they have been extremely useful in physics and engineering, especially in the description of certain electrical phenomena. Used in these fields, the "imaginary" numbers have significance which is quite as real as that of the "real" numbers.

A few quadratic equations in Chapter 7 and other equations in Chapter 9 have imaginary numbers as solutions. These were given as square roots of negative numbers, with no additional explanation at that time. Graphically, we noticed that the functions involved had real zeros only where the corresponding curves crossed or touched the horizontal axis. We are now able to write such solutions in terms of the imaginary symbol i.

EXAMPLE. Solve the equation $x^2 - 4x + 6 = 0$.

Solution. Using the quadratic formula Eq. (7–10), with $a = 1$, $b = -4$, and $c = 6$, we have

$$x = \frac{-(-4) \pm \sqrt{(-4)^2 - 4(1)(6)}}{2(1)}$$

$$= \frac{4 \pm \sqrt{16 - 24}}{2} = \frac{4 \pm \sqrt{-8}}{2}$$

$$= \frac{4 \pm 2\sqrt{-2}}{2} = 2 \pm \sqrt{2}\, i.$$

It is important to note that, although C is a field, it does not satisfy the Order Axioms given in Chapter 4, so that it is *not* an ordered field. (See Problem 18.)

PROBLEMS

In Problems 1 through 4, give the expression as a single complex number.

1. (a) $(2 + 5i) + (4 - i)$ (b) $(2 + 5i) - (4 - i)$

2. (a) $(2 + 5i)(4 - i)$ (b) $(2 + 5i)(4 + i)$

3. (a) $\dfrac{2 + 5i}{4 - i}$ (b) $\dfrac{2 + 5i}{4 + i}$

4. (a) $i^3 = i \cdot i^2$, (b) $i^4 = i^2 \cdot i^2$, (c) i^5, (d) $1/i$

5. Prove, for any positive integer n,

(a) $i^{4n} = 1$,   (b) $i^{4n+1} = i$,   (c) $i^{4n+2} = -1$,

(d) $i^{4n+3} = -i$,   (e) $i^{n+4} = i^n$.

In Problems 6 through 10 use the ordinary properties of the real numbers and the fact that $i^2 = -1$.

6. State Problems 17, 21, and 23 of Article 16–1, interpreting the ordered pairs as complex numbers, and solve.

7. If the complex number $x + yi = 0$, show algebraically that $x = 0$ and $y = 0$. [*Hint:* Since $x = -yi$, $x^2 = -y^2$. What can be said about x and y?]

8. If $x_1 + y_1 i$ and $x_2 + y_2 i$ are two complex numbers such that $x_1 + y_1 i = x_2 + y_2 i$, show by using algebra that $x_1 = x_2$ and $y_1 = y_2$. [*Hint:* Transpose so that $x_1 - x_2 + (y_1 - y_2)i = 0$. Then use Problem 7.]

9. Prove that the sum and product of two conjugate complex numbers are both real.

10. Prove that if the sum and product of two imaginary numbers are real, the numbers are conjugate complex numbers.

Solve the following equations, where some or all of the solutions may be imaginary.

11. $\dfrac{2x}{3} - 5i = 0$

12. $\dfrac{2x - 4i}{x + i} = 1$

13. $(2 + 5i)x + 2i = 0$

14. $\dfrac{ix}{2} = 3 - 4i$

15. $x^2 - (3 - i)x - 3i = 0$
    [*Hint:* Factor.]

16. $x^2 + ix - x - i = 0$

17. $ix^2 + 7x - 12i = 0$.

18. Show that the set of complex numbers C does not satisfy the four Order Axioms given in Chapter 4. [*Hint:* Consider the complex numbers i and 0. If Axiom O1 is to be satisfied, either $i = 0$, $i > 0$, or $i < 0$. (1) $i \neq 0$ since $i^2 = -1$, and $-1 \neq 0$. (2) If $i > 0$, by Axiom O4 we may multiply both sides by i so that $i^2 > 0$ or $-1 > 0$. But this is impossible. (3) If $i < 0$, what is the result?]

16–3 Complex roots of an equation. In an example of the preceding article the roots of the equation were the two conjugate imaginary numbers $2 + \sqrt{2}\, i$ and $2 - \sqrt{2}\, i$. In any polynomial equation with real coefficients, such roots always occur in pairs. This result may be stated as a fundamental theorem.

THEOREM 16–1. *If the complex number $a + bi$, $b \neq 0$, is a root of the polynomial equation*

$$f(x) = a_0 x^n + a_1 x^{n-1} + a_2 x^{n-2} + \cdots + a_{n-1}x + a_n = 0, \qquad (16\text{–}10)$$

where $a_0 \neq 0$, n is a positive integer, and a_i are real constants, then its conjugate $a - bi$ is also a root.

Proof. Since $a + bi$ is a root of $f(x) = 0$, $a + bi$ is a factor of $f(x)$. Let us divide $f(x)$ by the product $[x - (a + bi)][x - (a - bi)] \equiv x^2 - 2ax + a^2 + b^2$ until the remainder is of degree less than $x^2 - 2ax + a^2 + b^2$. The remainder will therefore be of the first degree at most. Symbolically, this can be expressed

$$\frac{f(x)}{x^2 - 2ax + a^2 + b^2} \equiv q(x) + \frac{Rx + S}{x^2 - 2ax + a^2 + b^2}, \qquad (16\text{–}11)$$

or

$$f(x) \equiv [x^2 - 2ax + a^2 + b^2]q(x) + Rx + S,$$

where R and S are real constants. Since this equality is true for all x, it is true for $x = a + bi$. Thus,

$$f(a + bi) = 0 \cdot q(a + bi) + R(a + bi) + S = 0.$$

Consequently, by the property stated in Problem 7,

$$Ra + S = 0 \quad \text{and} \quad Rbi = 0.$$

Since $b \neq 0$, $R = 0$, and therefore $S = 0$, which shows that the division in Eq. (16–11) is exact. Hence $a - bi$ is also a factor of $f(x)$; that is, $a - bi$ is a root of $f(x) = 0$.

As a result of the theorem, we note several properties of the roots of Eq. (16–10). (1) The imaginary roots of such an equation occur in pairs. (2) Any such equation has an even number of imaginary roots. (3) If the degree of such an equation is odd, the equation has at least one real root.

PROBLEMS

Find the third-degree equation with integral coefficients having the given numbers as roots.

1. $3, 2 - i$ 2. $-4, 6i$
3. $\frac{1}{2}, -5 + i$ 4. $\frac{3}{2}, i - 4$
5. $-\frac{1}{3}, 3 + \sqrt{2}\, i$ 6. $\frac{2}{3}, (-3 + \sqrt{5}\, i)/2$

Solve the following equations given the one root in parentheses. [*Hint:* Use division.]

7. $x^3 - 4x^2 + 9x - 36 = 0$, $(3i)$
8. $2x^3 + 9x^2 + 14x + 5 = 0$, $(-2 + i)$
9. $x^3 - 8x^2 + 23x - 22 = 0$, $(3 - \sqrt{2}\, i)$
10. $2x^3 - 8x^2 + 11x - 5 = 0$, $\frac{1}{2}(3 + i)$

16–4 Graphical representation of complex numbers. The interpretation of the ordered pair (x, y) as the complex number $x + yi$ lends itself to a simple graphical representation of the complex numbers. Since (x, y) may be plotted as a point in the rectangular coordinate system, every complex number $x + yi$ may be associated with some point in the plane, and every point in the plane with some complex number. This plane is called the *complex plane*, and the figure on which the complex numbers are plotted is called the *Argand diagram*.* The real numbers lie on the x-axis, the pure imaginaries on the y-axis, and a number such as $5 - 2i$ is represented by the point $(5, -2)$.

Any point $P(x, y)$ in the plane, other than $(0, 0)$, lies on some circle with center at $(0, 0)$ and radius r, where $r = \sqrt{x^2 + y^2}$. Let θ be the

---

* The system of representing complex numbers graphically was discovered independently by Wessel (Norwegian), Argand (French), and Gauss (German) about 1800.

FIGURE 16–1

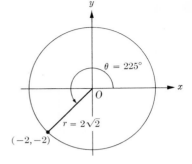

FIGURE 16–2

angle in standard position having OP as its terminal side (see Fig. 16–1), so that

$$x = r \cos \theta, \qquad y = r \sin \theta. \tag{16–12}$$

Thus the complex number, $x + yi$, may be written in trigonometric form,

$$x + yi = r\,(\cos \theta + i \sin \theta). \tag{16–13}*$$

Since $\sin \theta$ and $\cos \theta$ are both periodic with period $2\pi = 360°$, for $r > 0$ and any integer k,

$$r\,[\cos\,(\theta + k\,360°) + i \sin\,(\theta + k\,360°)]$$

is also a trigonometric form for $x + yi$. We note that r must be greater than zero. The value

$$r = \sqrt{x^2 + y^2} \tag{16–14}$$

is called the *absolute value* or *modulus* of $x + yi$. The angle θ is called the *amplitude* or *argument* of $x + yi$.

EXAMPLE 1. Express the complex number $-2 - 2i$ in trigonometric form.

Solution. By locating the point $(-2, -2)$ which corresponds to $-2 - 2i$ (see Fig. 16–2), we have

$$r = \sqrt{(-2)^2 + (-2)^2} = 2\sqrt{2}$$

---

* The form $r\,(\cos \theta + i \sin \theta)$ is sometimes abbreviated r cis θ.

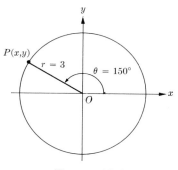

FIGURE 16–3

and $\tan \theta = 1$, with θ terminating in the third quadrant. Thus,

$$\theta = 225°, \quad \text{and} \quad -2 - 2i = 2\sqrt{2}\,(\cos 225° + i \sin 225°).$$

EXAMPLE 2. Express the complex number $3\,(\cos 150° + i \sin 150°)$ in the form $x + yi$.

Solution. On the terminal side of the angle of 150°, in standard position, locate the point P three units from the origin, as in Fig. 16–3. Since $P(x, y)$ represents the complex number, we have

$$x = 3 \cos 150° = \frac{-3\sqrt{3}}{2} \quad \text{and} \quad y = 3 \sin 150° = \frac{3}{2}.$$

Hence,

$$3\,(\cos 150° + i \sin 150°) = -\frac{3\sqrt{3}}{2} + \frac{3}{2}\, i.$$

One of the advantages of the trigonometric form for complex numbers is its usefulness in obtaining products. By letting $r_1\,(\cos \theta_1 + i \sin \theta_1)$ and $r_2\,(\cos \theta_2 + i \sin \theta_2)$ be two complex numbers, we have the following theorem.

THEOREM 16–2. *The modulus of the product of two complex numbers is the product of the moduli, and the amplitude is the sum of the amplitudes.*

Proof.

$$r_1\,(\cos \theta_1 + i \sin \theta_1) \cdot r_2\,(\cos \theta_2 + i \sin \theta_2)$$

$$= r_1 r_2\,(\cos \theta_1 \cos \theta_2 + i \cos \theta_1 \sin \theta_2 + i \sin \theta_1 \cos \theta_2$$
$$+ i^2 \sin \theta_1 \sin \theta_2)$$

$$= r_1 r_2\,[(\cos \theta_1 \cos \theta_2 - \sin \theta_1 \sin \theta_2)$$
$$+ i\,(\sin \theta_1 \cos \theta_2 + \cos \theta_1 \sin \theta_2)]$$

$$= r_1 r_2\,[\cos (\theta_1 + \theta_2) + i \sin (\theta_1 + \theta_2)]. \tag{16–15}$$

PROBLEMS

1. Locate the point representing graphically each of the following complex numbers. Give the trigonometric form for each, using the least positive or zero value of its amplitude.

(a) 2

(b) -2

(c) $3i$

(d) $-i$

(e) $2 - 2i$

(f) $-2 + 2i$

(g) $-\frac{1}{2} + \frac{\sqrt{3}}{2} i$

(h) $-\frac{1}{2} - \frac{\sqrt{3}}{2} i$

2. Express each of the following in the form $x + yi$.

(a) $3 (\cos 0° + i \sin 0°)$

(b) $2 (\cos 90° + i \sin 90°)$

(c) $\cos 180° + i \sin 180°$

(d) $2 (\cos 225° + i \sin 225°)$

(e) $2 (\cos 270° + i \sin 270°)$

(f) $8 (\cos 135° + i \sin 135°)$

(g) $4 (\cos 300° + i \sin 300°)$

(h) $6 (\cos 150° + i \sin 150°)$

3. Perform the indicated multiplications, expressing the final result in the form $x + yi$. Check your result by expressing each of the given numbers in the form $x + yi$ and then performing the multiplication algebraically.

(a) $3 (\cos 60° + i \sin 60°) \cdot 2 (\cos 30° + i \sin 30°)$

(b) $4 (\cos 120° + i \sin 120°) \cdot 2 (\cos 90° + i \sin 90°)$

(c) $3 (\cos 135° + i \sin 135°) \cdot 4 [\cos (-45°) + i \sin (-45°)]$

(d) $[2 (\cos 120° + i \sin 120°)]^3$

*4. Prove that the quotient of the two complex numbers $r_1 (\cos \theta_1 + i \sin \theta_1)$ and $r_2 (\cos \theta_2 + i \sin \theta_2)$ is given by

$$\frac{r_1}{r_2} [\cos (\theta_1 - \theta_2) + i \sin (\theta_1 - \theta_2)]. \tag{16–16}$$

5. Use Eq. (16–16) to perform the following divisions. Check as in Problem 3.

(a) $4 (\cos 60° + i \sin 60°) \div 2 (\cos 30° + i \sin 30°)$

(b) $6 (\cos 0° + i \sin 0°) \div 3 (\cos 240° + i \sin 240°)$

6. Prove that the reciprocal of $r (\cos \theta + i \sin \theta)$ is

$$\frac{1}{r} (\cos \theta - i \sin \theta).$$

7. Prove that $[r (\cos \theta + i \sin \theta)]^2 = r^2 (\cos 2\theta + i \sin 2\theta)$.

8. In considering Eq. (16–12), we recall a similar formula, Eq. (15–15). These are indeed the same if, in the ordered pairs considered in this chapter, the x and y are thought of as representing the x- and y-components of a vector from the origin to the point (x, y). The algebra of ordered pairs may be interpreted as a study of vectors in the plane. By plotting the following number pairs with their sum and drawing the appropriate vectors, show that the parallelogram law for the sum of two vectors is satisfied (see last paragraph in Article 15–5).

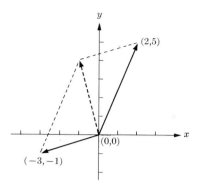

FIGURE 16–4

(a) $(2, 5) + (-3, -1) =$ [*Hint:* See Fig. 16–4.]
(b) $(-1, 2) + (4, -5) =$
(c) $(3, -2) + (-2, 3) =$
(d) $(-3, -2) + (6, 4) =$

Although C is not an ordered field, the modulus or absolute value of any complex number is real, and in fact positive, so that certain interesting inequalities result. In order to show these, we must also examine the relation between complex numbers and their conjugates. The following problems apply to this study and lead to the results stated in Problems 17 and 18. In the problems, we shall denote any complex number $x + iy$ by z and its conjugate $x - iy$ by $\bar{z}$. Recall that $|z| = |x + iy| = \sqrt{x^2 + y^2}$ (Eq. 16–14).

9. Show that the definition of absolute value of any complex number $z = x + iy$ is consistent with the previous definition of absolute value for real numbers.

10. Show that $|z| = |\bar{z}|$.

11. Show that the conjugate of the conjugate of a complex number is the number itself, that is, $\bar{\bar{z}} = z$.

12. Show that $z \cdot \bar{z} = |z|^2$.

13. Show that the sum of the conjugate of two complex numbers is the conjugate of their sum, that is, $\bar{z}_1 + \bar{z}_2 = \overline{z_1 + z_2}$.

14. Show that the product of the conjugate of two complex numbers is the conjugate of their product, that is, $\bar{z}_1 \cdot \bar{z}_2 = \overline{z_1 \cdot z_2}$.

15. For any complex number $z = x + iy$, show that $x \leq |z|$ and $y \leq |z|$.

16. For any complex number $z = x + iy$, show that $z + \bar{z} = 2x$.

17. Show that for any two complex numbers, the absolute value of the product is the product of the absolute values, that is, $|z_1 \cdot z_2| = |z_1| \cdot |z_2|$. [*Hint:* By using Problem 12, we have $|z_1 \cdot z_2|^2 = (z_1 \cdot z_2)(\overline{z_1 \cdot z_2})$. But $\overline{z_1 \cdot z_2} = \bar{z}_1 \cdot \bar{z}_2$ by Problem 14, so that $|z_1 \cdot z_2|^2 = z_1 \cdot \bar{z}_1 \cdot z_2 \cdot \bar{z}_2 = |z_1|^2 \cdot |z_2|^2$.]

18. It is possible to show that for any two complex numbers, the absolute value of their sum is less than or equal to the sum of their absolute values, that

is, $|z_1 + z_2| \leq |z_1| + |z_2|$. Give the reasons for each step in the following proof.

$$|z_1 + z_2|^2 = (z_1 + z_2)(\overline{z_1 + z_2}) = (z_1 + z_2)(\bar{z}_1 + \bar{z}_2)$$
$$= z_1\bar{z}_1 + z_2\bar{z}_1 + z_1\bar{z}_2 + z_2\bar{z}_2.$$

Now $z_1\bar{z}_2$ and $z_2\bar{z}_1$ are conjugates, so that

$$z_1\bar{z}_2 + z_2\bar{z}_1 = 2 \text{ (real part of } z_1\bar{z}_2)$$
$$\leq 2|z_1 \cdot \bar{z}_2|$$
$$= 2|z_1| \cdot |\bar{z}_2|$$
$$= 2|z_1| \cdot |z_2|.$$

Therefore, we have

$$|z_1 + z_2|^2 \leq z_1\bar{z}_1 + 2|z_1| \cdot |z_2| + z_2\bar{z}_2$$
$$= |z_1|^2 + 2|z_1| \cdot |z_2| + |z_2|^2 = (|z_1| + |z_2|)^2,$$

so that $|z_1 + z_2| \leq |z_1| + |z_2|$.

16–5 Powers and roots of complex numbers. In Article 16–4, we obtained an expression for the product of two complex numbers in trigonometric form. By using Eq. (16–15), we immediately have

$$[r \,(\cos \theta + i \sin \theta)]^2 = r^2 \,(\cos 2\theta + i \sin 2\theta),$$

and then,

$$[r \,(\cos \theta + i \sin \theta)]^3 = r^3 \,(\cos 3\theta + i \sin 3\theta).$$

In fact, we can prove by mathematical induction a general theorem known as De Moivre's Theorem, discovered by Abraham De Moivre (1667–1754).

THEOREM 16–3. *If n is any positive integer,*

$$\boxed{[r \,(\cos \theta + i \sin \theta)]^n = r^n \,(\cos n\theta + i \sin n\theta).}\qquad (16\text{–}17)$$

This theorem holds for rational, irrational, and even complex values of the exponent, but we shall make use of it only with integral values.

Proof. Part (a). Verification. This has been done at the beginning of this article.

Part (b). Assuming

$$[r \,(\cos \theta + i \sin \theta)]^k = r^k \,(\cos k\theta + i \sin k\theta),\qquad (16\text{–}18)$$

we must show

$$[r \,(\cos \theta + i \sin \theta)]^{k+1} = r^{k+1} \,[\cos (k + 1)\theta + i \sin (k + 1)\theta].\qquad (16\text{–}19)$$

Multiplying each member of Eq. (16–18) by $r (\cos \theta + i \sin \theta)$, we have

$$[r (\cos \theta + i \sin \theta)]^{k+1} = r^k (\cos k\theta + i \sin k\theta) r (\cos \theta + i \sin \theta),$$

and by Eq. (16–15),

$$[r (\cos \theta + i \sin \theta)]^{k+1} = r^{k+1} [\cos (k\theta + \theta) + i \sin (k\theta + \theta)]$$
$$= r^{k+1} [\cos (k + 1)\theta + i \sin (k + 1)\theta],$$

which is exactly Eq. (16–19).

Part (c) follows immediately.

EXAMPLE 1. Show that $z^3 = 1$ if $z = -\frac{1}{2} + (\sqrt{3}/2)i$.

Solution. Putting z in trigonometric form, we have

$$z = \cos 120° + i \sin 120°.$$

Thus,

$$z^3 = (\cos 120° + i \sin 120°)^3$$
$$= \cos 3(120°) + i \sin 3(120°)$$
$$= \cos 360° + i \sin 360° = 1.$$

A more important use of Eq. (16–17) is made in finding the roots of complex numbers. In our discussion we should recall that for r positive the notation $\sqrt[n]{r}$ represents the principal nth root of r, that is, the only nth root of r which is positive and real.

EXAMPLE 2. Find the three cube roots of $-2 - 2\sqrt{3}\, i$.

Solution. We wish to find values of r and θ such that

$$[r (\cos \theta + i \sin \theta)]^3 = -2 - 2\sqrt{3}\, i.$$

If we use Theorem 16–3, and express $-2 - 2\sqrt{3}\, i$ in trigonometric form, this becomes

$$r^3 (\cos 3\theta + i \sin 3\theta) = 4 (\cos 240° + i \sin 240°).$$

When two complex numbers are equal, their moduli are equal and their amplitudes are either equal or differ by integral multiples of 360°. Thus,

$$r^3 = 4 \qquad \text{and} \qquad 3\theta = 240° + k\,360°,$$

or

$$r = \sqrt[3]{4} \qquad \text{and} \qquad \theta = 80° + k\,120°,$$

where k is any positive or negative integer, or zero. Hence,

$$r (\cos \theta + i \sin \theta)$$

will be

$$\sqrt[3]{4} \,(\cos\ 80° + i\sin\ 80°), \qquad \text{for} \quad k = 0,$$
$$\sqrt[3]{4} \,(\cos 200° + i\sin 200°), \qquad \text{for} \quad k = 1,$$
$$\sqrt[3]{4} \,(\cos 320° + i\sin 320°), \qquad \text{for} \quad k = 2.$$

These three values are all distinct, and they represent the three different cube roots of $-2 - 2\sqrt{3}\,i$. For any other integral value of k, the expression will reduce to one of these three values, so that these three numbers are the only cube roots. A complex number has three and only three cube roots, four and only four fourth roots, and in general, n and only n nth roots. Should it be required to reduce our answers to the form $x + yi$, we can use tables to find $\sqrt[3]{4}$ and the values of the functions of $80°$, $200°$, and $320°$.

The general theorem concerning such roots should now be apparent.

THEOREM 16–4. *For any complex number* $r\,(\cos\theta + i\sin\theta)$ *and any positive integer* n,

$$\sqrt[n]{r}\,(\cos\theta_k + i\sin\theta_k), \tag{16–20}$$

where

$$\theta_k = \frac{\theta + k360°}{n}, \qquad k = 0, 1, 2, \ldots (n-1),$$

represents the n distinct nth roots of $r\,(\cos\theta + i\sin\theta)$.

Proof. To show that Eq. (16–20) is an nth root of $r\,(\cos\theta + i\sin\theta)$ for each k, we merely use Eq. (16–17) to raise it to the nth power:

$$[\sqrt[n]{r}\,(\cos\theta_k + i\sin\theta_k)]^n = r\,(\cos n\theta_k + i\sin n\theta_k)$$
$$= r\,[\cos(\theta + k360°) + i\sin(\theta + k360°)]$$
$$= r\,(\cos\theta + i\sin\theta).$$

Also, we must note that the n complex numbers given by Eq. (16–20) for the n different values of k are distinct, since no two of their amplitudes differ by a multiple of $360°$.

The use of Eq. (16–20) will enable us to find the n nth roots of any complex number directly by substitution.

PROBLEMS

Write each of the expressions in Problems 1 through 7 in the form $x + yi$.

1. $[2\,(\cos 15° + i\sin 15°)]^6$ 2. $[3\,(\cos 120° + i\sin 120°)]^5$

3. $[2\,(\cos 315° + i\sin 315°)]^3$ 4. $(\cos 36° + i\sin 36°)^{10}$

5. $\left(-\dfrac{\sqrt{3}}{2} + \dfrac{i}{2}\right)^5$ 6. $(1 - i)^8$ 7. $\left(\dfrac{1}{\sqrt{2}} + \dfrac{i}{\sqrt{2}}\right)^{200}$

Find and represent graphically the required roots in Problems 8 through 15.

8. The square roots of $4 + 4\sqrt{3}\,i$ 9. The square roots of $-16i$

10. The cube roots of 1   11. The cube roots of -8

12. The fourth roots of $4 - 4\sqrt{3}\,i$

13. The fourth roots of 16 $(\cos 120° + i \sin 120°)$

14. The cube roots of 8 $(\cos 300° + i \sin 300°)$

15. The tenth roots of 1. Compare the figure with Fig. 6–14.

Solve the equations in Problems 16 through 19, expressing the roots in the form $x + yi$, and represent them graphically.

16. $z^6 = 64$ 17. $z^4 = 1$

18. $z^3 + i = 0$ 19. $z^5 + 32 = 0$

Degrees	Radians	Sine	Tangent	Cotangent	Cosine		
0° 00′	.0000	.0000	.0000		1.0000	1.5708	90° 00′
10′	.0029	.0029	.0029	343.77	1.0000	1.5679	50′
20′	.0058	.0058	.0058	171.89	1.0000	1.5650	40′
30′	.0087	.0087	.0087	114.59	1.0000	1.5621	30′
40′	.0116	.0116	.0116	85.940	.9999	1.5592	20′
50′	.0145	.0145	.0145	68.750	.9999	1.5563	10′
1° 00′	.0175	.0175	.0175	57.290	.9998	1.5533	89° 00′
10′	.0204	.0204	.0204	49.104	.9998	1.5504	50′
20′	.0233	.0233	.0233	42.964	.9997	1.5475	40′
30′	.0262	.0262	.0262	38.188	.9997	1.5446	30′
40′	.0291	.0291	.0291	34.368	.9996	1.5417	20′
50′	.0320	.0320	.0320	31.242	.9995	1.5388	10′
2° 00′	.0349	.0349	.0349	28.636	.9994	1.5359	88° 00′
10′	.0378	.0378	.0378	26.432	.9993	1.5330	50′
20′	.0407	.0407	.0407	24.542	.9992	1.5301	40′
30′	.0436	.0436	.0437	22.904	.9990	1.5272	30′
40′	.0465	.0465	.0466	21.470	.9989	1.5243	20′
50′	.0495	.0494	.0495	20.206	.9988	1.5213	10′
3° 00′	.0524	.0523	.0524	19.081	.9986	1.5184	87° 00′
10′	.0553	.0552	.0553	18.075	.9985	1.5155	50′
20′	.0582	.0581	.0582	17.169	.9983	1.5126	40′
30′	.0611	.0610	.0612	16.350	.9981	1.5097	30′
40′	.0640	.0640	.0641	15.605	.9980	1.5068	20′
50′	.0669	.0669	.0670	14.924	.9978	1.5039	10′
4° 00′	.0698	.0698	.0699	14.301	.9976	1.5010	86° 00′
10′	.0727	.0727	.0729	13.727	.9974	1.4981	50′
20′	.0756	.0756	.0758	13.197	.9971	1.4952	40′
30′	.0785	.0785	.0787	12.706	.9969	1.4923	30′
40′	.0814	.0814	.0816	12.251	.9967	1.4893	20′
50′	.0844	.0843	.0846	11.826	.9964	1.4864	10′
5° 00′	.0873	.0872	.0875	11.430	.9962	1.4835	85° 00′
10′	.0902	.0901	.0904	11.059	.9959	1.4806	50′
20′	.0931	.0929	.0934	10.712	.9957	1.4777	40′
30′	.0960	.0958	.0963	10.385	.9954	1.4748	30′
40′	.0989	.0987	.0992	10.078	.9951	1.4719	20′
50′	.1018	.1016	.1022	9.7882	.9948	1.4690	10′
6° 00′	.1047	.1045	.1051	9.5144	.9945	1.4661	84° 00′
10′	.1076	.1074	.1080	9.2553	.9942	1.4632	50′
20′	.1105	.1103	.1110	9.0098	.9939	1.4603	40′
30′	.1134	.1132	.1139	8.7769	.9936	1.4573	30′
40′	.1164	.1161	.1169	8.5555	.9932	1.4544	20′
50′	.1193	.1190	.1198	8.3450	.9929	1.4515	10′
7° 00′	.1222	.1219	.1228	8.1443	.9925	1.4486	83° 00′
10′	.1251	.1248	.1257	7.9530	.9922	1.4457	50′
20′	.1280	.1276	.1287	7.7704	.9918	1.4428	40′
30′	.1309	.1305	.1317	7.5958	.9914	1.4399	30′
40′	.1338	.1334	.1346	7.4287	.9911	1.4370	20′
50′	.1367	.1363	.1376	7.2687	.9907	1.4341	10′
8° 00′	.1396	.1392	.1405	7.1154	.9903	1.4312	82° 00′
10′	.1425	.1421	.1435	6.9682	.9899	1.4283	50′
20′	.1454	.1449	.1465	6.8269	.9894	1.4254	40′
30′	.1484	.1478	.1495	6.6912	.9890	1.4224	30′
40′	.1513	.1507	.1524	6.5606	.9886	1.4195	20′
50′	.1542	.1536	.1554	6.4348	.9881	1.4166	10′
9° 00′	.1571	.1564	.1584	6.3138	.9877	1.4137	81° 00′
		Cosine	Cotangent	Tangent	Sine	Radians	Degrees

TABLE I. VALUES OF TRIGONOMETRIC FUNCTIONS (*cont.*) 339

Degrees	Radians	Sine	Tangent	Cotangent	Cosine		
9° 00′	.1571	.1564	.1584	6.3138	.9877	1.4137	81° 00′
10′	.1600	.1593	.1614	6.1970	.9872	1.4108	50′
20′	.1629	.1622	.1644	6.0844	.9868	1.4079	40′
30′	.1658	.1650	.1673	5.9758	.9863	1.4050	30′
40′	.1687	.1679	.1703	5.8708	.9858	1.4021	20′
50′	.1716	.1708	.1733	5.7694	.9853	1.3992	10′
10° 00′	.1745	.1736	.1763	5.6713	.9848	1.3963	80° 00′
10′	.1774	.1765	.1793	5.5764	.9843	1.3934	50′
20′	.1804	.1794	.1823	5.4845	.9838	1.3904	40′
30′	.1833	.1822	.1853	5.3955	.9833	1.3875	30′
40′	.1862	.1851	.1883	5.3093	.9827	1.3846	20′
50′	.1891	.1880	.1914	5.2257	.9822	1.3817	10′
11° 00′	.1920	.1908	.1944	5.1446	.9816	1.3788	79° 00′
10′	.1949	.1937	.1974	5.0658	.9811	1.3759	50′
20′	.1978	.1965	.2004	4.9894	.9805	1.3730	40′
30′	.2007	.1994	.2035	4.9152	.9799	1.3701	30′
40′	.2036	.2022	.2065	4.8430	.9793	1.3672	20′
50′	.2065	.2051	.2095	4.7729	.9787	1.3643	10′
12° 00′	.2094	.2079	.2126	4.7046	.9781	1.3614	78° 00′
10′	.2123	.2108	.2156	4.6382	.9775	1.3584	50′
20′	.2153	.2136	.2186	4.5736	.9769	1.3555	40′
30′	.2182	.2164	.2217	4.5107	.9763	1.3526	30′
40′	.2211	.2193	.2247	4.4494	.9757	1.3497	20′
50′	.2240	.2221	.2278	4.3897	.9750	1.3468	10′
13° 00′	.2269	.2250	.2309	4.3315	.9744	1.3439	77° 00′
10′	.2298	.2278	.2339	4.2747	.9737	1.3410	50′
20′	.2327	.2306	.2370	4.2193	.9730	1.3381	40′
30′	.2356	.2334	.2401	4.1653	.9724	1.3352	30′
40′	.2385	.2363	.2432	4.1126	.9717	1.3323	20′
50′	.2414	.2391	.2462	4.0611	.9710	1.3294	10′
14° 00′	.2443	.2419	.2493	4.0108	.9703	1.3265	76° 00′
10′	.2473	.2447	.2524	3.9617	.9696	1.3235	50′
20′	.2502	.2476	.2555	3.9136	.9689	1.3206	40′
30′	.2531	.2504	.2586	3.8667	.9681	1.3177	30′
40′	.2560	.2532	.2617	3.8208	.9674	1.3148	20′
50′	.2589	.2560	.2648	3.7760	.9667	1.3119	10′
15° 00′	.2618	.2588	.2679	3.7321	.9659	1.3090	75° 00′
10′	.2647	.2616	.2711	3.6891	.9652	1.3061	50′
20′	.2676	.2644	.2742	3.6470	.9644	1.3032	40′
30′	.2705	.2672	.2773	3.6059	.9636	1.3003	30′
40′	.2734	.2700	.2805	3.5656	.9628	1.2974	20′
50′	.2763	.2728	.2836	3.5261	.9621	1.2945	10′
16° 00′	.2793	.2756	.2867	3.4874	.9613	1.2915	74° 00′
10′	.2822	.2784	.2899	3.4495	.9605	1.2886	50′
20′	.2851	.2812	.2931	3.4124	.9596	1.2857	40′
30′	.2880	.2840	.2962	3.3759	.9588	1.2828	30′
40′	.2909	.2868	.2994	3.3402	.9580	1.2799	20′
50′	.2938	.2896	.3026	3.3052	.9572	1.2770	10′
17° 00′	.2967	.2924	.3057	3.2709	.9563	1.2741	73° 00′
10′	.2996	.2952	.3089	3.2371	.9555	1.2712	50′
20′	.3025	.2979	.3121	3.2041	.9546	1.2683	40′
30′	.3054	.3007	.3153	3.1716	.9537	1.2654	30′
40′	.3083	.3035	.3185	3.1397	.9528	1.2625	20′
50′	.3113	.3062	.3217	3.1084	.9520	1.2595	10′
18° 00′	.3142	.3090	.3249	3.0777	.9511	1.2566	72° 00′
		Cosine	Cotangent	Tangent	Sine	Radians	Degrees

Degrees	Radians	Sine	Tangent	Cotangent	Cosine		
18° 00′	.3142	.3090	.3249	3.0777	.9511	1.2566	72° 00′
10′	.3171	.3118	.3281	3.0475	.9502	1.2537	50′
20′	.3200	.3145	.3314	3.0178	.9492	1.2508	40′
30′	.3229	.3173	.3346	2.9887	.9483	1.2479	30′
40′	.3258	.3201	.3378	2.9600	.9474	1.2450	20′
50′	.3287	.3228	.3411	2.9319	.9465	1.2421	10′
19° 00′	.3316	.3256	.3443	2.9042	.9455	1.2392	71° 00′
10′	.3345	.3283	.3476	2.8770	.9446	1.2363	50′
20′	.3374	.3311	.3508	2.8502	.9436	1.2334	40′
30′	.3403	.3338	.3541	2.8239	.9426	1.2305	30′
40′	.3432	.3365	.3574	2.7980	.9417	1.2275	20′
50′	.3462	.3393	.3607	2.7725	.9407	1.2246	10′
20° 00′	.3491	.3420	.3640	2.7475	.9397	1.2217	70° 00′
10′	.3520	.3448	.3673	2.7228	.9387	1.2188	50′
20′	.3549	.3475	.3706	2.6985	.9377	1.2159	40′
30′	.3578	.3502	.3739	2.6746	.9367	1.2130	30′
40′	.3607	.3529	.3772	2.6511	.9356	1.2101	20′
50′	.3636	.3557	.3805	2.6279	.9346	1.2072	10′
21° 00′	.3665	.3584	.3839	2.6051	.9336	1.2043	69° 00′
10′	.3694	.3611	.3872	2.5826	.9325	1.2014	50′
20′	.3723	.3638	.3906	2.5605	.9315	1.1985	40′
30′	.3752	.3665	.3939	2.5386	.9304	1.1956	30′
40′	.3782	.3692	.3973	2.5172	.9293	1.1926	20′
50′	.3811	.3719	.4006	2.4960	.9283	1.1897	10′
22° 00′	.3840	.3746	.4040	2.4751	.9272	1.1868	68° 00′
10′	.3869	.3773	.4074	2.4545	.9261	1.1839	50′
20′	.3898	.3800	.4108	2.4342	.9250	1.1810	40′
30′	.3927	.3827	.4142	2.4142	.9239	1.1781	30′
40′	.3956	.3854	.4176	2.3945	.9228	1.1752	20′
50′	.3985	.3881	.4210	2.3750	.9216	1.1723	10′
23° 00′	.4014	.3907	.4245	2.3559	.9205	1.1694	67° 00′
10′	.4043	.3934	.4279	2.3369	.9194	1.1665	50′
20′	.4072	.3961	.4314	2.3183	.9182	1.1636	40′
30′	.4102	.3987	.4348	2.2998	.9171	1.1606	30′
40′	.4131	.4014	.4383	2.2817	.9159	1.1577	20′
50′	.4160	.4041	.4417	2.2637	.9147	1.1548	10′
24° 00′	.4189	.4067	.4452	2.2460	.9135	1.1519	66° 00′
10′	.4218	.4094	.4487	2.2286	.9124	1.1490	50′
20′	.4247	.4120	.4522	2.2113	.9112	1.1461	40′
30′	.4276	.4147	.4557	2.1943	.9100	1.1432	30′
40′	.4305	.4173	.4592	2.1775	.9088	1.1403	20′
50′	.4334	.4200	.4628	2.1609	.9075	1.1374	10′
25° 00′	.4363	.4226	.4663	2.1445	.9063	1.1345	65° 00′
10′	.4392	.4253	.4699	2.1283	.9051	1.1316	50′
20′	.4422	.4279	.4734	2.1123	.9038	1.1286	40′
30′	.4451	.4305	.4770	2.0965	.9026	1.1257	30′
40′	.4480	.4331	.4806	2.0809	.9013	1.1228	20′
50′	.4509	.4358	.4841	2.0655	.9001	1.1199	10′
26° 00′	.4538	.4384	.4877	2.0503	.8988	1.1170	64° 00′
10′	.4567	.4410	.4913	2.0353	.8975	1.1141	50′
20′	.4596	.4436	.4950	2.0204	.8962	1.1112	40′
30′	.4625	.4462	.4986	2.0057	.8949	1.1083	30′
40′	.4654	.4488	.5022	1.9912	.8936	1.1054	20′
50′	.4683	.4514	.5059	1.9768	.8923	1.1025	10′
27° 00′	.4712	.4540	.5095	1.9626	.8910	1.0996	63° 00′
		Cosine	Cotangent	Tangent	Sine	Radians	Degrees

TABLE I. VALUES OF TRIGONOMETRIC FUNCTIONS (*cont.*)   341

Degrees	Radians	Sine	Tangent	Cotangent	Cosine		
27° 00′	.4712	.4540	.5095	1.9626	.8910	1.0996	63° 00′
10′	.4741	.4566	.5132	1.9486	.8897	1.0966	50′
20′	.4771	.4592	.5169	1.9347	.8884	1.0937	40′
30′	.4800	.4617	.5206	1.9210	.8870	1.0908	30′
40′	.4829	.4643	.5243	1.9074	.8857	1.0879	20′
50′	.4858	.4669	.5280	1.8940	.8843	1.0850	10′
28° 00′	.4887	.4695	.5317	1.8807	.8829	1.0821	62° 00′
10′	.4916	.4720	.5354	1.8676	.8816	1.0792	50′
20′	.4945	.4746	.5392	1.8546	.8802	1.0763	40′
30′	.4974	.4772	.5430	1.8418	.8788	1.0734	30′
40′	.5003	.4797	.5467	1.8291	.8774	1.0705	20′
50′	.5032	.4823	.5505	1.8165	.8760	1.0676	10′
29° 00′	.5061	.4848	.5543	1.8040	.8746	1.0647	61° 00′
10′	.5091	.4874	.5581	1.7917	.8732	1.0617	50′
20′	.5120	.4899	.5619	1.7796	.8718	1.0588	40′
30′	.5149	.4924	.5658	1.7675	.8704	1.0559	30′
40′	.5178	.4950	.5696	1.7556	.8689	1.0530	20′
50′	.5207	.4975	.5735	1.7437	.8675	1.0501	10′
30° 00′	.5236	.5000	.5774	1.7321	.8660	1.0472	60° 00′
10′	.5265	.5025	.5812	1.7205	.8646	1.0443	50′
20′	.5294	.5050	.5851	1.7090	.8631	1.0414	40′
30′	.5323	.5075	.5890	1.6977	.8616	1.0385	30′
40′	.5352	.5100	.5930	1.6864	.8601	1.0356	20′
50′	.5381	.5125	.5969	1.6753	.8587	1.0327	10′
31° 00′	.5411	.5150	.6009	1.6643	.8572	1.0297	59° 00′
10′	.5440	.5175	.6048	1.6534	.8557	1.0268	50′
20′	.5469	.5200	.6088	1.6426	.8542	1.0239	40′
30′	.5498	.5225	.6128	1.6319	.8526	1.0210	30′
40′	.5527	.5250	.6168	1.6212	.8511	1.0181	20′
50′	.5556	.5275	.6208	1.6107	.8496	1.0152	10′
32° 00′	.5585	.5299	.6249	1.6003	.8480	1.0123	58° 00′
10′	.5614	.5324	.6289	1.5900	.8465	1.0094	50′
20′	.5643	.5348	.6330	1.5798	.8450	1.0065	40′
30′	.5672	.5373	.6371	1.5697	.8434	1.0036	30′
40′	.5701	.5398	.6412	1.5597	.8418	1.0007	20′
50′	.5730	.5422	.6453	1.5497	.8403	.9977	10′
33° 00′	.5760	.5446	.6494	1.5399	.8387	.9948	57° 00′
10′	.5789	.5471	.6536	1.5301	.8371	.9919	50′
20′	.5818	.5495	.6577	1.5204	.8355	.9890	40′
30′	.5847	.5519	.6619	1.5108	.8339	.9861	30′
40′	.5876	.5544	.6661	1.5013	.8323	.9832	20′
50′	.5905	.5568	.6703	1.4919	.8307	.9803	10′
34° 00′	.5934	.5592	.6745	1.4826	.8290	.9774	56° 00′
10′	.5963	.5616	.6787	1.4733	.8274	.9745	50′
20′	.5992	.5640	.6830	1.4641	.8258	.9716	40′
30′	.6021	.5664	.6873	1.4550	.8241	.9687	30′
40′	.6050	.5688	.6916	1.4460	.8225	.9657	20′
50′	.6080	.5712	.6959	1.4370	.8208	.9628	10′
35° 00′	.6109	.5736	.7002	1.4281	.8192	.9599	55° 00′
10′	.6138	.5760	.7046	1.4193	.8175	.9570	50′
20′	.6167	.5783	.7089	1.4106	.8158	.9541	40′
30′	.6196	.5807	.7133	1.4019	.8141	.9512	30′
40′	.6225	.5831	.7177	1.3934	.8124	.9483	20′
50′	.6254	.5854	.7221	1.3848	.8107	.9454	10′
36° 00′	.6283	.5878	.7265	1.3764	.8090	.9425	54° 00′
		Cosine	Cotangent	Tangent	Sine	Radians	Degrees

Degrees	Radians	Sine	Tangent	Cotangent	Cosine		
36° 00′	.6283	.5878	.7265	1.3764	.8090	.9425	**54° 00′**
10′	.6312	.5901	.7310	1.3680	.8073	.9396	50′
20′	.6341	.5925	.7355	1.3597	.8056	.9367	40′
30′	.6370	.5948	.7400	1.3514	.8039	.9338	30′
40′	.6400	.5972	.7445	1.3432	.8021	.9308	20′
50′	.6429	.5995	.7490	1.3351	.8004	.9279	10′
37° 00′	.6458	.6018	.7536	1.3270	.7986	.9250	**53° 00′**
10′	.6487	.6041	.7581	1.3190	.7969	.9221	50′
20′	.6516	.6065	.7627	1.3111	.7951	.9192	40′
30′	.6545	.6088	.7673	1.3032	.7934	.9163	30′
40′	.6574	.6111	.7720	1.2954	.7916	.9134	20′
50′	.6603	.6134	.7766	1.2876	.7898	.9105	10′
38° 00′	.6632	.6157	.7813	1.2799	.7880	.9076	**52° 00′**
10′	.6661	.6180	.7860	1.2723	.7862	.9047	50′
20′	.6690	.6202	.7907	1.2647	.7844	.9018	40′
30′	.6720	.6225	.7954	1.2572	.7826	.8988	30′
40′	.6749	.6248	.8002	1.2497	.7808	.8959	20′
50′	.6778	.6271	.8050	1.2423	.7790	.8930	10′
39° 00′	.6807	.6293	.8098	1.2349	.7771	.8901	**51° 00′**
10′	.6836	.6316	.8146	1.2276	.7753	.8872	50′
20′	.6865	.6338	.8195	1.2203	.7735	.8843	40′
30′	.6894	.6361	.8243	1.2131	.7716	.8814	30′
40′	.6923	.6383	.8292	1.2059	.7698	.8785	20′
50′	.6952	.6406	.8342	1.1988	.7679	.8756	10′
40° 00′	.6981	.6428	.8391	1.1918	.7660	.8727	**50° 00′**
10′	.7010	.6450	.8441	1.1847	.7642	.8698	50′
20′	.7039	.6472	.8491	1.1778	.7623	.8668	40′
30′	.7069	.6494	.8541	1.1708	.7604	.8639	30′
40′	.7098	.6517	.8591	1.1640	.7585	.8610	20′
50′	.7127	.6539	.8642	1.1571	.7566	.8581	10′
41° 00′	.7156	.6561	.8693	1.1504	.7547	.8552	**49° 00′**
10′	.7185	.6583	.8744	1.1436	.7528	.8523	50′
20′	.7214	.6604	.8796	1.1369	.7509	.8494	40′
30′	.7243	.6626	.8847	1.1303	.7490	.8465	30′
40′	.7272	.6648	.8899	1.1237	.7470	.8436	20′
50′	.7301	.6670	.8952	1.1171	.7451	.8407	10′
42° 00′	.7330	.6691	.9004	1.1106	.7431	.8378	**48° 00′**
10′	.7359	.6713	.9057	1.1041	.7412	.8348	50′
20′	.7389	.6734	.9110	1.0977	.7392	.8319	40′
30′	.7418	.6756	.9163	1.0913	.7373	.8290	30′
40′	.7447	.6777	.9217	1.0850	.7353	.8261	20′
50′	.7476	.6799	.9271	1.0786	.7333	.8232	10′
43° 00′	.7505	.6820	.9325	1.0724	.7314	.8203	**47° 00′**
10′	.7534	.6841	.9380	1.0661	.7294	.8174	50′
20′	.7563	.6862	.9435	1.0599	.7274	.8145	40′
30′	.7592	.6884	.9490	1.0538	.7254	.8116	30′
40′	.7621	.6905	.9545	1.0477	.7234	.8087	20′
50′	.7650	.6926	.9601	1.0416	.7214	.8058	10′
44° 00′	.7679	.6947	.9657	1.0355	.7193	.8029	**46° 00′**
10′	.7709	.6967	.9713	1.0295	.7173	.7999	50′
20′	.7738	.6988	.9770	1.0235	.7153	.7970	40′
30′	.7767	.7009	.9827	1.0176	.7133	.7941	30′
40′	.7796	.7030	.9884	1.0117	.7112	.7912	20′
50′	.7825	.7050	.9942	1.0058	.7092	.7883	10′
45° 00′	.7854	.7071	1.0000	1.0000	.7071	.7854	**45° 00′**
		Cosine	Cotangent	Tangent	Sine	Radians	Degrees

TABLE II. LOGARITHMS OF NUMBERS 343

N	0	1	2	3	4	5	6	7	8	9
1.0	.0000	.0043	.0086	.0128	.0170	.0212	.0253	.0294	.0334	.0374
1.1	.0414	.0453	.0492	.0531	.0569	.0607	.0645	.0682	.0719	.0755
1.2	.0792	.0828	.0864	.0899	.0934	.0969	.1004	.1038	.1072	.1106
1.3	.1139	.1173	.1206	.1239	.1271	.1303	.1335	.1367	.1399	.1430
1.4	.1461	.1492	.1523	.1553	.1584	.1614	.1644	.1673	.1703	.1732
1.5	.1761	.1790	.1818	.1847	.1875	.1903	.1931	.1959	.1987	.2014
1.6	.2041	.2068	.2095	.2122	.2148	.2175	.2201	.2227	.2253	.2279
1.7	.2304	.2330	.2355	.2380	.2405	.2430	.2455	.2480	.2504	.2529
1.8	.2553	.2577	.2601	.2625	.2648	.2672	.2695	.2718	.2742	.2765
1.9	.2788	.2810	.2833	.2856	.2878	.2900	.2923	.2945	.2967	.2989
2.0	.3010	.3032	.3054	.3075	.3096	.3118	.3139	.3160	.3181	.3201
2.1	.3222	.3243	.3263	.3284	.3304	.3324	.3345	.3365	.3385	.3404
2.2	.3424	.3444	.3464	.3483	.3502	.3522	.3541	.3560	.3579	.3598
2.3	.3617	.3636	.3655	.3674	.3692	.3711	.3729	.3747	.3766	.3784
2.4	.3802	.3820	.3838	.3856	.3874	.3892	.3909	.3927	.3945	.3962
2.5	.3979	.3997	.4014	.4031	.4048	.4065	.4082	.4099	.4116	.4133
2.6	.4150	.4166	.4183	.4200	.4216	.4232	.4249	.4265	.4281	.4298
2.7	.4314	.4330	.4346	.4362	.4378	.4393	.4409	.4425	.4440	.4456
2.8	.4472	.4487	.4502	.4518	.4533	.4548	.4564	.4579	.4594	.4609
2.9	.4624	.4639	.4654	.4669	.4683	.4698	.4713	.4728	.4742	.4757
3.0	.4771	.4786	.4800	.4814	.4829	.4843	.4857	.4871	.4886	.4900
3.1	.4914	.4928	.4942	.4955	.4969	.4983	.4997	.5011	.5024	.5038
3.2	.5051	.5065	.5079	.5092	.5105	.5119	.5132	.5145	.5159	.5172
3.3	.5185	.5198	.5211	.5224	.5237	.5250	.5263	.5276	.5289	.5302
3.4	.5315	.5328	.5340	.5353	.5366	.5378	.5391	.5403	.5416	.5428
3.5	.5441	.5453	.5465	.5478	.5490	.5502	.5514	.5527	.5539	.5551
3.6	.5563	.5575	.5587	.5599	.5611	.5623	.5635	.5647	.5658	.5670
3.7	.5682	.5694	.5705	.5717	.5729	.5740	.5752	.5763	.5775	.5786
3.8	.5798	.5809	.5821	.5832	.5843	.5855	.5866	.5877	.5888	.5899
3.9	.5911	.5922	.5933	.5944	.5955	.5966	.5977	.5988	.5999	.6010
4.0	.6021	.6031	.6042	.6053	.6064	.6075	.6085	.6096	.6107	.6117
4.1	.6128	.6138	.6149	.6160	.6170	.6180	.6191	.6201	.6212	.6222
4.2	.6232	.6243	.6253	.6263	.6274	.6284	.6294	.6304	.6314	.6325
4.3	.6335	.6345	.6355	.6365	.6375	.6385	.6395	.6405	.6415	.6425
4.4	.6435	.6444	.6454	.6464	.6474	.6484	.6493	.6503	.6513	.6522
4.5	.6532	.6542	.6551	.6561	.6571	.6580	.6590	.6599	.6609	.6618
4.6	.6628	.6637	.6646	.6656	.6665	.6675	.6684	.6693	.6702	.6712
4.7	.6721	.6730	.6739	.6749	.6758	.6767	.6776	.6785	.6794	.6803
4.8	.6812	.6821	.6830	.6839	.6848	.6857	.6866	.6875	.6884	.6893
4.9	.6902	.6911	.6920	.6928	.6937	.6946	.6955	.6964	.6972	.6981
5.0	.6990	.6998	.7007	.7016	.7024	.7033	.7042	.7050	.7059	.7067
5.1	.7076	.7084	.7093	.7101	.7110	.7118	.7126	.7135	.7143	.7152
5.2	.7160	.7168	.7177	.7185	.7193	.7202	.7210	.7218	.7226	.7235
5.3	.7243	.7251	.7259	.7267	.7275	.7284	.7292	.7300	.7308	.7316
5.4	.7324	.7332	.7340	.7348	.7356	.7364	.7372	.7380	.7388	.7396
N	0	1	2	3	4	5	6	7	8	9

N	0	1	2	3	4	5	6	7	8	9
5.5	.7404	.7412	.7419	.7427	.7435	.7443	.7451	.7459	.7466	.7474
5.6	.7482	.7490	.7497	.7505	.7513	.7520	.7528	.7536	.7543	.7551
5.7	.7559	.7566	.7574	.7582	.7589	.7597	.7604	.7612	.7619	.7627
5.8	.7634	.7642	.7649	.7657	.7664	.7672	.7679	.7686	.7694	.7701
5.9	.7709	.7716	.7723	.7731	.7738	.7745	.7752	.7760	.7767	.7774
6.0	.7782	.7789	.7796	.7803	.7810	.7818	.7825	.7832	.7839	.7846
6.1	.7853	.7860	.7868	.7875	.7882	.7889	.7896	.7903	.7910	.7917
6.2	.7924	.7931	.7938	.7945	.7952	.7959	.7966	.7973	.7980	.7987
6.3	.7993	.8000	.8007	.8014	.8021	.8028	.8035	.8041	.8048	.8055
6.4	.8062	.8069	.8075	.8082	.8089	.8096	.8102	.8109	.8116	.8122
6.5	.8129	.8136	.8142	.8149	.8156	.8162	.8169	.8176	.8182	.8189
6.6	.8195	.8202	.8209	.8215	.8222	.8228	.8235	.8241	.8248	.8254
6.7	.8261	.8267	.8274	.8280	.8287	.8293	.8299	.8306	.8312	.8319
6.8	.8325	.8331	.8338	.8344	.8351	.8357	.8363	.8370	.8376	.8382
6.9	.8388	.8395	.8401	.8407	.8414	.8420	.8426	.8432	.8439	.8445
7.0	.8451	.8457	.8463	.8470	.8476	.8482	.8488	.8494	.8500	.8506
7.1	.8513	.8519	.8525	.8531	.8537	.8543	.8549	.8555	.8561	.8567
7.2	.8573	.8579	.8585	.8591	.8597	.8603	.8609	.8615	.8621	.8627
7.3	.8633	.8639	.8645	.8651	.8657	.8663	.8669	.8675	.8681	.8686
7.4	.8692	.8698	.8704	.8710	.8716	.8722	.8727	.8733	.8739	.8745
7.5	.8751	.8756	.8762	.8768	.8774	.8779	.8785	.8791	.8797	.8802
7.6	.8808	.8814	.8820	.8825	.8831	.8837	.8842	.8848	.8854	.8859
7.7	.8865	.8871	.8876	.8882	.8887	.8893	.8899	.8904	.8910	.8915
7.8	.8921	.8927	.8932	.8938	.8943	.8949	.8954	.8960	.8965	.8971
7.9	.8976	.8982	.8987	.8993	.8998	.9004	.9009	.9015	.9020	.9025
8.0	.9031	.9036	.9042	.9047	.9053	.9058	.9063	.9069	.9074	.9079
8.1	.9085	.9090	.9096	.9101	.9106	.9112	.9117	.9122	.9128	.9133
8.2	.9138	.9143	.9149	.9154	.9159	.9165	.9170	.9175	.9180	.9186
8.3	.9191	.9196	.9201	.9206	.9212	.9217	.9222	.9227	.9232	.9238
8.4	.9243	.9248	.9253	.9258	.9263	.9269	.9274	.9279	.9284	.9289
8.5	.9294	.9299	.9304	.9309	.9315	.9320	.9325	.9330	.9335	.9340
8.6	.9345	.9350	.9355	.9360	.9365	.9370	.9375	.9380	.9385	.9390
8.7	.9395	.9400	.9405	.9410	.9415	.9420	.9425	.9430	.9435	.9440
8.8	.9445	.9450	.9455	.9460	.9465	.9469	.9474	.9479	.9484	.9489
8.9	.9494	.9499	.9504	.9509	.9513	.9518	.9523	.9528	.9533	.9538
9.0	.9542	.9547	.9552	.9557	.9562	.9566	.9571	.9576	.9581	.9586
9.1	.9590	.9595	.9600	.9605	.9609	.9614	.9619	.9624	.9628	.9633
9.2	.9638	.9643	.9647	.9652	.9657	.9661	.9666	.9671	.9675	.9680
9.3	.9685	.9689	.9694	.9699	.9703	.9708	.9713	.9717	.9722	.9727
9.4	.9731	.9736	.9741	.9745	.9750	.9754	.9759	.9763	.9768	.9773
9.5	.9777	.9782	.9786	.9791	.9795	.9800	.9805	.9809	.9814	.9818
9.6	.9823	.9827	.9832	.9836	.9841	.9845	.9850	.9854	.9859	.9863
9.7	.9868	.9872	.9877	.9881	.9886	.9890	.9894	.9899	.9903	.9908
9.8	.9912	.9917	.9921	.9926	.9930	.9934	.9939	.9943	.9948	.9952
9.9	.9956	.9961	.9965	.9969	.9974	.9978	.9983	.9987	.9991	.9996
N	0	1	2	3	4	5	6	7	8	9

TABLE III. LOGARITHMS OF TRIGONOMETRIC FUNCTIONS   345

Degrees	Log₁₀ Sine	Log₁₀ Tangent	Log₁₀ Cotangent	Log₁₀ Cosine	
0° 00′					90° 00′
10′	.4637 −3	.4637 −3	2.5363	.0000	50′
20′	.7648 −3	.7648 −3	2.2352	.0000	40′
30′	9408 −3	.9409 −3	2.0591	.0000	30′
40′	.0658 −2	.0658 −2	1.9342	.0000	20′
50′	.1627 −2	.1627 −2	1.8373	.0000	10′
1° 00′	.2419 −2	.2419 −2	1.7581	.9999 −1	89° 00′
10′	.3088 −2	.3089 −2	1.6911	.9999 −1	50′
20′	.3668 −2	.3669 −2	1.6331	.9999 −1	40′
30′	.4179 −2	.4181 −2	1.5819	.9999 −1	30′
40′	.4637 −2	.4638 −2	1.5362	.9998 −1	20′
50′	.5050 −2	.5053 −2	1.4947	.9998 −1	10′
2° 00′	.5428 −2	.5431 −2	1.4569	.9997 −1	88° 00′
10′	.5776 −2	.5779 −2	1.4221	.9997 −1	50′
20′	.6097 −2	.6101 −2	1.3899	.9996 −1	40′
30′	.6397 −2	.6401 −2	1.3599	.9996 −1	30′
40′	.6677 −2	.6682 −2	1.3318	.9995 −1	20′
50′	.6940 −2	.6945 −2	1.3055	.9995 −1	10′
3° 00′	.7188 −2	.7194 −2	1.2806	.9994 −1	87° 00′
10′	.7423 −2	.7429 −2	1.2571	.9993 −1	50′
20′	.7645 −2	.7652 −2	1.2348	.9993 −1	40′
30′	.7857 −2	.7865 −2	1.2135	.9992 −1	30′
40′	.8059 −2	.8067 −2	1.1933	.9991 −1	20′
50′	.8251 −2	.8261 −2	1.1739	.9990 −1	10′
4° 00′	.8436 −2	.8446 −2	1.1554	.9989 −1	86° 00′
10′	.8613 −2	.8624 −2	1.1376	.9989 −1	50′
20′	.8783 −2	.8795 −2	1.1205	.9988 −1	40′
30′	.8946 −2	.8960 −2	1.1040	.9987 −1	30′
40′	.9104 −2	.9118 −2	1.0882	.9986 −1	20′
50′	.9256 −2	.9272 −2	1.0728	.9985 −1	10′
5° 00′	.9403 −2	.9420 −2	1.0580	.9983 −1	85° 00′
10′	.9545 −2	.9563 −2	1.0437	.9982 −1	50′
20′	.9682 −2	.9701 −2	1.0299	.9981 −1	40′
30′	.9816 −2	.9836 −2	1.0164	.9980 −1	30′
40′	.9945 −2	.9966 −2	1.0034	.9979 −1	20′
50′	.0070 −1	.0093 −1	.9907	.9977 −1	10′
6° 00′	.0192 −1	.0216 −1	.9784	.9976 −1	84° 00′
10′	.0311 −1	.0336 −1	.9664	.9975 −1	50′
20′	.0426 −1	.0453 −1	.9547	.9973 −1	40′
30′	.0539 −1	.0567 −1	.9433	.9972 −1	30′
40′	.0648 −1	.0678 −1	.9322	.9971 −1	20′
50′	.0755 −1	.0786 −1	.9214	.9969 −1	10′
7° 00′	.0859 −1	.0891 −1	.9109	.9968 −1	83° 00′
10′	.0961 −1	.0995 −1	.9005	.9966 −1	50′
20′	.1060 −1	.1096 −1	.8904	.9964 −1	40′
30′	.1157 −1	.1194 −1	.8806	.9963 −1	30′
40′	.1252 −1	.1291 −1	.8709	.9961 −1	20′
50′	.1345 −1	.1385 −1	.8615	.9959 −1	10′
8° 00′	.1436 −1	.1478 −1	.8522	.9958 −1	82° 00′
10′	.1525 −1	.1569 −1	.8431	.9956 −1	50′
20′	.1612 −1	.1658 −1	.8342	.9954 −1	40′
30′	.1697 −1	.1745 −1	.8255	.9952 −1	30′
40′	.1781 −1	.1831 −1	.8169	.9950 −1	20′
50′	.1863 −1	.1915 −1	.8085	.9948 −1	10′
9° 00′	.1943 −1	.1997 −1	.8003	.9946 −1	81° 00′
	Log₁₀ Cosine	Log₁₀ Cotangent	Log₁₀ Tangent	Log₁₀ Sine	Degrees

Degrees	Log_{10} Sine	Log_{10} Tangent	Log_{10} Cotangent	Log_{10} Cosine	
9° 00′	.1943 − 1	.1997 − 1	.8003	.9946 − 1	81° 00′
10′	.2022 − 1	.2078 − 1	.7922	.9944 − 1	50′
20′	.2100 − 1	.2158 − 1	.7842	.9942 − 1	40′
30′	.2176 − 1	.2236 − 1	.7764	.9940 − 1	30′
40′	.2251 − 1	.2313 − 1	.7687	.9938 − 1	20′
50′	.2324 − 1	.2389 − 1	.7611	.9936 − 1	10′
10° 00′	.2397 − 1	.2463 − 1	.7537	.9934 − 1	80° 00′
10′	.2468 − 1	.2536 − 1	.7464	.9931 − 1	50′
20′	.2538 − 1	.2609 − 1	.7391	.9929 − 1	40′
30′	.2606 − 1	.2680 − 1	.7320	.9927 − 1	30′
40′	.2674 − 1	.2750 − 1	.7250	.9924 − 1	20′
50′	.2740 − 1	.2819 − 1	.7181	.9922 − 1	10′
11° 00′	.2806 − 1	.2887 − 1	.7113	.9919 − 1	79° 00′
10′	.2870 − 1	.2953 − 1	.7047	.9917 − 1	50′
20′	.2934 − 1	.3020 − 1	.6980	.9914 − 1	40′
30′	.2997 − 1	.3085 − 1	.6915	.9912 − 1	30′
40′	.3058 − 1	.3149 − 1	.6851	.9909 − 1	20′
50′	.3119 − 1	.3212 − 1	.6788	.9907 − 1	10′
12° 00′	.3179 − 1	.3275 − 1	.6725	.9904 − 1	78° 00′
10′	.3238 − 1	.3336 − 1	.6664	.9901 − 1	50′
20′	.3296 − 1	.3397 − 1	.6603	.9899 − 1	40′
30′	.3353 − 1	.3458 − 1	.6542	.9896 − 1	30′
40′	.3410 − 1	.3517 − 1	.6483	.9893 − 1	20′
50′	.3466 − 1	.3576 − 1	.6424	.9890 − 1	10′
13° 00′	.3521 − 1	.3634 − 1	.6366	.9887 − 1	77° 00′
10′	.3575 − 1	.3691 − 1	.6309	.9884 − 1	50′
20′	.3629 − 1	.3748 − 1	.6252	.9881 − 1	40′
30′	.3682 − 1	.3804 − 1	.6196	.9878 − 1	30′
40′	.3734 − 1	.3859 − 1	.6141	.9875 − 1	20′
50′	.3786 − 1	.3914 − 1	.6086	.9872 − 1	10′
14° 00′	.3837 − 1	.3968 − 1	.6032	.9869 − 1	76° 00′
10′	.3887 − 1	.4021 − 1	.5979	.9866 − 1	50′
20′	.3937 − 1	.4074 − 1	.5926	.9863 − 1	40′
30′	.3986 − 1	.4127 − 1	.5873	.9859 − 1	30′
40′	.4035 − 1	.4178 − 1	.5822	.9856 − 1	20′
50′	.4083 − 1	.4230 − 1	.5770	.9853 − 1	10′
15° 00′	.4130 − 1	.4281 − 1	.5719	.9849 − 1	75° 00′
10′	.4177 − 1	.4331 − 1	.5669	.9846 − 1	50′
20′	.4223 − 1	.4381 − 1	.5619	.9843 − 1	40′
30′	.4269 − 1	.4430 − 1	.5570	.9839 − 1	30′
40′	.4314 − 1	.4479 − 1	.5521	.9836 − 1	20′
50′	.4359 − 1	.4527 − 1	.5473	.9832 − 1	10′
16° 00′	.4403 − 1	.4575 − 1	.5425	.9828 − 1	74° 00′
10′	.4447 − 1	.4622 − 1	.5378	.9825 − 1	50′
20′	.4491 − 1	.4669 − 1	.5331	.9821 − 1	40′
30′	.4533 − 1	.4716 − 1	.5284	.9817 − 1	30′
40′	.4576 − 1	.4762 − 1	.5238	.9814 − 1	20′
50′	.4618 − 1	.4808 − 1	.5192	.9810 − 1	10′
17° 00′	.4659 − 1	.4853 − 1	.5147	.9806 − 1	73° 00′
10′	.4700 − 1	.4898 − 1	.5102	.9802 − 1	50′
20′	.4741 − 1	.4943 − 1	.5057	.9798 − 1	40′
30′	.4781 − 1	.4987 − 1	.5013	.9794 − 1	30′
40′	.4821 − 1	.5031 − 1	.4969	.9790 − 1	20′
50′	.4861 − 1	.5075 − 1	.4925	.9786 − 1	10′
18° 00′	.4900 − 1	.5118 − 1	.4882	.9782 − 1	72° 00′
	Log_{10} Cosine	Log_{10} Cotangent	Log_{10} Tangent	Log_{10} Sine	Degrees

TABLE III. LOGARITHMS OF TRIGONOMETRIC FUNCTIONS (*cont.*) 347

Degrees	Log₁₀ Sine	Log₁₀ Tangent	Log₁₀ Cotangent	Log₁₀ Cosine	
18° 00′	.4900 −1	.5118 −1	.4882	.9782 −1	72° 00′
10′	.4939 −1	.5161 −1	.4839	.9778 −1	50′
20′	.4977 −1	.5203 −1	.4797	.9774 −1	40′
30′	.5015 −1	.5245 −1	.4755	.9770 −1	30′
40′	.5052 −1	.5287 −1	.4713	.9765 −1	20′
50′	.5090 −1	.5329 −1	.4671	.9761 −1	10′
19° 00′	.5126 −1	.5370 −1	.4630	.9757 −1	71° 00′
10′	.5163 −1	.5411 −1	.4589	.9752 −1	50′
20′	.5199 −1	.5451 −1	.4549	.9748 −1	40′
30′	.5235 −1	.5491 −1	.4509	.9743 −1	30′
40′	.5270 −1	.5531 −1	.4469	.9739 −1	20′
50′	.5306 −1	.5571 −1	.4429	.9734 −1	10′
20° 00′	.5341 −1	.5611 −1	.4389	.9730 −1	70° 00′
10′	.5375 −1	.5650 −1	.4350	.9725 −1	50′
20′	.5409 −1	.5689 −1	.4311	.9721 −1	40′
30′	.5443 −1	.5727 −1	.4273	.9716 −1	30′
40′	.5477 −1	.5766 −1	.4234	.9711 −1	20′
50′	.5510 −1	.5804 −1	.4196	.9706 −1	10′
21° 00′	.5543 −1	.5842 −1	.4158	.9702 −1	69° 00′
10′	.5576 −1	.5879 −1	.4121	.9697 −1	50′
20′	.5609 −1	.5917 −1	.4083	.9692 −1	40′
30′	.5641 −1	.5954 −1	.4046	.9687 −1	30′
40′	.5673 −1	.5991 −1	.4009	.9682 −1	20′
50′	.5704 −1	.6028 −1	.3972	.9677 −1	10′
22° 00′	.5736 −1	.6064 −1	.3936	.9672 −1	68° 00′
10′	.5767 −1	.6100 −1	.3900	.9667 −1	50′
20′	.5798 −1	.6136 −1	.3864	.9661 −1	40′
30′	.5828 −1	.6172 −1	.3828	.9656 −1	30′
40′	.5859 −1	.6208 −1	.3792	.9651 −1	20′
50′	.5889 −1	.6243 −1	.3757	.9646 −1	10′
23° 00′	.5919 −1	.6279 −1	.3721	.9640 −1	67° 00′
10′	.5948 −1	.6314 −1	.3686	.9635 −1	50′
20′	.5978 −1	.6348 −1	.3652	.9629 −1	40′
30′	.6007 −1	.6383 −1	.3617	.9624 −1	30′
40′	.6036 −1	.6417 −1	.3583	.9618 −1	20′
50′	.6065 −1	.6452 −1	.3548	.9613 −1	10′
24° 00′	.6093 −1	.6486 −1	.3514	.9607 −1	66° 00′
10′	.6121 −1	.6520 −1	.3480	.9602 −1	50′
20′	.6149 −1	.6553 −1	.3447	.9596 −1	40′
30′	.6177 −1	.6587 −1	.3413	.9590 −1	30′
40′	.6205 −1	.6620 −1	.3380	.9584 −1	20′
50′	.6232 −1	.6654 −1	.3346	.9579 −1	10′
25° 00′	.6259 −1	.6687 −1	.3313	.9573 −1	65° 00′
10′	.6286 −1	.6720 −1	.3280	.9567 −1	50′
20′	.6313 −1	.6752 −1	.3248	.9561 −1	40′
30′	.6340 −1	.6785 −1	.3215	.9555 −1	30′
40′	.6366 −1	.6817 −1	.3183	.9549 −1	20′
50′	.6392 −1	.6850 −1	.3150	.9543 −1	10′
26° 00′	.6418 −1	.6882 −1	.3118	.9537 −1	64° 00′
10′	.6444 −1	.6914 −1	.3086	.9530 −1	50′
20′	.6470 −1	.6946 −1	.3054	.9524 −1	40′
30′	.6495 −1	.6977 −1	.3023	.9518 −1	30′
40′	.6521 −1	.7009 −1	.2991	.9512 −1	20′
50′	.6546 −1	.7040 −1	.2960	.9505 −1	10′
27° 00′	.6570 −1	.7072 −1	.2928	.9499 −1	63° 00′
	Log₁₀ Cosine	Log₁₀ Cotangent	Log₁₀ Tangent	Log₁₀ Sine	Degrees

Degrees	Log₁₀ Sine	Log₁₀ Tangent	Log₁₀ Cotangent	Log₁₀ Cosine	
27° 00′	.6570 − 1	.7072 − 1	.2928	.9499 − 1	**63° 00′**
10′	.6595 − 1	.7103 − 1	.2897	.9492 − 1	50′
20′	.6620 − 1	.7134 − 1	.2866	.9486 − 1	40′
30′	.6644 − 1	.7165 − 1	.2835	.9479 − 1	30′
40′	.6668 − 1	.7196 − 1	.2804	.9473 − 1	20′
50′	.6692 − 1	.7226 − 1	.2774	.9466 − 1	10′
28° 00′	.6716 − 1	.7257 − 1	.2743	.9459 − 1	**62° 00′**
10′	.6740 − 1	.7287 − 1	.2713	.9453 − 1	50′
20′	.6763 − 1	.7317 − 1	.2683	.9446 − 1	40′
30′	.6787 − 1	.7348 − 1	.2652	.9439 − 1	30′
40′	.6810 − 1	.7378 − 1	.2622	.9432 − 1	20′
50′	.6833 − 1	.7408 − 1	.2592	.9425 − 1	10′
29° 00′	.6856 − 1	.7438 − 1	.2562	.9418 − 1	**61° 00′**
10′	.6878 − 1	.7467 − 1	.2533	.9411 − 1	50′
20′	.6901 − 1	.7497 − 1	.2503	.9404 − 1	40′
30′	.6923 − 1	.7526 − 1	.2474	.9397 − 1	30′
40′	.6946 − 1	.7556 − 1	.2444	.9390 − 1	20′
50′	.6968 − 1	.7585 − 1	.2415	.9383 − 1	10′
30° 00′	.6990 − 1	.7614 − 1	.2386	.9375 − 1	**60° 00′**
10′	.7012 − 1	.7644 − 1	.2356	.9368 − 1	50′
20′	.7033 − 1	.7673 − 1	.2327	.9361 − 1	40′
30′	.7055 − 1	.7701 − 1	.2299	.9353 − 1	30′
40′	.7076 − 1	.7730 − 1	.2270	.9346 − 1	20′
50′	.7097 − 1	.7759 − 1	.2241	.9338 − 1	10′
31° 00′	.7118 − 1	.7788 − 1	.2212	.9331 − 1	**59° 00′**
10′	.7139 − 1	.7816 − 1	.2184	.9323 − 1	50′
20′	.7160 − 1	.7845 − 1	.2155	.9315 − 1	40′
30′	.7181 − 1	.7873 − 1	.2127	.9308 − 1	30′
40′	.7201 − 1	.7902 − 1	.2098	.9300 − 1	20′
50′	.7222 − 1	.7930 − 1	.2070	.9292 − 1	10′
32° 00′	.7242 − 1	.7958 − 1	.2042	.9284 − 1	**58° 00′**
10′	.7262 − 1	.7986 − 1	.2014	.9276 − 1	50′
20′	.7282 − 1	.8014 − 1	.1986	.9268 − 1	40′
30′	.7302 − 1	.8042 − 1	.1958	.9260 − 1	30′
40′	.7322 − 1	.8070 − 1	.1930	.9252 − 1	20′
50′	.7342 − 1	.8097 − 1	.1903	.9244 − 1	10′
33° 00′	.7361 − 1	.8125 − 1	.1875	.9236 − 1	**57° 00′**
10′	.7380 − 1	.8153 − 1	.1847	.9228 − 1	50′
20′	.7400 − 1	.8180 − 1	.1820	.9219 − 1	40′
30′	.7419 − 1	.8208 − 1	.1792	.9211 − 1	30′
40′	.7438 − 1	.8235 − 1	.1765	.9203 − 1	20′
50′	.7457 − 1	.8263 − 1	.1737	.9194 − 1	10′
34° 00′	.7476 − 1	.8290 − 1	.1710	.9186 − 1	**56° 00′**
10′	.7494 − 1	.8317 − 1	.1683	.9177 − 1	50′
20′	.7513 − 1	.8344 − 1	.1656	.9169 − 1	40′
30′	.7531 − 1	.8371 − 1	.1629	.9160 − 1	30′
40′	.7550 − 1	.8398 − 1	.1602	.9151 − 1	20′
50′	.7568 − 1	.8425 − 1	.1575	.9142 − 1	10′
35° 00′	.7586 − 1	.8452 − 1	.1548	.9134 − 1	**55° 00′**
10′	.7604 − 1	.8479 − 1	.1521	.9125 − 1	50′
20′	.7622 − 1	.8506 − 1	.1494	.9116 − 1	40′
30′	.7640 − 1	.8533 − 1	.1467	.9107 − 1	30′
40′	.7657 − 1	.8559 − 1	.1441	.9098 − 1	20′
50′	.7675 − 1	.8586 − 1	.1414	.9089 − 1	10′
36° 00′	.7692 − 1	.8613 − 1	.1387	.9080 − 1	**54° 00′**
	Log₁₀ Cosine	Log₁₀ Cotangent	Log₁₀ Tangent	Log₁₀ Sine	Degrees

Table III. Logarithms of Trigonometric Functions (*cont.*) 349

Degrees	Log₁₀ Sine	Log₁₀ Tangent	Log₁₀ Cotangent	Log₁₀ Cosine	
36° 00′	.7692 −1	.8613 −1	.1387	.9080 −1	**54° 00′**
10′	.7710 −1	.8639 −1	.1361	.9070 −1	50′
20′	.7727 −1	.8666 −1	.1334	.9061 −1	40′
30′	.7744 −1	.8692 −1	.1308	.9052 −1	30′
40′	.7761 −1	.8718 −1	.1282	.9042 −1	20′
50′	.7778 −1	.8745 −1	.1255	.9033 −1	10′
37° 00′	.7795 −1	.8771 −1	.1229	.9023 −1	**53° 00′**
10′	.7811 −1	.8797 −1	.1203	.9014 −1	50′
20′	.7828 −1	.8824 −1	.1176	.9004 −1	40′
30′	.7844 −1	.8850 −1	.1150	.8995 −1	30′
40′	.7861 −1	.8876 −1	.1124	.8985 −1	20′
50′	.7877 −1	.8902 −1	.1098	.8975 −1	10′
38° 00′	.7893 −1	.8928 −1	.1072	.8965 −1	**52° 00′**
10′	.7910 −1	.8954 −1	.1046	.8955 −1	50′
20′	.7926 −1	.8980 −1	.1020	.8945 −1	40′
30′	.7941 −1	.9006 −1	.0994	.8935 −1	30′
40′	.7957 −1	.9032 −1	.0968	.8925 −1	20′
50′	.7973 −1	.9058 −1	.0942	.8915 −1	10′
39° 00′	.7989 −1	.9084 −1	.0916	.8905 −1	**51° 00′**
10′	.8004 −1	.9110 −1	.0890	.8895 −1	50′
20′	.8020 −1	.9135 −1	.0865	.8884 −1	40′
30′	.8035 −1	.9161 −1	.0839	.8874 −1	30′
40′	.8050 −1	.9187 −1	.0813	.8864 −1	20′
50′	.8066 −1	.9212 −1	.0788	.8853 −1	10′
40° 00′	.8081 −1	.9238 −1	.0762	.8843 −1	**50° 00′**
10′	.8096 −1	.9264 −1	.0736	.8832 −1	50′
20′	.8111 −1	.9289 −1	.0711	.8821 −1	40′
30′	.8125 −1	.9315 −1	.0685	.8810 −1	30′
40′	.8140 −1	.9341 −1	.0659	.8800 −1	20′
50′	.8155 −1	.9366 −1	.0634	.8789 −1	10′
41° 00′	.8169 −1	.9392 −1	.0608	.8778 −1	**49° 00′**
10′	.8184 −1	.9417 −1	.0583	.8767 −1	50′
20′	.8198 −1	.9443 −1	.0557	.8756 −1	40′
30′	.8213 −1	.9468 −1	.0532	.8745 −1	30′
40′	.8227 −1	.9494 −1	.0506	.8733 −1	20′
50′	.8241 −1	.9519 −1	.0481	.8722 −1	10′
42° 00′	.8255 −1	.9544 −1	.0456	.8711 −1	**48° 00′**
10′	.8269 −1	.9570 −1	.0430	.8699 −1	50′
20′	.8283 −1	.9595 −1	.0405	.8688 −1	40′
30′	.8297 −1	.9621 −1	.0379	.8676 −1	30′
40′	.8311 −1	.9646 −1	.0354	.8665 −1	20′
50′	.8324 −1	.9671 −1	.0329	.8653 −1	10′
43° 00′	.8338 −1	.9697 −1	.0303	.8641 −1	**47° 00′**
10′	.8351 −1	.9722 --1	.0278	.8629 −1	50′
20′	.8365 −1	.9747 −1	.0253	.8618 −1	40′
30′	.8378 −1	.9772 −1	.0228	.8606 −1	30′
40′	.8391 −1	.9798 −1	.0202	.8594 −1	20′
50′	.8405 −1	.9823 −1	.0177	.8582 −1	10′
44° 00′	.8418 −1	.9848 −1	.0152	.8569 −1	**46° 00′**
10′	.8431 −1	.9874 −1	.0126	.8557 −1	50′
20′	.8444 −1	.9899 −1	.0101	.8545 −1	40′
30′	.8457 −1	.9924 −1	.0076	.8532 −1	30′
40′	.8469 −1	.9949 −1	.0051	.8520 −1	20′
50′	.8482 −1	.9975 −1	.0025	.8507 −1	10′
45° 00′	.8495 −1	.0000	.0000	.8495 −1	**45° 00′**
	Log₁₀ Cosine	Log₁₀ Cotangent	Log₁₀ Tangent	Log₁₀ Sine	Degrees

TABLE IV. POWERS AND ROOTS

No.	Sq.	Sq. Root	Cube	Cube Root	No.	Sq.	Sq. Root	Cube	Cube Root
1	1	1.000	1	1.000	51	2,601	7.141	132,651	3.708
2	4	1.414	8	1.260	52	2,704	7.211	140,608	3.733
3	9	1.732	27	1.442	53	2,809	7.280	148,877	3.756
4	16	2.000	64	1.587	54	2,916	7.348	157,464	3.780
5	25	2.236	125	1.710	55	3,025	7.416	166,375	3.803
6	36	2.449	216	1.817	56	3,136	7.483	175,616	3.826
7	49	2.646	343	1.913	57	3,249	7.550	185,193	3.849
8	64	2.828	512	2.000	58	3,364	7.616	195,112	3.871
9	81	3.000	729	2.080	59	3,481	7.681	205,379	3.893
10	100	3.162	1,000	2.154	60	3,600	7.746	216,000	3.915
11	121	3.317	1.331	2.224	61	3,721	7.810	226,981	3.936
12	144	3.464	1,728	2.289	62	3,844	7.874	238,328	3.958
13	169	3.606	2,197	2.351	63	3,969	7.937	250,047	3.979
14	196	3.742	2,744	2.410	64	4,096	8.000	262,144	4.000
15	225	3.873	3,375	2.466	65	4,225	8.062	274,625	4.021
16	256	4.000	4,096	2.520	66	4,356	8.124	287,496	4.041
17	289	4.123	4,913	2.571	67	4,489	8.185	300,763	4.062
18	324	4.243	5,832	2.621	68	4,624	8.246	314,432	4.082
19	361	4.359	6,859	2.668	69	4,761	8.307	328,509	4.102
20	400	4.472	8,000	2.714	70	4,900	8.367	343,000	4.121
21	441	4.583	9,261	2.759	71	5,041	8.426	357,911	4.141
22	484	4.690	10,648	2.802	72	5,184	8.485	373,248	4.160
23	529	4.796	12,167	2.844	73	5,329	8.544	389,017	4.179
24	576	4.899	13,824	2.884	74	5,476	8.602	405,224	4.198
25	625	5.000	15,625	2.924	75	5,625	8.660	421,875	4.217
26	676	5.099	17,576	2.962	76	5,776	8.718	438,976	4.236
27	729	5.196	19,683	3.000	77	5,929	8.775	456,533	4.254
28	784	5.292	21,952	3.037	78	6,084	8.832	474,552	4.273
29	841	5.385	24,389	3.072	79	6,241	8.888	493,039	4.291
30	900	5.477	27,000	3.107	80	6,400	8.944	512,000	4.309
31	961	5.568	29,791	3.141	81	6,561	9.000	531,441	4.327
32	1,024	5.657	32,768	3.175	82	6,724	9.055	551,368	4.344
33	1,089	5.745	35,937	3.208	83	6,889	9.110	571,787	4.362
34	1,156	5.831	39,304	3.240	84	7,056	9.165	592,704	4.380
35	1,225	5.916	42,875	3.271	85	7,225	9.220	614,125	4.397
36	1,296	6.000	46,656	3.302	86	7,396	9.274	636,056	4.414
37	1,369	6.083	50,653	3.332	87	7,569	9.327	658,503	4.431
38	1,444	6.164	54,872	3.362	88	7,744	9.381	681,472	4.448
39	1,521	6.245	59,319	3.391	89	7,921	9.434	704,969	4.465
40	1,600	6.325	64,000	3.420	90	8,100	9.487	729,000	4.481
41	1,681	6.403	68,921	3.448	91	8,281	9.539	753,571	4.498
42	1,764	6.481	74,088	3.476	92	8,464	9.592	778,688	4.514
43	1,849	6.557	79,507	3.503	93	8,649	9.644	804,357	4.531
44	1,936	6.633	85,184	3.530	94	8,836	9.695	830,584	4.547
45	2,025	6.708	91,125	3.557	95	9,025	9.747	857,375	4.563
46	2,116	6.782	97,336	3.583	96	9,216	9.798	884,736	4.579
47	2,209	6.856	103,823	3.609	97	9,409	9.849	912,673	4.595
48	2,304	6.928	110,592	3.634	98	9,604	9.899	941,192	4.610
49	2,401	7.000	117,649	3.659	99	9,801	9.950	970,299	4.626
50	2,500	7.071	125,000	3.684	100	10,000	10.000	1,000,000	4.642

ANSWERS TO SELECTED ODD-NUMBERED PROBLEMS

CHAPTER 1

ARTICLE 1–1

3. $\{1, \frac{1}{2}, \frac{1}{3}, \frac{1}{4}, \frac{1}{5}, \frac{1}{6}, \frac{1}{7}, \frac{1}{8}, \frac{1}{9}\}$, $\{1/x \,|\, x$ is a counting number and less than 10$\}$
5. $\{6, 12, 18, 24, 30, 36, 42, 48\}$, $\{x \,|\, x$ is a multiple of 6 and less than 50$\}$
7. $\{x^2 \,|\, x$ is a counting number and less than 6$\}$
9. $\{3x - 2 \,|\, x$ is a counting number and less than 6$\}$
17. (a) Same size, equal $\qquad$ (b) Same size, not equal
    (c) Same size, equal $\qquad$ (d) Not same size
    (e) Same size, equal $\qquad$ (f) Not same size

ARTICLE 1–2

5. (a) Not true $\qquad$ (b) Not true $\qquad$ (c) True
   (d) Not true $\qquad$ (e) True $\qquad$ (f) Not true
   (g) True $\qquad$ (h) True $\qquad$ (i) Not true
7. $Y = \{1, 2\}$ or $\{1, 3\}$ or $\{1\}$
9. (a) $\{a, b, c, d\}$
   (b) $\{a, b, c\}, \{a, b, d\}, \{a, c, d\}, \{b, c, d\}$
   (c) $\{a, b\}, \{a, c\}, \{a, d\}, \{b, c\}, \{b, d\}, \{c, d\}$
   (d) $\{a\}, \{b\}, \{c\}, \{d\}$
   (e) $\emptyset$
11. (a) True $\qquad$ (b) Not true $\qquad$ (c) True
    (d) Not true $\qquad$ (e) True $\qquad$ (f) Not true
    (g) Not true $\qquad$ (h) True $\qquad$ (i) Not true
    (j) Not true
13. If $a \in A$, then $a \in B$, and if $b \in B$, then $b \in A$

ARTICLE 1–3

1. (a) $\{0, 1, 2, 3, 4, 5\}$ $\quad$ (b) $\{2, 3, 4, 5, 6, 7\}$ $\quad$ (c) $\{6, 7\}$
   (d) U $\qquad$ (e) $\emptyset$ $\qquad$ (f) $\{4, 5\}$
   (g) A $\qquad$ (h) $\emptyset$ $\qquad$ (i) U
   (j) D $\qquad$ (k) $\{0, 1, 6, 7, 8, 9\}$ $\quad$ (l) $\{0, 1, 2, 3, 8, 9\}$
   (m) $\{6, 7, 8, 9\}$ $\qquad$ (n) U $\qquad$ (o) $\emptyset$
3. (a) $X \cup U = U$
9. (a) A and B disjoint, or A or $B = \emptyset$

ARTICLE 1–4(1)

1. (a) Yes $\qquad$ (b) No
3. (a) Closed under multiplication (b) Not closed under either
   (c) Closed under multiplication
5. (a) No $\qquad$ (b) Yes

ARTICLE 1–4(2)

1. 1, 2, 3, 4, 6, 12 are factors of 12; 1, 2, 3, 4, 5, 6, 8, 10, 12, 15, 20, 24, 30, 40, 60, 120 are factors of 120
3. (a) I (b) $\emptyset$
5. The set consisting of integral multiples of $2 \cdot 3 \cdot 5 = 30$
7. (a) No   (b) No
9. (a) 41, 43, 47, 53, 61   (b) 113, 131, 151
   (c) Yes   (d) 41^2, no

ARTICLE 1–5

1. (a) $\frac{3}{5}$ (b) $\frac{31}{7}$
   (c) $-\frac{1473}{100}$ (d) $\frac{0}{1}$
3. (a) $0.6666\ldots$ (b) $0.571428571428\ldots$
   (c) 0.03125 (d) $0.0588235294117647\ldots$
5. (b) $\frac{69}{11}$ (c) $\frac{64}{11}$
   (d) $\frac{5}{9}$ (e) $\frac{1}{7}$

CHAPTER 2

ARTICLE 2–2(1)

1. The union of two sets is a set; the intersection of two sets is a set.
5. Yes, no   7. No

ARTICLE 2–2(2)

1. $A5$ 3. $A5$ 5. $A5$ 7. $A5$
9. $A3$ and $A6$ 11. $A6$ 13. $A6$ 15. $A5$
17. $A3, A1, A6$ 19. $A1, A5, A3, A6$
23. $a + 0 = a$ (Axiom 5), $a \cdot 1 = a$ (Axiom 5)

CHAPTER 3

ARTICLE 3–1

1. $3a + b - 1$, $a + 5b - 7$ 3. $6x + 6y - z$, $2x + 3z$
5. $-8x - 11y$, $12x - y$ 7. $-2x - 4y$
9. $-6x - 9y - 4$ 11. $16x - 3y - 9$
13. $13x - 10y$ 15. $a^2 - (b^2 - 2bc + c^2)$
17. $4x^2 - (4y^2 + 4y + 1)$ 19. $(c - a)x$, $-(a - c)x$
21. $(a + b)x$, $-(-a - b)x$ 23. 7
25. 17 27. 5
29. 35

ARTICLE 3–2

1. a^9 3. $3x^{12}$ 5. y^{24} 7. a^{20}
9. $125c^3$ 11. $32a^{15}$ 13. $a^{(r+s)t}$ 15. $2^n x^{n^2}$
17. $2x^2 + x - 15$ 19. $16x^2 - 4y^2$
21. $r^3 - r^2s - rs^2 + s^3$ 23. $x^3 + y^3$
25. $2x^4 - 3x^3 - 10x^2 + 6x + 8$ 27. $x^3 - 2x^2 - 5x + 6$

29. $x^6 - 8y^6$

31. $a^{2n+1} - a^{2n} - 7a^{n+1} + 7a^n + 10a - 10$

33. $x^{4n} - 2x^{2n}y^{2n} + y^{4n}$ 35. $x^4 - 4x^3y + 6x^2y^2 - 4xy^3 + y^4$

ARTICLE 3–3(1)

1. $3y^2 - 2x^2$ 3. $2x^2/y - 3x^3$

5. $3x - 4y + 6x^2y^2$ 7. $x^2 - 7x + 10 \equiv (x - 2)(x - 5)$

9. $3x^2 - 13x + 4 \equiv (3x - 1)(x - 4)$

11. $2x^3 - 7x^2 + 11x - 4 \equiv (x^2 - 3x + 4)(2x - 1)$

13. $x^2y - 6x^3 - 12xy^2 - 6y^3 \equiv (-3x^2 - 4xy - 12y^2)(2x - 3y) - 42y^3$

15. $4x^3 + 5 + 4x^2 - 13x \equiv (2x^2 - 3x + 1)(2x + 5)$

17. $5x^3 - 2x^2 + 3x - 4 \equiv (5x + 8)(x^2 - 2x + 1) + (14x - 12)$

19. $x^6 - y^6 \equiv (x^5 + x^4y + x^3y^2 + x^2y^3 + xy^4 + y^5)(x - y)$

ARTICLE 3–3(2)

1. $Q = 3x + 7, \ R = 17$

3. $Q = x^2 - 4x + 8, \ R = -7$

5. (a) $Q = x^3 - 3x - 10, \ R = -28$

   (b) $Q = x^3 - 3x^2 - 4, \ R = -4$

7. (a) $Q = 3x^3 + 6x^2 + 12x + 17, \ R = 14$

   (b) $Q = 3x^3 - 6x^2 + 12x - 31, \ R = 42$

9. $x^3 - 2x^2 + 3x - 4 \equiv (x^2 + x + 6)(x - 3) + 14$

11. $x^4 - 5x^3 + x^2 - 6 \equiv (x^3 - 4x^2 - 3x - 3)(x - 1) - 9$

ARTICLE 3–4

1. $6ax - 8ay$ 3. $-21x^3y - 28xy^2$

5. $4x^2 - 9y^2$ 7. $x^4 - 16y^4$

9. $4x^2 + 28xy + 49y^2$ 11. $x^2 - 7x + 10$

13. $x^2y^4 - 2xy^2z^2w + z^4w^2$ 15. $28x^2 - 9xy - 9y^2$

17. $4x^2 + 12xy + 9y^2 - 9$ 19. $x^2 + 4y^2 + z^2 - 4xy - 2xz + 4yz$

21. $x^3 + 8$

23. $x^2 + 6xy + 9y^2 - 4z^2 + 16zw - 16w^2$

25. $a^2 + b^2 + c^2 + d^2 - 2ab + 2ac - 2ad - 2bc + 2bd - 2cd$

27. $4(x + 2y)^2 + 2(x + 2y) - 12$

29. $8x^3 + 36x^2y + 54xy^2 + 27y^3$

ARTICLE 3–5(1)

1. $4(x - 5)$ 3. $3y(y - 3)$

5. $xyz^2(yz - 3x + 5y^2)$ 7. $(2x + 5)(3y - 4x)$

9. $2z(x + 3y)(z - 3x)$ 11. $(3 - a)(3 + a)$

13. $(15a^4 - 8b)(15a^4 + 8b)$ 15. $x(xy^2 - 5d^3)(xy^2 + 5d^3)$

17. $(x + 2y - z)(x + 2y + z)$ 19. $(a + b + c + d)(a + b - c - d)$

21. $[9(4x - 3y) + 5(3z + w)][9(4x - 3y) - 5(3z + w)]$

23. $(x - 4)^2$ 25. $(3xy + 11)^2$

27. $5(z - 3w)^2$ 29. $(7 - x)^2$

31. $(a - 2)(a^2 + 2a + 4)$ 33. $(2x^{2n} + 3y^m)(4x^{4n} - 6x^{2n}y^m + 9y^{2m})$

35. $(x - 5y)(19x^2 - 10xy + 7y^2)$ 37. $(x - 4)(x - 3)$

39. $(ab - 5)(ab + 4)$ 41. $(7x - 2)(5x - 2)$

43. $(3a - 4)(2a + 5)$ 45. $(x + y - 5)(x + y - 2)$

47. $(4x + 2y - 5)(2x + y + 2)$

49. $2(2a + 2b + c + d)(3a + 3b - 5c - 5d)$

ARTICLE 3–5(2)

1. $(a + b)(x - y)$ 3. $(x - 2)(x^2 + 4)$

5. $(a - 3)(2 - b^2)$ 7. $(x - 1 + y)(x - 1 - y)$

9. $(2x + y - 2)(2x - y + 2)$ 11. $(x + y + z - w)(x + y - z + w)$

13. $(x + 2y - 3)(x + 2y + 2)$ 15. $(x^2 - xy - 3y^2)(x^2 + xy - 3y^2)$

17. $(a^2 - 2ab + 3b^2)(a^2 + 2ab + 3b^2)$

19. $(a^4 + b^4)(a^2 + b^2)(a + b)(a - b)$

21. $(x - z)(x + 2y + z)$

23. $3(z - x)(x + 2y + z)$

ARTICLE 3–6

1. $\dfrac{4}{9}$ 3. $\dfrac{a^2 x^2}{y^2}$ 5. $\dfrac{a}{x + y}$

7. $\dfrac{x + 1}{x}$ 9. $\dfrac{x + 4}{x - 4}$ 11. $\dfrac{y + 2}{y + 5}$

13. $\dfrac{3a + 1}{2a - 1}$ 15. $\dfrac{2(3 - x)}{x + 5}$ 17. $\dfrac{x + 6}{x^2 + 6x + 36}$

19. $\dfrac{x^2 + 2xy + y^2}{x^2 + y^2}$

ARTICLE 3–7

1. $\dfrac{6}{5}$ 3. $\dfrac{(3x - 4y)(3x + 4y)}{12xy}$

5. $\dfrac{23 - 2x}{18}$ 7. $\dfrac{2x^2 - y^2}{x - y}$

9. $\dfrac{x - y}{5x - 3}$ 11. $\dfrac{5yz - 4xz + 3xy}{xyz}$

13. $\dfrac{5(1 - x)}{3(x - 4)}$ 15. $\dfrac{2x^2 - 9x - 9}{(2x - 3)(x - 5)(x - 6)}$

17. $\dfrac{4a^2 + 9a + 29}{a^3 - 27}$ 19. $-\dfrac{5}{(x + 2)(x + 3)}$

21. $\dfrac{8y^4 - 28y^3 + 21y^2 + 27y - 35}{(2y - 3)^2(y + 1)}$

23. $\dfrac{xz - x^2 + xy - y^2 + yz - z^2}{(x - y)(y - z)(z - x)}$

ARTICLE 3–8(1)

1. $\frac{20}{21}$

3. $\frac{1}{6}$

5. $\frac{3}{10}$

7. $\frac{15x}{4y}$

9. $\frac{40x^3}{81}$

11. $\frac{x}{x^2 + xy + y^2}$

13. $\frac{1}{x + 3}$

15. y

17. 1

19. $-\frac{2 + 3x}{x^2(x + 1)}$

ARTICLE 3–8(2)

1. $-\frac{57}{5}$

3. $\frac{x}{z}$

5. $\frac{2y + 5x}{2y - 5x}$

7. $x - 1$

9. $(3x + 2y)(y - 2x)$

ARTICLE 3–9

1. 8

3. $\frac{3y^4}{x^2}$

5. $\frac{2x^5}{3y^5}$

7. $\frac{cd(a + b)}{ab}$

9. $\frac{(a + b)^2}{ab}$

11. $x^{nm}y^{2m}$

ARTICLE 3–10

1. 5

3. $\frac{4}{7}$

5. $\frac{16}{9}$

7. $\frac{1}{64}$

9. 81

11. $\sqrt[20]{x}$

13. $\sqrt[20]{x}$

15. $\sqrt[20]{x}$

17. $\frac{1}{64xy^5}$

19. $\frac{5x^2}{3y}$

21. $a + 2\sqrt{ab} + b$

23. $x + y$

25. $x^2 + \frac{2x}{y} + \frac{1}{y^2}$

ARTICLE 3–11

1. $2\sqrt{2}$

3. $\frac{5}{2}$

5. $-5\sqrt[3]{5}$

7. $3xy^2\sqrt{3xy}$

9. $3zx^2y\sqrt[3]{3zy^2}$

11. $5\sqrt{35}/21$

13. $b\sqrt{a^2 + c^2}$

15. $\sqrt{3xy}/y^2$

17. $xy\sqrt[4]{27x^3y^2}/9$

19. $\sqrt{5}$

21. $\sqrt[3]{45x}/3x$

23. $x\sqrt{13xz}/y$

ARTICLE 3–12

1. $4\sqrt{3}$

3. $11\sqrt{2}$

5. $-\sqrt{x + y}$

7. $(ac^2 + b^3c + a^4b^2)\sqrt{abc}$

9. $32\sqrt{3}/3$

11. 5, 2

ARTICLE 3–13

1. $\sqrt{65}$

3. $2\sqrt[3]{13}$

5. $(x - y)\sqrt{x + y}$

7. $(x + y)\sqrt{x^2 - xy + y^2}$

9. $2\sqrt[3]{3}$

11. $2(\sqrt{3} + \sqrt{7})$

13. -2

15. $-13 - \sqrt{15}$

17. $(3 - \sqrt{5})/2$

19. $\frac{8}{3}$

21. $\sqrt[3]{9}/3$

23. $\sqrt[4]{3a^2b^2}/b$

25. $\sqrt{15}/10$

27. $\sqrt[3]{4}$

29. $(5\sqrt{7} + 5\sqrt{3})/4$

31. $\dfrac{x^2 - x\sqrt{y}}{x^2 - y}$

33. $-(57 + 13\sqrt{21})/12$

35. $2(4 + 2\sqrt[3]{3} + \sqrt[3]{9})/5$

37. $(2\sqrt{3} + 3\sqrt{2} - \sqrt{30})/12$

CHAPTER 4

ARTICLE 4–2

1. -6.5, -5, -1, 0, 0.333, $\frac{1}{3}$, $\sqrt{4}$, 2.3, 2^3

5. (0), (-1), (1), $\left(\dfrac{\sqrt{2} + \sqrt{3}}{2}\right)$, $\left(\dfrac{x_1 + x_2}{2}\right)$

7. (a) ± 2 (b) $\pm\sqrt{5}$ (c) ± 3

(d) $\pm\frac{1}{4}$ (e) $7, -3$ (f) 4

(g) $9, -3$ (h) $6, -4$ (i) $6, -2$

(j) None   (k) None   (l) $8, 2$

15. Two

ARTICLE 4–3

1. (a) lub $- 3$, no glb   (b) No lub, glb$\sqrt{2}$

(c) lub 1, glb $- 3$ (d) No lub, glb 0

ARTICLE 4–4

3. (a) $(3, 2)$ 5. II, IV, III, I, II, IV

(b) $(-4, 6)$

(c) $(5, 0)$

7. (a) $(8, 4)$, $(4, -4)$, $(-4, 4)$ 11. (a) $(-1, \frac{7}{2})$

(b) $(-1, 6)$, $(3, -2)$, $(-3, -4)$ (b) $(\frac{11}{2}, -\frac{9}{2})$

(c) $(-1, 0)$

ARTICLE 4–5

1. (a) $\sqrt{34}$ (b) $\sqrt{106}$ (c) $3\sqrt{2}/4$ (d) 13

(e) 8 (f) $\sqrt{(x + 1)^2 + (y - 3)^2}$

7. Yes; no

9. $(2\sqrt{3}, -1 - 4\sqrt{3})$ or $(-2\sqrt{3}, -1 + 4\sqrt{3})$

11. $(\pm a\sqrt{2}/2, 0)$ and $(0, \pm a\sqrt{2}/2)$
13. $(1, 0)$, $(0, -1)$, $(1/\sqrt{2}, 1/\sqrt{2})$, $(-\frac{1}{2}, \sqrt{3}/2)$

ARTICLE 4–6

1. (a) $(x - 3)^2 + (y - 1)^2 = 25$
   (b) $(x - 4)^2 + (y + 2)^2 = 9$
   (c) $(x + 1)^2 + (y - 3)^2 = 9$
   (d) $(x - 2)^2 + (y + 4)^2 = 25$

3. (a) All points on the circle
   (b) All points inside or on the circle
   (c) All points outside or on the circle
   (d) The point $(3, -1)$
   (e) No points

5. $4r\sqrt{2}$

7. 2π, $\pi/2$, $\pi/3$

CHAPTER 5

ARTICLE 5–1

1. (a) Domain, all real numbers; range, all real numbers
   (b) Domain, all non-negative real numbers; range, all non-negative real numbers
   (c) Domain, all real numbers; range, all non-negative real numbers
   (d) Domain, all real numbers between 2 and -2 inclusive; range, all real numbers between 0 and 2 inclusive
   (e) Domain, all real numbers greater than or equal to 1 or less than or equal to -1; range, all nonnegative real numbers
   (f) Domain, all real numbers except 1; range, all real numbers except -1
   (g) Domain, all real numbers except 1 and -1; range, all real numbers except those equal to or between -1 and 0
   (h) Domain, all real numbers; range, all real numbers greater than or equal to -2
3. (a) Domain 1, 2, 3; range 2, 3, 4
   (b) Domain 1, 2; range 2, 3, 4
   (c) Domain R; range R
   (d) Domain R; range R
   (e) Domain, all real numbers less than or equal to 1; range R
   (f) Domain R; range, all real numbers less than or equal to 1
   (g) Domain, all real numbers between -1 and 5 inclusive; range, all real numbers between 0 and 6 inclusive
   (h) Domain R; range R
   (i) Domain, R except 7; range, R except 3
   (j) Domain, all real numbers between -1 and 1 inclusive; range, all real numbers between -1 and 1 inclusive
5. 0, 0, -2, 10
7. 1, 2, 32, $\frac{1}{32}$
9. 0, 1, 2, -2
11. 6, -3, 4
13. $A = \pi x^2$, $x \rightarrow \pi x^2$
15. 0, 12, 16, 12, 0
17. 1, 0, -1, 0, 0, 1

ARTICLE 5–2

1. $-\frac{5}{2}$
3. 0
5. 2, 5
7. 1
9. 1
11. 0, ± 1

CHAPTER 6

ARTICLE 6–2

1. $+$ 3. $+$ 5. $+$
7. $-$ 9. $-$ 11. $+$
13. $+$ 15. $-$ 17. I or IV
19. III or IV   21. I or IV   23. IV
25. II
27. $\sin\theta = \frac{4}{5}$ 29. $\sin\theta = \frac{3}{5}$
   $\cos\theta = \frac{3}{5}$ $\cos\theta = -\frac{4}{5}$
31. $\sin\theta = -\frac{15}{17}$ 33. $\sin\theta = -1$
   $\cos\theta = -\frac{8}{17}$ $\cos\theta = 0$
35. $\sin\theta = 0$ 37. $\sin\theta = -\frac{3}{5}$
   $\cos\theta = 1$ $\tan\theta = \frac{3}{4}$
39. $\cos\theta = -\sqrt{5}/3$ 41. $\sin\theta = -\sqrt{11}/6$
   $\tan\theta = -2/\sqrt{5}$ $\tan\theta = -\sqrt{11}/5$
43. $\cos\theta = -\frac{4}{5}$ 45. $\sin\theta = \pm2/\sqrt{13}$
   $\tan\theta = \frac{3}{4}$ $\cos\theta = \pm3/\sqrt{13}$
47. $\cos\theta = \pm\sqrt{95}/12$ 49. $\sin\theta = -\frac{15}{17}$
   $\tan\theta = \pm7/\sqrt{95}$ $\cos\theta = -\frac{8}{17}$
51. $\sin\theta = -\frac{15}{17}$
   $\cos\theta = -\frac{8}{17}$

ARTICLE 6–3

1. Same
3. (a) $\sin\theta = 0$ (b) $\sin\theta = -1$ (c) $\sin\theta = 1$
       $\cos\theta = -1$ $\cos\theta = 0$ $\cos\theta = 0$
   (d) $\sin\theta = 0$ (e) $\sin\theta = 0$ (f) $\sin\theta = 0$
       $\cos\theta = 1$ $\cos\theta = -1$ $\cos\theta = 1$
   (g) $\sin\theta = 1$ (h) $\sin\theta = 0$ (i) $\sin\theta = 0$
       $\cos\theta = 0$ $\cos\theta = 1$ $\cos\theta = -1$
13. (a) $\sqrt{2}$,   (b) 2

ARTICLE 6–4

11. (a) 1,   (b) 1   13. $-\sqrt{3}$ 15. $\frac{5}{2} - \sqrt{3}$
17. -1 19. 2   21. $\pi/6,\ 5\pi/6$
23. $\pi/6,\ 7\pi/6$ 25. $3\pi/4,\ 7\pi/4$ 27. $\pi/4,\ 3\pi/4$
29. $5\pi/6,\ 11\pi/6$

ARTICLE 6–6

1. $1/\sin\theta$ 3. $\pm\sqrt{1 - \sin^2\theta}$
5. $\pm\sin\theta/\sqrt{1 - \sin^2\theta}$ 7. $1/\cos\theta$
9. $\pm\sqrt{1 - \cos^2\theta}$ 11. $\pm\sqrt{1 - \cos^2\theta}/\cos\theta$
13. $\sin\theta = \pm\tan\theta/\sqrt{1 + \tan^2\theta}$, $\cos\theta = \pm1/\sqrt{1 + \tan^2\theta}$
    $\cot\theta = 1/\tan\theta$, $\sec\theta = \pm\sqrt{1 + \tan^2\theta}$, $\csc\theta = \pm\sqrt{1 + \tan^2\theta}/\tan\theta$
15. $1/(1 - \cos^2\theta)$

ARTICLE 6–9

1. $\sin \dfrac{5\pi}{12} = \dfrac{\sqrt{6} + \sqrt{2}}{4}$, $\cos \dfrac{5\pi}{12} = \dfrac{\sqrt{6} - \sqrt{2}}{4}$, $\tan \dfrac{5\pi}{12} = 2 + \sqrt{3}$

3. $\cos \dfrac{7\pi}{12} = \dfrac{\sqrt{2} - \sqrt{6}}{4}$, $\tan \dfrac{7\pi}{12} = -(2 + \sqrt{3})$

5. (a) $\frac{56}{65}$ (b) $-\frac{33}{65}$ 7. (a) II

    (c) $-\frac{56}{33}$ (d) $-\frac{16}{65}$ (b) IV

    (e) $\frac{63}{65}$ (f) $-\frac{16}{63}$

9. $\sin(\alpha + \beta) = -\frac{304}{425}$, $\cos(\alpha + \beta) = \frac{297}{425}$

11. $\dfrac{\sqrt{3}\tan\theta + 1}{\sqrt{3} - \tan\theta}$ 13. $\dfrac{1 - \tan\theta}{1 + \tan\theta}$.

15. $\dfrac{2}{\sqrt{3}\sin\theta - \cos\theta}$ 17. $\dfrac{\sin\theta - \cos\theta}{\sqrt{2}}$

29. $13\sin(\theta + \theta_1)$, where $\sin\theta_1 = \frac{12}{13}$ and $\cos\theta_1 = \frac{5}{13}$

31. $5\sin(\theta + \theta_1)$, where $\sin\theta_1 = -\frac{3}{5}$ and $\cos\theta_1 = \frac{4}{5}$

33. $\sqrt{2}\sin\left(\theta + \dfrac{\pi}{4}\right)$

ARTICLE 6–10

1. $-\sin 0.2793$ 3. $-\sin 0.7156$ 5. $-\cot 0.3665$

7. $\cos 0.0873$ 9. $-\cot 0.2443$ 11. $-\sin 0.4292$

13. $-\sin 0.7124$ 15. $-\sin 0.2832$ 27. π

ARTICLE 6–11

3. $\sin 7\pi/12 = \sqrt{2 + \sqrt{3}}/2$ 5. (a) $-\frac{120}{169}$ (b) $-\frac{119}{169}$

    $\cos 7\pi/12 = -\sqrt{2 - \sqrt{3}}/2$ (c) $\frac{120}{119}$ (d) $3/\sqrt{13}$

    $\tan 7\pi/12 = -(2 + \sqrt{3})$ (e) $2/\sqrt{13}$ (f) $\frac{3}{2}$

7. $\dfrac{3 + 4\cos 2\theta + \cos 4\theta}{8}$

ARTICLE 6–12

1. $(\sin 8\theta - \sin 2\theta)/2$ 3. $(\sin 12\theta - \sin 2\theta)/2$

5. $(\sin 7\theta + \sin 3\theta)/2$ 7. $[\sin(3\theta/2) - \sin(2\theta)]/2$

9. $2\sin(\pi/6)\cos(\pi/18)$ 11. $2\cos(\pi/2)\cos(5\pi/18)$

13. $2\sin 6\theta\cos 2\theta$ 15. $2\cos(5\theta/4)\sin(5\theta/12)$

ARTICLE 6–13

3. $11\pi/60 = \pi/12 + \pi/10$, $13\pi/60 = 5\pi/12 - \pi/5$,

    $7\pi/30 = \pi/3 - \pi/10$

5. (a) 0.4566 (b) 0.9261 (c) 2.2286 (d) 0.1679

    (e) -0.9903 (f) 1.1571 (g) -0.9881 (h) -0.9528

CHAPTER 7

ARTICLE 7–1

1. -2 3. $\frac{5}{6}$ 5. -3

7. -7 9. $\frac{11}{9}$ 11. -5

13. $-\frac{16}{9}$ 15. $\pi/3,\ 2\pi/3$ 17. $0.3217,\ 3.4633$

19. $0.2195,\ 2.3985,\ 3.3611,\ 5.5401$

21. $\dfrac{c}{a-b}$ 23. $2A/h$ 25. $\dfrac{l-a}{n-1}$

27. $\dfrac{Sr+a-S}{r}$ 29. $\dfrac{2S-an}{n}$ 31. $\dfrac{a\tan\theta_1}{\tan\theta_2-\tan\theta_1}$

41. 18 years   43. \$45,000   45. $1\frac{5}{7}$ hr

ARTICLE 7–2

1. $10,\ 13,\ 16;\ t_9=25,\ S_9=117$ 3. $1,\ -2,\ -5;\ t_{15}=-32,\ S_{15}=-165$

5. $t_{12}=46,\ S_{12}=288$ 7. $d=\frac{48}{91},\ t_{14}=\frac{34}{7}$

9. $t_1=-\frac{31}{28},\ t_{14}=\frac{151}{28}$ 11. $n=7,\ S_7=147$

13. $8,\ 9,\ 10$ 15. $187{,}026$

17. $2,\ 5,\ 8,\ 11$ 19. $-\frac{25}{2},\ -7,\ -\frac{3}{2}$

21. (a) -4; (b) $\frac{17}{15}$ 25. 27 numbers; $S=2835$

27. 1092 times   29. 1610 ft

31. \$5075

ARTICLE 7–3

1. Minimum -4, when $x=-3$ 3. Minimum $-\frac{121}{8}$, when $x=-\frac{5}{4}$

5. Minimum $-\frac{169}{24}$, when $x=\frac{17}{12}$ 7. Minimum 2, when $x=-3$

9. $8,\ 8$ 11. 40 ft, 40 ft

ARTICLE 7–4(1)

1. $-1,\ -5$ 3. $\frac{3}{2},\ 4$ 5. $\frac{1}{3},\ \frac{5}{2}$ 7. None

9. $\pm\frac{4}{3}$ 11. $\pi/6,\ 5\pi/6,\ 7\pi/6,\ 11\pi/6$

13. $\frac{10}{3},\ -\frac{5}{2}$ 15. $\pi/4,\ 3\pi/4,\ 5\pi/4,\ 7\pi/4$

17. $-\frac{5}{3},\ 2$ 19. $\pi/3,\ \pi/2,\ 3\pi/2,\ 5\pi/3$

21. $-a\pm b$ 23. $\pi/2,\ 7\pi/6,\ 11\pi/6$

25. $-\frac{1}{2},\ -\frac{14}{3}$

ARTICLE 7–4(2)

1. $\frac{3}{2},\ -4$ 3. $\dfrac{-1\pm\sqrt{5}}{2}$

5. $0,\ \pi/3,\ 5\pi/3$ 7. $a,\ b$

9. $1,\ \dfrac{c-a}{a-b}$ 11. $3\pi/4,\ 7\pi/4,\ 0.5880,\ 3.7295$

13. $1,\ -5/4$ 15. $0.3142,\ 0.9425,\ 2.1991,\ 2.8275$
$3.4558,\ 4.0841,\ 5.3407,\ 5.9691$

17. $\dfrac{v_0\pm\sqrt{v_0^2-2gs}}{g}$ 19. -3

21. $\frac{3}{5}$ or $\frac{5}{3}$ 23. 1

25. $\dfrac{-27 + \sqrt{909}}{2}$ yd

ARTICLE 7–5(1)

1. $x > 9$ 3. $x < 7$
5. $x > 9$ or $x < -11$ 7. $-\frac{1}{2} < x < \frac{1}{3}$
9. $x > -1 + \sqrt{13}$ or $x < -1 - \sqrt{13}$
11. No real values   13. $x > 5$ or $x < 0$
15. $3 < x < 5$ 17. $-\frac{1}{2} \le x \le \frac{7}{2}$
19. $x \le -26$ or $x \ge -22$

21. $\dfrac{3\pi}{4} < \theta < \dfrac{5\pi}{4}$ or $0 \le \theta < \dfrac{\pi}{4}$ or $\dfrac{7\pi}{4} < \theta \le 2\pi$

23. $\pi < \theta < 2\pi$ 25. $\dfrac{4\pi}{3} < \theta < 2\pi$

27. $0 \le \theta < \dfrac{7\pi}{6}$ or $\dfrac{11\pi}{6} < \theta < 2\pi$ 29. All values

31. $\dfrac{\pi}{4} < \theta < \dfrac{5\pi}{4}$

ARTICLE 7–6

1. The sums of the zeros are -6, -1, $-\frac{5}{2}$, $\frac{11}{2}$, $\frac{17}{6}$, $\frac{5}{2}$, -6, and $\frac{5}{3}$
   The products of the zeros are 5, -6, -6, $\frac{15}{2}$, $\frac{5}{6}$, -4, 11, $\frac{4}{3}$
3. $x^2 + x - 20 = 0$ 5. $12x^2 + x - 6 = 0$
7. $x^2 - 4x + 1 = 0$ 9. $8x^2 + 12x + 1 = 0$
11. $5x^2 - 8x - 4 = 0$ 13. $2x^2 + 5x - 3 = 0$
15. $36x^2 + 24x - 5 = 0$ 17. $6x^2 - 5x - 1 = 0$
19. $k = -1$ 21. $k = 1$
23. $k = \frac{49}{12}$ 25. $k = -5$
27. $k = 0$ 29. All values of k
31. $-8 < k < 8$ 33. $k = \frac{27}{4}$
35. $k > \frac{3}{2}$ or $k < -1$

ARTICLE 7–7

1. ± 2, $\pm \sqrt{7}$ 3. $\pm \frac{1}{3}$, $\pm \frac{1}{2}$
5. Real roots: -2, 1   7. -64, 8

9. 5, 2, $\dfrac{7 \pm \sqrt{53}}{2}$ 11. 0, 0

13. $-\dfrac{23}{9}$ 15. 5, $-5/2$, $\dfrac{5 \pm \sqrt{57}}{4}$

ARTICLE 7–8

1. $\frac{11}{2}$ 3. 7, 1   5. 16
7. -5 9. 6   11. 2.09, 6.05 (approx.)
13. 0, $\pi/2$ 15. $3\pi/4$, 5.99 (approx.)

ARTICLE 7–9

1. $z = \dfrac{kx}{y}$ 3. $z = 6xy$ 5. $C = kd$

7. $A = kx^2$ 9. $y = 2x/3$ 11. 90

13. 576π in^2 15. 72 ergs   17. 2 ft

19. Multiplied by 16

ARTICLE 7–10

1. $x = 2$, $y = -1$ 3. $x = 3$, $y = 5$

5. $x = \frac{2}{3}$, $y = \frac{3}{2}$ 7. $\alpha = \pi/6$, $5\pi/6$
$\beta = 0$

9. $\alpha = \pi/6$, $11\pi/6$ 11. $x = 5$, $y = -2$
$\beta = \pi/6$, $7\pi/6$

13. $x = \dfrac{a^3 + a^2 b + 3ab^2 + b^3}{a^2 + b^2}$ 15. $x = \dfrac{a}{\tan k_2 - \tan k_1}$

$y = \dfrac{a^3 - a^2 b + ab^2 + b^3}{a^2 + b^2}$ $y = \dfrac{a \tan k_1}{\tan k_2 - \tan k_1}$

17. $x' = x \cos \alpha + y \sin \alpha$ 29. $\frac{27}{36}$
$y' = y \cos \alpha - x \sin \alpha$

31. 150 mi/hr, 10 mi/hr   33. 12 hr, 15 hr

35. $(-1, 2)$, $(2, 5)$, $(3, -1)$

37. $(\frac{18}{7}, \frac{8}{7})$, $(\frac{30}{7}, \frac{4}{7})$, $(\frac{23}{7}, -\frac{10}{7})$, $(\frac{11}{7}, -\frac{6}{7})$

39. (a) $y = -\dfrac{x}{3} + \dfrac{11}{3}$ (b) $y = -\dfrac{3}{10} x + \dfrac{4}{5}$

ARTICLE 7–11

1. $x = 1$, $y = 2$, $z = 3$ 3. $x = 3$, $y = -1$, $z = 4$

5. $x = \frac{1}{3}$, $y = -\frac{2}{5}$, $z = \frac{1}{2}$ 7. $x = 5$, $y = 6$, $z = 7$

9. $x = 3$, $y = 4$, $z = 6$ 11. $\{(-1, 2, 3)\}$

13. 10 nickels, 10 dimes, 5 quarters

15. $x^2 + y^2 - x - 7y + 6 = 0$ 17. $x = y + 2z - 1$

ARTICLE 7–12

1. $x = 0$, 2   3. No real values
$y = 0$, 16

5. $x = \dfrac{3 \pm \sqrt{7}}{2}$, $y = \dfrac{5 \mp \sqrt{7}}{2}$ 7. $\{(2, 1), (-8/5), -1/5)\}$

9. $\left\{\left(\dfrac{-2 + 2\sqrt{5}}{3}, 1 + \sqrt{5}\right), \left(\dfrac{-2 - 2\sqrt{5}}{3}, 1 - \sqrt{5}\right)\right\}$

11. $b = \pm a\sqrt{1 + m^2}$ 13. 23, 32

15. 7, 4

CHAPTER 8

ARTICLE 8–1(1)

1. -2 3. 3   5. 1   11. $x = 1$

15. Real; equal; imaginary

ARTICLE 8–1(2)

1. 5   3. 0

15. $\dfrac{4x + 3y - 17}{2}$ 17. $9x - 5y - 2 = 0$ 19. $x = -1,\ y = 4$

ARTICLE 8–2

1. Rows and columns are interchanged
3. Two columns are identical   5. 1008
9. $x = a,\ b$ 11. $x = 3,\ 1$

ARTICLE 8–3

1. -110 3. -484 5. 0

ARTICLE 8–4

3. $x = -4,\ y = -3,\ z = 2,\ w = 1$
7. $f(x) = 2x^2 - 5x + 4$

CHAPTER 9

ARTICLE 9–1(1)

1. $R = 17$ 3. $R = -7$ 5. (a) -6,   (b) 57
7. Yes   9. No   11. Yes

ARTICLE 9–1(2)

1. 2, one; 3, two; -4, three   3. -7, single; $\frac{3}{2}$, three
5. $-\frac{5}{3}$, single; 3, four   7. Upper bound 3, lower bound -4
9. Upper bound 3, lower bound -2 11. Upper bound 3, lower bound -3
13. Upper bound 2, lower bound -1 15. Upper bound 2, lower bound -3

ARTICLE 9–2

5. 2, double; single between 1 and 2; single between -5 and -6
7. Single at -3; double between 0 and 1
9. Single between -2 and -3

ARTICLE 9–4

1. $-2,\ 3,\ \frac{1}{2}$ 3. 1, 3, 5, 7

5. 1, 2, 3, -5 7. $-\dfrac{3}{2},\ -\dfrac{3}{2},\ \dfrac{1 \pm \sqrt{5}}{2}$

9. 1, 1, 1, 1   11. $\frac{1}{2},\ \frac{1}{2},\ \frac{1}{2},\ \pm\sqrt{-1}$
13. $\pi/6,\ 5\pi/6,\ 7\pi/6,\ 11\pi/6,\ 3\pi/2$
15. $\pi/6,\ 5\pi/6,\ 7\pi/6,\ 11\pi/6,\ 3\pi/4,\ 7\pi/4$

ARTICLE 9–5

1. 0.75   3. 0.45   5. 1.36, 1.69
7. -0.62, 1.62   9. 1.817   11. 1.189
13. (a) 0.9549   (b) 0.8765   (c) 0.7957   (d) 0.4480
    (e) 0.8183   (f) 0.7815   (g) -0.8932 (h) 0.1419

CHAPTER 10

ARTICLE 10–1

1. $y = 5x - 6$, domain R; inverse $y = (x + 6)/5$, domain R
3. $y = x^2 - 4x$, domain $x > 2$; inverse $y = 2 + \sqrt{x + 4}$, domain
   $x > -4$, domain $x < 2$; inverse $y = 2 - \sqrt{x + 4}$, domain $x > -4$
5. $y = (x^2 - 1)/x^2$, domain $x > 0$; inverse $y = 1/\sqrt{1 - x}$, domain
   $x < 1$, domain $x < 0$; inverse $y = 1/(-\sqrt{1 - x})$, domain $x < 1$
7. Depends on whether n is even or odd
9. $y = \sqrt{x^2 - 4}$, domain $x > 2$; inverse $y = \sqrt{x^2 + 4}$, domain $x > 0$
   domain $x < -2$; inverse $y = -\sqrt{x^2 + 4}$, domain $x > 0$
11. $y = x/(x^2 - 1)$, domain $x > 0$ and $x \neq 1$; inverse $y = (1 + \sqrt{1 + 4x^2})/2x$,
    domain $x < 0$ and $x \neq -1$; inverse $y = (1 - \sqrt{1 + 4x^2})/2x$

ARTICLE 10–3

3. $\pm 2\pi/3 + 2n\pi$	5. $n\pi$	7. $\pm \pi/4 + 2n\pi$
9. $\pi/2$	11. $-\pi/2$	13. $(-1)^n(0.4189) + n\pi$
15. $\pm 0.8901 + 2n\pi$	17. 1.4719	21. $\frac{1}{2}\arctan(y/3)$
23. $\frac{1}{2}\operatorname{arcsec}(y/2)$	27. $\frac{1}{4}(4 + \cos 3y)$	29. $\tan(y + 2)$

31. $\dfrac{\cos(2y - \pi/12) - 1}{2}$

ARTICLE 10–4

1. $\pm \frac{3}{5}$	3. $\pm \frac{12}{5}$	5. $\sqrt{11}/6$
7. u	9. $\pm \sqrt{1 - u^2}/u$	11. $\pi/7$
13. $\pi/18$	15. $2\pi/5$	17. 0
19. $uv \pm \sqrt{(1 - u^2)(1 - v^2)}$		21. $\pm \frac{3}{5}$
23. 1 or $-\frac{7}{8}$	25. $-\frac{16}{63}$	27. $(24\sqrt{5} - 14)/75$
37. $2n\pi \pm (\pi/2 - \theta)$		39. $n\pi + \theta$
41. 1	43. 0	45. 0

CHAPTER 11

ARTICLE 11–1

1. 4	3. 120	5. 240
7. 1920	9. 60	11. (a) 56, (b) 64

ARTICLE 11–2

1. 504	3. 585	5. (a) 5040, (b) 144
7. 5040	9. 103,680	11. 1440
13. 468,000	15. 3780	17. 360
19. $n = 8$		

ARTICLE 11–3

1. (a) 35, (b) 45, (c) 210	3. 12,650
5. 84,456	7. 18,375
9. 560	11. $384C(36, 6)$

13. (a) 36, (b) 84   15. 126
17. (a) 28, (b) 56, (c) 247   19. $n = 7$

ARTICLE 11–4

1. $a^7 + 7a^6b + 21a^5b^2 + 35a^4b^3 + 35a^3b^4 + 21a^2b^5 + 7ab^6 + b^7$

3. $32x^5 + 80x^4y^2 + 80x^3y^4 + 40x^2y^6 + 10xy^8 + y^{10}$

5. $625x^4 - 500x^3y^2 + 150x^2y^4 - 20xy^6 + y^8$

7. $x^2 + 6x^{5/3}y^{1/3} + 15x^{4/3}y^{2/3} + 20xy + 15x^{2/3}y^{4/3} + 6x^{1/3}y^{5/3} + y^2$

9. $x^2 - \dfrac{15x^{8/5}}{y^2} + \dfrac{90x^{6/5}}{y^4} - \dfrac{270x^{4/5}}{y^6} + \dfrac{405x^{2/5}}{y^8} - \dfrac{243}{y^{10}}$

11. $\dfrac{x^{24}}{4096} + \dfrac{3x^{22}}{256y^2} + \dfrac{33x^{20}}{128y^4} + \dfrac{55x^{18}}{16y^6} + \cdots$

13. $x^{11/3} - \dfrac{11x^{10/3}}{y^{1/3}} + \dfrac{55x^3}{y^{2/3}} - \dfrac{165x^{8/3}}{y} + \cdots$

15. $1 + kx + \dfrac{k(k-1)}{2}x^2 + \dfrac{k(k-1)(k-2)}{3!}x^3 + \cdots$

17. $59{,}136x^6y^6$ 19. $\dfrac{35y^8}{8}$

21. $-414{,}720x^7$ 23. $(7/2)x^5$

ARTICLE 11–5

1. $1 - x + x^2 - x^3 + \cdots$ 3. $1 + \dfrac{x}{2} + \dfrac{3x^2}{8} + \dfrac{5x^3}{16} + \cdots$

5. 0.9803   7. 1.005   9. 5.745   11. 4.932

13. $\frac{23}{4}, \frac{65}{32}, \frac{74}{15}$

CHAPTER 13

ARTICLE 13–2

1. $64, 256, 1024$; $t_n = 16{,}384$, $S_8 = 21{,}845$

3. $-1, 5, -25$; $t_n = 125$, $S_7 = 13{,}021/125$

5. $t_n = 486$, $S_6 = 728$

7. $r = 3$, or -4; $t_n = 9$, or 16 9. $t_1 = \frac{36}{121}$; $t_n = \frac{4}{1089}$

11. $n = 6$; $S = -126$ 13. $t_1 = \frac{625}{16}, \frac{125}{8}, \frac{25}{4}$

15. $n = 9$ 17. $\pm\frac{9}{4}, \frac{3}{2}, \pm 1$

19. $\pm\sqrt{ab}$ 23. $\frac{1}{81}$ ft; $26\frac{79}{81}$ ft

25. \$1583   27. Second

ARTICLE 13–3

1. $\frac{3}{2}$ 3. $\frac{64}{5}$ 5. $4 + 2\sqrt{2}$

7. $\frac{10}{3}$ 9. $\frac{5}{9}$ 11. $\frac{64}{11}$

13. $r = \frac{1}{7}$ 15. $16[2 + \sqrt{2}]$ 17. 240 ft

ARTICLE 13–4

1. $\log_3 27 = 3$ 3. $\log_4 1 = 0$ 5. $\log_8 16 = \frac{4}{3}$
7. $\log_{10} 0.001 = -3$ 9. $\log_4 4 = 1$ 11. $36^{1/2} = 6$
13. $x = 2$ 15. $x = -1$ 17. $u = 25$

19. $x = 14$ 21. $a = \frac{27}{8}$ 27. $\log_b \dfrac{a + 2}{a - 3}$

29. $\log_a \dfrac{\sqrt{x}}{\sqrt[3]{y^2}}$ 31. $\log_a x^5 (x - 1)^6$ 33. $4 \log_{10} 60.3$

35. $3 \log_{10} 54.3 + \log_{10} 67 - \log_{10} 93.9 - 2 \log 32.5$

ARTICLE 13–5(1)

1. 0.4099   3. 0.8401   5. 0.6730   7. 0.8373
9. 0.5153   11. 0.8858   13. 2.43   15. 4.12
17. 8.74   19. 1.851   21. 8.374   23. 3.213

ARTICLE 13–5(2)

1. Characteristic, 1; mantissa, 0.3782
3. Characteristic, -3; mantissa, 0.5728
5. Characteristic, 5; mantissa, 0.8723
7. Characteristic, -4; mantissa, 0.2715
9. 2.5172   11. 3.6747   13. $8.8623 - 10$
15. 6650   17. 267.2   19. 0.003653

ARTICLE 13–6

1. 32000   3. 34.6   5. 158,800   7. 0.5152
9. 2.642   11. 0.1313   13. 8.52   15. 0.923

ARTICLE 13–7

(All problems worked with four-place tables in back of book.)

1. (a) \$295.80, (b) \$297.10, (c) \$297.10 [larger than (b) if more accurate
   tables were used], (d) \$298.30
3. (a) 11.9 yr   5. $r = 0.3467$ 7. (a) -0.2746
   (b) 11.55 yr   (b) 0.002

ARTICLE 13–8

1. 3.808   3. 2.493   5. 1.947
7. 0.5824   9. 7.052×10^{13} 11. 26.6
13. 2.33   17. 5   19. 3.155
21. 6.14   23. 0.402   25. $\log_e (1 \pm \sqrt{2})$
27. $\frac{2}{11}$ 29. $\frac{1}{297}$

CHAPTER 14

ARTICLE 14–1

1. Amp 5, period 1
5. Amp 1.5, period $4\pi/3$
9. Amp 0.5, period $2\pi/3$

3. Amp 3, period 6
7. Amp 2, period 8π
11. Amp 100, period 200 (approx.)

ARTICLE 14–3

1. Amp 2, period 2π, phase displacement $\pi/6$
3. Amp 5, period π, phase displacement $\pi/16$
5. Amp 1, period 2π, phase displacement 0.25
7. Amp 1, period 2π, phase displacement 1.176
9. Amp 17, period 2π, phase displacement 0.4900
11. Amp $\sqrt{29}$, period 2π, phase displacement 1.1903
13. Period 2π 15. Period 4π 17. Period 2π

ARTICLE 14–4

1. P_x has an x-coordinate, $x = a \cos \omega t$
3. Yes; period π 5. $E = 8 \sin 120\pi t$ 7. $y = 0.001 \sin 800\pi t$

ARTICLE 14–5

1. Amp a
3. $A_0 = 80$, $A_1 = 9.5$, $A_2 = 1.44$, $\alpha_1 = 0.53$, $\alpha_2 = 2.16$

CHAPTER 15

ARTICLE 15–1

5. Problem 2: (a) $\frac{1}{8}$ (b) $\frac{3}{8}$ (c) $-\frac{5}{8}$ (d) $-\frac{5}{6}$
(e) $\frac{2}{3}$ (f) $\frac{5}{4}$ (g) 2 (h) $-\frac{1}{3}$

Problem 3: (a) $\frac{1}{12}$ (b) $\frac{1}{3}$ (c) $\frac{1}{8}$ (d) $\frac{2}{9}$
(e) $-\frac{3}{4}$ (f) $-\frac{5}{12}$ (g) $\frac{5}{24}$ (h) $-\frac{5}{2}$

7. (a) 0.4712   (b) 2.7285   (c) 0.8203
(d) 3.3080   (e) 4.4186   (f) -6.6116
9. (a) 47°41′   (b) 33°53′   (c) 51°
(d) 151°   (e) 81°21′   (f) 85°17′
(g) 164°47′   (h) 42°22′   (i) 212°37′
(j) 206°12′   (k) 37°38′   (l) 4°26′
11. $\frac{3}{2}$ radians, 85°57′   13. 120°, 30°, 172°30′, 108°30′
15. 60 radians

ARTICLE 15–2

1. -1 3. $-\frac{1}{4}$ 5. 30°, 150°   7. 30°, 210°
9. 135°, 315°   11. 45°, 135°   13. 150°, 330°
15. (a) $\sin 2 = 0.9088 > \sin 2° = 0.0349$
(b) $\cos 4 = -0.6539 < \cos 4° = 0.9976$
(c) $\tan 1 = 1.5597 > \tan 1° = 0.0175$

17. (a) $-\sin 16°$ (b) $-\cos 33°$ 19. (a) 0.2476   (b) 1.3111
    (c) $-\sin 41°$ (d) $-\sin 16°$ (c) 0.8760   (d) 0.8949
    (e) $-\cot 24°$ (f) $\cos 8°$ (e) 0.3872   (f) 0.3035
    (g) $\cos 5°$ (h) $\sin 15°$ (g) 0.9026   (h) -0.9465

23. (a) $25°10'$ (b) $48°20'$ (c) $27°40'$ (d) $57°40'$
    (e) $12°10'$ (f) $75°50'$ (g) $20°20'$ (h) $38°20'$

33. 54.1   35. 43,000

ARTICLE 15–5

1. (a) $\beta = 52°40'$, $b = 319$, $c = 401$
   (b) $\beta = 27°20'$, $a = 1540$, $c = 1730$
   (c) $\alpha = 29°40'$, $\beta = 60°20'$, $c = 6.63$
   (d) $\alpha = 44°40'$, $\beta = 45°20'$, $a = 67.6$
   (e) $\alpha = 38°50'$, $a = 0.522$, $b = 0.648$
   (f) $\beta = 52°20'$, $b = 71.0$, $c = 89.7$
   (g) $\alpha = 33°30'$, $\beta = 56°30'$, $c = 68.7$
   (h) $\alpha = 48°35'$, $a = 2448$, $b = 2160$
   (i) $\alpha = 59°36'$, $\beta = 30°24'$, $b = 3185$
   (j) $\alpha = 23°10'$, $\beta = 66°50'$, $c = 8.320$
   (k) $\alpha = 27°3'$, $b = 1.619$, $c = 1.818$
   (l) $\alpha = 42°37'$, $a = 66.74$, $c = 98.58$
   (m) $\alpha = 42°30'$, $\beta = 47°30'$, $a = 3274$
   (n) $\beta = 65°13'$, $a = 147.0$, $c = 350.8$

3. 313 ft, $19°0'$ 5. 474 in^2

7. 55°   9. 7.075 in, 7.075 in, 10.62 in

11. 172 ft   13. 78.8 ft

15. 2770 ft   17. 6.30 mi from A, 9.09 mi from B

19. 3195 ft south, 3485 ft west   21. (a) $v = 5$, $\theta = 53°$
                                   (b) $v = 50$, $\theta = 63°$
                                   (c) $v = 32.9$, $\theta = 119°30'$
                                   (d) $v = 858.2$, $\theta = 296°27'$

23. 56°, 22 ft/sec   25. N $47°0'$ W

27. (a) $f = 43$, $\theta = 122°$
   (b) $f = 8250$, $\theta = 21°10'$
   (c) $f = 3000$, $\theta = 255°$

ARTICLE 15–7

1. (a) $\gamma = 38°$, $b = 163$, $c = 102$
   (b) $\alpha = 40°26'$, $a = 36.27$, $b = 55.35$
   (c) $\beta = 13°52'$, $a = 270,400$, $c = 321,000$
   (d) $\alpha = 112°16'$, $a = 30.72$, $c = 26.56$

3. No

5. (a) $\alpha_1 = 91°50'$, $\gamma_1 = 49°30'$, $a_1 = 95.0$
      $\alpha_2 = 10°50'$, $\gamma_2 = 130°30'$, $a_2 = 17.9$
   (b) $\beta = 127°40'$, $\gamma = 7°10'$, $b = 55.0$
   (c) $\alpha = 17°49'$, $\gamma = 14°24'$, $c = 11.96$
   (d) $\alpha = 76°42'$, $\beta = 46°0'$, $a = 6.667$

7. (a) $\beta = 31°19'$, $\gamma = 96°23'$, $a = 28.35$
   (b) $\alpha = 45°50'$, $\beta = 76°30'$, $c = 545$
9. (a) $\alpha = 41°$, $\beta = 56°$, $\gamma = 83°$
   (b) $\alpha = 30°$, $\beta = 63°$, $\gamma = 87°$
15. 29.80 in, 48.52 in
17. 100 mi, 60 mi
19. 25.5 ft
21. N 79°20' W
23. 148 mi/hr, S 63° E

CHAPTER 16

ARTICLE 16–1

15. $(0, -1)$ 17. $(6, 8)$ 19. $(-1, 1)$ 21. $(3, 11)$
23. $(-\frac{1}{2}, -\frac{1}{2})$ 25. $(1, 0)$

ARTICLE 16–2

1. (a) $6 + 4i$
   (b) $-2 + 6i$
11. $-15i/2$
15. $3, -i$
3. (a) $\frac{3}{17} + \frac{22}{17}i$
   (b) $\frac{13}{17} + \frac{18}{17}i$
13. $-(4i + 10)/29$
17. $3i, 4i$

ARTICLE 16–3

1. $x^3 - 7x^2 + 17x - 15 = 0$
3. $2x^3 + 19x^2 + 42x - 26 = 0$
5. $3x^3 - 17x^2 + 27x + 11 = 0$
7. $4, \pm 3i$
9. $2, 3 \pm \sqrt{2}\, i$

ARTICLE 16–4

1. (a) $2 (\cos 0° + i \sin 0°)$
   (c) $3 (\cos 90° + i \sin 90°)$
   (e) $2\sqrt{2} (\cos 315° + i \sin 315°)$
   (g) $\cos 120° + i \sin 120°$
   (b) $2 (\cos 180° + i \sin 180°)$
   (d) $\cos 270° + i \sin 270°$
   (f) $2\sqrt{2} (\cos 135° + i \sin 135°)$
   (h) $\cos 240° + i \sin 240°$
3. (a) $6i$ (b) $-4\sqrt{3} - 4i$
   (c) $12i$ (d) 8
5. (a) $\sqrt{3} + i$
   (b) $-1 + \sqrt{3}\, i$

ARTICLE 16–5

1. $64i$
3. $-4\sqrt{2} - 4\sqrt{2}\, i$
5. $\dfrac{\sqrt{3}}{2} + \dfrac{i}{2}$
7. 1
9. $-2\sqrt{2} + 2\sqrt{2}\, i, \; 2\sqrt{2} - 2\sqrt{2}\, i$
11. $1 + \sqrt{3}\, i, \; -2, \; 1 - \sqrt{3}\, i$
13. $\sqrt{3} + i, \; -1 + \sqrt{3}\, i, \; -\sqrt{3} - i, \; 1 - \sqrt{3}\, i$
15. $(\cos 36° + i \sin 36°), \; (\cos 72° + i \sin 72°), \ldots$
17. $1, i, -1, -i$
19. $\dfrac{\sqrt{5} + 1}{2} + \sqrt{\dfrac{5 - \sqrt{5}}{2}}\, i, \quad \dfrac{1 - \sqrt{5}}{2} + \sqrt{\dfrac{5 + \sqrt{5}}{2}}\, i, \quad -2,$

$\dfrac{1 - \sqrt{5}}{2} - \sqrt{\dfrac{5 + \sqrt{5}}{2}}\, i, \quad \dfrac{\sqrt{5} + 1}{2} - \sqrt{\dfrac{5 - \sqrt{5}}{2}}\, i$

INDEX